ADMINISTRATION OF
SCHOOL HEALTH AND PHYSICAL
EDUCATION PROGRAMS

Administration of School Health and Physical Education Programs

By

CHARLES A. BUCHER, A.B., M.A., Ed.D.

Associate Professor of Education and Coordinator of
Undergraduate and Graduate Physical Education for Men and Women
School of Education, New York University

ILLUSTRATED

ST. LOUIS
THE C. V. MOSBY COMPANY
1955

Press of
The C. V. Mosby Company
St. Louis

TO
MY WIFE JACKIE AND MY CHILDREN
DIANA, RICHARD, AND NANCY

PREFACE

The manner in which organizations are administered influences the lives of many human beings. It affects their way of living, their goals, their ambitions, their happiness, and their achievements. A knowledge of administration encourages the use of democratic procedures, promotes associated effort, furthers human relations, and insures the continuance of organizations that have proved worth while. A study of administration can contribute to more efficiently run organizations, which are so essential to human endeavor. Through a democratic approach to administration the individual can aid in carrying on what has proved to be good in the past and steer a course which will insure progress in the future.

Administration is rapidly becoming a science, the study of which is essential to everyone. Such work is not confined to executives. Most individuals perform some administrative duties. Through an understanding of sound principles in this area, such assignments will be carried out more efficiently.

This book is concerned with administration as it is related to the school programs of health and physical education, with implications for recreation. The first part of this book is written on the premise that many factors concerned with administration are governed to a great degree by common principles, which may be applied in an industrial concern, government agency, school, public health agency, recreation program, physical education program, or other organization. Such factors as policies concerned with planning, human relations, and personnel are of concern to all administration, regardless of specialization. Furthermore, there are certain additional elements that are common to the areas of health, physical education, and recreation, such as legal liability, leadership, and public relations. These are also considered.

This book is written with the administrative problems in mind that confront the teacher and leader in the field. It is important that the student in training as well as the specialist on the job understand the various ramifications of such problems. An attempt has been made to write this treatise in simple, clear language adapted to the reader's experience and understanding.

At times the author has referred to administrators, teachers, and students by using the pronoun "he." This was done to facilitate writing. He wishes to emphasize, however, that this book refers to both men and women. It is not confined to one sex. The professions can look with pride to the excellent job being done by women administrators, teachers, and students.

The author wishes to express his appreciation to the many individuals, schools, publishing firms, and others who furnished and/or granted permission to use quotations, illustrations, and other material.   He is particularly indebted to his wife, Jacqueline D. Bucher, for the many hours she spent editing and typing the manuscript.

The writer wishes to thank Dr. Leslie Irwin of Boston University and Dr. H. F. Kilander of New York University for reading and making suggestions for improvement of the manuscript.

CHARLES A. BUCHER

New York, N. Y.

CONTENTS

CHAPTER   PAGE

I. THE MEANING OF ADMINISTRATION _ _ _ _ _ _ _ _ _ _ _ 17

    DEFINITION OF ADMINISTRATION _ _ _ _ _ _ _ _ _ _ _ _ 17
    HISTORY OF ADMINISTRATION _ _ _ _ _ _ _ _ _ _ _ _ _ 18
    IMPORTANCE OF ADMINISTRATION _ _ _ _ _ _ _ _ _ _ _ 20
    QUALIFICATIONS OF A GOOD ADMINISTRATOR _ _ _ _ _ _ 22
    DEVELOPMENT AND SELECTION OF ADMINISTRATORS _ _ _ _ _ 25
    MAJOR ADMINISTRATIVE DUTIES _ _ _ _ _ _ _ _ _ _ _ 26
    CODE FOR ADMINISTRATORS _ _ _ _ _ _ _ _ _ _ _ _ _ 30

II. ADMINISTRATION AND PERSONNEL POLICIES _ _ _ _ _ _ 32

    PRINCIPLES OF COOPERATION _ _ _ _ _ _ _ _ _ _ _ _ _ 32
    THE INDIVIDUAL AS A MEMBER OF AN ORGANIZATION _ _ _ _ 32
    THE FALLACY OF FINAL AUTHORITY _ _ _ _ _ _ _ _ _ _ 33
    DECISIONS _ _ _ _ _ _ _ _ _ _ _ _ _ _ _ _ _ _ 35
    STAFF MORALE _ _ _ _ _ _ _ _ _ _ _ _ _ _ _ _ _ 36
    PERSONNEL MANAGEMENT _ _ _ _ _ _ _ _ _ _ _ _ _ 38
    INCENTIVES _ _ _ _ _ _ _ _ _ _ _ _ _ _ _ _ _ _ 41
    COMMUNICATION AND PERSONNEL RELATIONS _ _ _ _ _ _ _ 43

III. MANAGEMENT _ _ _ _ _ _ _ _ _ _ _ _ _ _ _ _ _ 47

    THE IMPORTANCE AND PURPOSE OF ORGANIZATION _ _ _ _ _ 47
    ORGANIZATIONAL PATTERNS _ _ _ _ _ _ _ _ _ _ _ _ 48
    LINE AND STAFF _ _ _ _ _ _ _ _ _ _ _ _ _ _ _ _ 51
    ADMINISTRATION AND COORDINATION _ _ _ _ _ _ _ _ _ 53
    ADMINISTRATION AND REORGANIZATION _ _ _ _ _ _ _ _ 54
    BUDGETING AND FINANCIAL CONTROL _ _ _ _ _ _ _ _ _ 56
    PLANNING _ _ _ _ _ _ _ _ _ _ _ _ _ _ _ _ _ _ 57
    RESEARCH _ _ _ _ _ _ _ _ _ _ _ _ _ _ _ _ _ _ 59
    PUBLIC RELATIONS _ _ _ _ _ _ _ _ _ _ _ _ _ _ _ 59
    OFFICE MANAGEMENT _ _ _ _ _ _ _ _ _ _ _ _ _ _ 60

IV. DEMOCRATIC ADMINISTRATION _ _ _ _ _ _ _ _ _ _ 62

    EDUCATION AND GROUP PROCESS _ _ _ _ _ _ _ _ _ _ _ 62
    THE IMPORTANCE OF DEMOCRACY IN OUR SOCIETY _ _ _ _ _ 64
    PROBLEMS ASSOCIATED WITH THE DEMOCRATIC PROCESS _ _ _ 64
    ELEMENTS OF DEMOCRATIC ADMINISTRATION _ _ _ _ _ _ 67
    EDUCATING DEMOCRATIC ADMINISTRATORS _ _ _ _ _ _ _ 70

V. GOVERNMENTAL ASPECTS OF EDUCATIONL ADMINISTRATION _ 73

    PURPOSE OF EDUCATION _ _ _ _ _ _ _ _ _ _ _ _ _ _ 73
    GROWTH OF EDUCATION IN RELATION TO GOVERNMENT _ _ _ _ 74
    INTEREST OF FEDERAL GOVERNMENT IN EDUCATION _ _ _ _ _ 78

Chapter	Page
THE FUNCTION OF THE STATE IN EDUCATION	81
COMMUNITY RESPONSIBILITY IN EDUCATION	85
GOVERNMENTAL RELATIONSHIPS	86
GOVERNMENT AND HEALTH	87
GOVERNMENT AND PHYSICAL EDUCATION	91

VI. SCHOOL AND COMMUNITY ORGANIZATION AND ADMINISTRATION — 95

SCHOOL STRUCTURE — 95
  Board of Education or School Committees — 95
  General Administrative Personnel — 97
  Lay Groups — 98
  Health Within the School Structure — 98
  Physical Education Within the School Structure — 104

COMMUNITY STRUCTURE — 109
  Village Government — 109
  Municipal Government — 110
  Public Health Organization at the Local Level — 115

VII. ADMINISTRATIVE RELATIONSHIPS AND OBJECTIVES OF HEALTH AND PHYSICAL EDUCATION — 119

CLOSELY ALLIED BUT SEPARATE AREAS OF ENDEAVOR — 119
OBJECTIVES OF SCHOOL HEALTH AND PHYSICAL EDUCATION PROGRAMS — 120
  Objectives of the School Health Program — 120
  Objectives of the School Physical Education Program — 124
THE ROLE OF THE ADMINISTRATOR IN PROMOTING OBJECTIVES AND COOPERATION — 130

VIII. LEGAL LIABILITY — 133

LIABILITY AND PLAY — 133
TORT — 135
NEGLIGENCE — 136
DEFENSES AGAINST NEGLIGENCE — 138
NUISANCE — 139
GOVERNMENTAL VERSUS PROPRIETARY FUNCTIONS — 141
FEES — 141
LIABILITY OF THE MUNICIPALITY — 142
LIABILITY OF THE SCHOOL DISTRICT — 142
LIABILITY OF SCHOOL, PARK, AND RECREATION BOARD MEMBERS — 142
LIABILITY OF TEACHERS AND LEADERS — 143
ACCIDENT-PRONE SETTINGS — 144
SAFETY — 146
SUPERVISION — 152
WAIVERS AND CONSENT SLIPS — 152
ATHLETIC PROTECTION FUNDS — 152

IX. THE PROFESSIONAL PREPARATION PROGRAM — 155

WHERE ARE WE HEADING IN PROFESSIONAL PREPARATION? — 155
QUALIFICATIONS FOR HEALTH EDUCATORS — 160
QUALIFICATIONS FOR PHYSICAL EDUCATORS — 161
THE IMPORTANCE OF BEING PROFESSIONAL — 163
THE NEED FOR A CULTURAL BACKGROUND — 164
GREATER STRESS ON COMPETENCIES — 165
ACCREDITING PROFESSIONAL PREPARING INSTITUTIONS — 168

CHAPTER   PAGE

X. MEASUREMENT AND EVALUATION _ _ _ _ _ _ _ _ _ _ 171

    PURPOSES OF MEASUREMENT AND EVALUATION _ _ _ _ _ _ _ 171
    FRAMEWORK FOR MEASUREMENT PROCEDURES _ _ _ _ _ _ _ 172
    FRAMEWORK FOR EVALUATION PROCEDURES _ _ _ _ _ _ _ _ 177
    GENERAL ADMINISTRATIVE GUIDES IN MEASUREMENT AND EVALUATION _ _ 178
    CRITERIA FOR TEST CONSTRUCTION AND SELECTION _ _ _ _ _ 179
    THE NEED FOR A STANDARDIZATION OF MEASUREMENT AND EVALUATION MA-
        TERIALS _ _ _ _ _ _ _ _ _ _ _ _ _ _ _ _ _ 181
    AVAILABLE SCIENTIFIC MEASUREMENT AND EVALUATION MATERIALS _ _ 181
    MINIMUM AND DESIRABLE STANDARDS _ _ _ _ _ _ _ _ _ 183

XI. PUBLIC RELATIONS _ _ _ _ _ _ _ _ _ _ _ _ _ _ 186

    WHAT IS PUBLIC RELATIONS? _ _ _ _ _ _ _ _ _ _ _ _ 186
    THE IMPORTANCE OF PUBLIC RELATIONS TO ADMINISTRATORS _ _ _ _ 188
    PUBLIC RELATIONS MEDIA _ _ _ _ _ _ _ _ _ _ _ _ _ 189
    GET THE FACTS _ _ _ _ _ _ _ _ _ _ _ _ _ _ _ _ 193
    QUALIFICATIONS FOR THE PUBLIC RELATIONS PERSON _ _ _ _ _ 194
    SOME PRINCIPLES OF PUBLIC RELATIONS _ _ _ _ _ _ _ _ _ 195
    PUBLIC RELATIONS AND EDUCATION _ _ _ _ _ _ _ _ _ _ 196
    PUBLIC RELATIONS IN SCHOOL HEALTH AND PHYSICAL EDUCATION PROGRAMS 198

XII. FACILITIES FOR A HEALTHFUL ENVIRONMENT _ _ _ _ _ _ 204

    BASIC CONSIDERATIONS IN PLANNING _ _ _ _ _ _ _ _ _ _ 204
    GENERAL TRENDS IN SCHOOL CONSTRUCTION _ _ _ _ _ _ _ _ 210
    GENERAL HEALTH FEATURES OF SCHOOL CONSTRUCTION _ _ _ _ _ 211
    INDOOR FACILITIES _ _ _ _ _ _ _ _ _ _ _ _ _ _ _ 216
    OUTDOOR FACILITIES _ _ _ _ _ _ _ _ _ _ _ _ _ _ _ 225

XIII. ADMINISTRATIVE PRACTICES FOR A HEALTHFUL ENVIRONMENT 232

    ASPECTS OF HEALTH _ _ _ _ _ _ _ _ _ _ _ _ _ _ _ 232
    ADMINISTRATIVE PRACTICES _ _ _ _ _ _ _ _ _ _ _ _ _ 233
    THE TEACHER _ _ _ _ _ _ _ _ _ _ _ _ _ _ _ _ _ 238
    IMPLICATIONS OF THE PHYSICAL ENVIRONMENT _ _ _ _ _ _ _ 239
    HUMAN RELATIONSHIPS _ _ _ _ _ _ _ _ _ _ _ _ _ _ 240
    SCHOOL-COMMUNITY RELATIONSHIPS _ _ _ _ _ _ _ _ _ _ 241
    PROFESSIONAL SERVICES _ _ _ _ _ _ _ _ _ _ _ _ _ _ 242

XIV. THE HEALTH EDUCATION PROGRAM _ _ _ _ _ _ _ _ _ 245

    HEALTH EDUCATION AND THE SCHOOLS _ _ _ _ _ _ _ _ _ 245
    HEALTH EDUCATION AND THE SCHOOL HEALTH PROGRAM _ _ _ _ _ 246
    ADMINISTRATION OF HEALTH EDUCATION _ _ _ _ _ _ _ _ _ 247
    CONTENT AREAS OF HEALTH EDUCATION _ _ _ _ _ _ _ _ _ 248
    HEALTH EDUCATION AT THE ELEMENTARY LEVEL _ _ _ _ _ _ _ 254
    HEALTH EDUCATION AT THE SECONDARY LEVEL _ _ _ _ _ _ _ 256
    HEALTH EDUCATION AT THE COLLEGE AND UNIVERSITY LEVEL _ _ _ _ 257
    HEALTH EDUCATION FOR ADULTS _ _ _ _ _ _ _ _ _ _ _ 259
    CONCENTRATED, CORRELATED, AND INCIDENTAL HEALTH TEACHING _ _ 259
    ORGANIZATION OF CLASSES _ _ _ _ _ _ _ _ _ _ _ _ _ 261
    RESOURCES _ _ _ _ _ _ _ _ _ _ _ _ _ _ _ _ _ _ 263

XV. AREAS OF THE SCHOOL HEALTH SERVICES PROGRAM _ _ _ _ 268

    THE PLACE OF HEALTH SERVICES IN THE SCHOOLS _ _ _ _ _ _ _ 269
    THE RESPONSIBILITY FOR SCHOOL HEALTH SERVICES _ _ _ _ _ _ 271

CHAPTER   PAGE

EDUCATION VERSUS TREATMENT _ _ _ _ _ _ _ _ _ _ _ _ _ _   271
SCHOOL HEALTH SERVICES _ _ _ _ _ _ _ _ _ _ _ _ _ _ _ _   272
  Health Appraisal _ _ _ _ _ _ _ _ _ _ _ _ _ _ _ _ _ _   273
  Health Counseling _ _ _ _ _ _ _ _ _ _ _ _ _ _ _ _ _   288
  Correction of Remediable Defects _ _ _ _ _ _ _ _ _ _ _   290
  Care and Education of Exceptional Children _ _ _ _ _ _ _   292
  Communicable Disease Control _ _ _ _ _ _ _ _ _ _ _ _   298
  Emergency Care _ _ _ _ _ _ _ _ _ _ _ _ _ _ _ _ _ _   303

XVI. THE REQUIRED PHYSICAL EDUCATION CLASS PROGRAM _ _ _   309

  SOME INITIAL CONSIDERATIONS _ _ _ _ _ _ _ _ _ _ _ _ _   309
  SCHEDULING _   312
  ADMINISTRATIVE POLICIES _ _ _ _ _ _ _ _ _ _ _ _ _ _ _   318
  CLASS MANAGEMENT _ _ _ _ _ _ _ _ _ _ _ _ _ _ _ _ _   322
  PHYSICAL EDUCATION ACTIVITIES _ _ _ _ _ _ _ _ _ _ _ _   329
  PROGRAM _   334
  INTERRELATIONSHIPS OF ELEMENTARY, SECONDARY, AND COLLEGE AND UNI-
    VERSITY LEVELS _ _ _ _ _ _ _ _ _ _ _ _ _ _ _ _ _   342
  MODIFIED PROGRAM _ _ _ _ _ _ _ _ _ _ _ _ _ _ _ _ _   343
  PROVIDING FOR THE HEALTH OF THE INDIVIDUAL _ _ _ _ _ _ _   343

XVII. INTRAMURAL AND EXTRAMURAL ATHLETICS _ _ _ _ _ _ _   346

  NATURE AND SCOPE _ _ _ _ _ _ _ _ _ _ _ _ _ _ _ _ _   346
  OBJECTIVES _   347
  RELATION TO INTERSCHOOL ATHLETICS _ _ _ _ _ _ _ _ _ _ _   349
  PLAY, SPORTS, AND INVITATION DAYS _ _ _ _ _ _ _ _ _ _ _   350
  ACTIVITIES _   356
  UNITS AND TYPES OF COMPETITION FOR INTRAMURAL AND EXTRAMURAL ATH-
    LETICS _   357
  AWARDS, POINTS, ELIGIBILITY _ _ _ _ _ _ _ _ _ _ _ _ _   359
  INTRAMURAL AND EXTRAMURAL ATHLETICS IN THE ELEMENTARY SCHOOL _   361
  INTRAMURAL AND EXTRAMURAL ATHLETICS IN THE JUNIOR HIGH SCHOOL _   362
  INTRAMURAL AND EXTRAMURAL ATHLETICS IN THE SENIOR HIGH SCHOOL,
    COLLEGE, AND UNIVERSITY _ _ _ _ _ _ _ _ _ _ _ _ _   363
  INTRAMURAL AND EXTRAMURAL ATHLETICS FOR GIRLS _ _ _ _ _ _   363
  GENERAL ADMINISTRATIVE POLICIES FOR ORGANIZATION AND ADMINISTRATION
    OF INTRAMURAL AND EXTRAMURAL ATHLETICS _ _ _ _ _ _ _   365

XVIII. THE INTERSCHOOL ATHLETICS PROGRAM _ _ _ _ _ _ _ _   369

  RELATIONSHIP TO TOTAL PHYSICAL EDUCATION PROGRAM _ _ _ _ _   369
  THE COACH _   371
  SOME ADMINISTRATIVE CONSIDERATIONS IN THE INTERSCHOOL ATHLETICS
    PROGRAM _   373
  SOME ADMINISTRATIVE PROBLEMS _ _ _ _ _ _ _ _ _ _ _ _ _   380
    Gate Receipts _ _ _ _ _ _ _ _ _ _ _ _ _ _ _ _ _ _   380
    Tournaments and Play-offs _ _ _ _ _ _ _ _ _ _ _ _ _   382
    Eligibility _ _ _ _ _ _ _ _ _ _ _ _ _ _ _ _ _ _ _   384
    Scholarships _ _ _ _ _ _ _ _ _ _ _ _ _ _ _ _ _ _   384
    Recruitment _ _ _ _ _ _ _ _ _ _ _ _ _ _ _ _ _ _   385
    Proselyting _ _ _ _ _ _ _ _ _ _ _ _ _ _ _ _ _ _   385
    Scouting _ _ _ _ _ _ _ _ _ _ _ _ _ _ _ _ _ _ _   386
  ATHLETIC ASSOCIATIONS _ _ _ _ _ _ _ _ _ _ _ _ _ _ _ _   386

CHAPTER   PAGE

  GIRLS' INTERSCHOOL ATHLETICS _ _ _ _ _ _ _ _ _ _ _ _ _ _   388
  INTERSCHOOL ATHLETICS AT THE ELEMENTARY AND JUNIOR HIGH SCHOOL
   LEVELS _   389
  INTERSCHOOL ATHLETICS AT THE HIGH SCHOOL LEVEL _ _ _ _ _ _   390
  INTERSCHOOL ATHLETICS AT THE COLLEGE AND UNIVERSITY LEVEL _ _ _   394
  SUMMARY _   398

XIX. COMMUNITY RECREATION _ _ _ _ _ _ _ _ _ _ _ _ _   400

  OBJECTIVES OF RECREATION _ _ _ _ _ _ _ _ _ _ _ _ _ _   400
   The Health Development Objective _ _ _ _ _ _ _ _ _ _   400
   The Human Relations Objective _ _ _ _ _ _ _ _ _ _ _   400
   The Civic Development Objective _ _ _ _ _ _ _ _ _ _   401
   The Self-Development Objective _ _ _ _ _ _ _ _ _ _ _   402
  RECREATION IN RETROSPECT _ _ _ _ _ _ _ _ _ _ _ _ _ _   402
  THE RECREATION LEADER _ _ _ _ _ _ _ _ _ _ _ _ _ _ _   408

XX. CAMPING AND OUTDOOR EDUCATION _ _ _ _ _ _ _ _ _   410

ADMINISTRATION OF
SCHOOL HEALTH AND PHYSICAL
EDUCATION PROGRAMS

Chapter I

THE MEANING OF ADMINISTRATION

It has been estimated that there are at least 5,000,000 individuals in the United States today performing administrative work as their main function. At least 100,000 of these could be classified as holding major executive positions. This number is large, but as the technology and the specialized functions of this country advance, there will be an increasing number of individuals needed to perform the myriad administrative duties characteristic of the thousands of organizations in society. Administration offers many career opportunities for both women and men.

It is essential that individuals who perform administrative work know the many aspects of this particular field. If they are not aware of certain basic facts and are not acquainted with acceptable administrative procedures, many errors may be made. This could result in loss of efficiency, production, staff morale, and in poor human relations, to mention only a few of the possible outcomes. Administration is rapidly becoming a science with a body of specialized knowledge which should be known by all who would administer in a wise and effective manner. Plato in his book, *Laws,* summed it up in a few words which still hold true today: ". . . that God governs all things, and that chance and opportunity cooperate with Him in the government of human affairs. There is, however, a third and less extreme view, that art should be there also; for I should say that in a storm there must surely be a great advantage in having the aid of the pilot's art. You would agree?"

I. DEFINITION OF ADMINISTRATION

In an organization where the associated efforts of many individuals are necessary, there is no spontaneous and automatic working together of the individuals involved. There is no miraculous thought and planning which results in the achievement of goals and purposes. It is not a natural trait of human beings to cooperate and work side by side in a happy and purposeful manner. This is accomplished through direction, and administration gives this direction.

To a considerable degree, the actions of human beings in society are determined through their association with formal organizations. Formal organizations have leaders and purposes. They depend upon the cooperative efforts of individuals to achieve the objectives which have been set. Many times organizations have failed

17

when their leaders have been of low caliber, there has been a lack of cooperative effort among members, or the objectives have not been in conformance with what is essential and good for society.

Administration determines in great measure whether an organization is going to progress, operate efficiently, achieve its objectives, and have a group of individuals within its framework who are happy, cooperative, and productive. It has to do with directing, guiding, and integrating the efforts of human beings so that specific aims may be accomplished. It refers particularly to a group of individuals, many times called executives, who have as their major responsibility this direction, guidance, integration, and achievement.

Administration is especially concerned with achievement—proof that the organization is producing those things for which it has been established. To be able to achieve these results in a satisfactory manner presupposes an understanding of human relationships, and the ability to foresee the future and plan for any eventuality. It demands capacity to coordinate many different and conflicting types of human personalities. Good administration should insure that the associated efforts of individuals are productive. To accomplish this, administrators should possess those attributes which are conducive to bringing out the most creative and best efforts on the part of the members of the organization.

Administration also requires close supervision of the facilities, materials, supplies, and equipment essential to the life of the organization. It implies a logical formulation of policies and the effective operation of the organization.

In light of the above discussion, the author would like to propose as a definition of administration, the following:

Administration *is concerned with the functions and responsibilities essential to the achievement of established goals through associated effort. It is also concerned with that group of individuals sometimes called executives. These individuals are responsible for directing, guiding, coordinating, and inspiring the associated efforts of individual members, so that the purposes for which an organization has been established may be accomplished in the most effective and efficient manner possible.*

II. HISTORY OF ADMINISTRATION

Most of the facts concerning the history of administration have to do with public administration. To some, therefore, it may seem that they are not pertinent to the type of administration discussed in this book. However, it is well to remind the reader that this book has been written with the assumption there is certain basic knowledge which is applicable to all phases of administration whether it is associated with a church, school, public agency, government, or industry. Therefore, it is essential to examine all available administrative facts, whatever their specialized design.

The history of administration can be traced back as early as 1300 B.C., when the Egyptians were spreading their culture throughout the world. They had a system of large-scale administration. The decrees of Ramses III were recorded for history. The administrative setup of the Ptolemies provides some evidence of a systematic, though not always the most efficient, public administration. They had a planned economy with such work as industry, cattle breeding, and agriculture conducted along definite and prescribed lines.

The Byzantine Empire (330-1453) and the Ottoman Empire (1520-1566) under Suleiman contributed a system of civil service to administration.

Ancient Chinese records show that this people had a very good civil service system. They were aware that the public government had to abide by certain basic administrative principles.

The Greeks introduced democracy into administration when it placed government in the hands of all men. It recognized such basic facts as: all men are equal before the law; a citizen should be interested not only in his own personal affairs, but also in the affairs of state; all citizens have a responsibility for deciding public policy; and full discussion of important public issues is an essential to good government.

The Romans showed their ability in large-scale management, which included the administration of their own affairs as well as the affairs of their subject colonies. They established a paid system of civil service under Augustus about 25 B.C.

During the Middle Ages evidence points to considerable administrative thinking. The royal domains, ecclesiastical provinces, and feudal manors provided opportunity for various types of administrative practice. Local government administration was carried on by manor officials or ecclesiastical personnel. According to some historians and church people, the Catholic prelates and parish clergy could be given an excellent administrative rating in the light of present-day standards. Also, during the Middle Ages a fiscal procedure was developed for the Exchequer in England and additional administrative work was performed by such organizations as parliaments, synods, and councils.

A group of individuals to whom history owes much for their contributions to the science of administration were the Cameralists in Germany and Austria. The Cameralists were professors and public administrators whose work and influence have been traced back to around 1550. They were especially prominent during the 1700's. They were interested in scientific administration and did a great deal of work in connection with finance and other pertinent topics. They were scholars and applied their scholarship and practice to making administration a science.

During the eighteenth century, the formation of the United States Government stands out as the most important development in administration. It represents an attempt to devise a system of public government based on democratic principles. This great experiment attracted world-wide attention and many of its basic features have been copied by other peoples.

Woodrow Wilson, while at Princeton University, studied and wrote concerning the science of administration. Wilson recognized the importance of administration in government.

One of the outstanding developments of the twentieth century in the field of administration has been the stress placed upon scientific administration by industry. The industrial revolution pointed to the necessity for good organization and administration in order that industry might be most efficient and productive. Consequently, much literature has been published on the subject, educational institutions have initiated courses, and more and more stress has been placed on the necessity for trained administrators.

The trend in industry has been contagious. All types of organizations, whether they relate to education, religion, government, or industry, are starting to recognize more and more the importance of administration as a science. These organizations realize the important part administration plays in achieving objectives which are essential to their success and to their ways of life and government. Teachers College, Columbia University, recently created a new Department of Educational Administration at a cost of $1,000,000, one which will cost $500,000 a year to operate. The purpose of this new department is to develop better principals, superintendents, and other school administrators. It is being increasingly recognized that administrative *savoir-faire* is most essential for the welfare of mankind.

Another development which has been much in evidence in recent years is the increased number of women in administrative positions. This is true of education, business, government, and all forms of endeavor. It is right that more women should occupy important administrative positions because qualifications are not restricted to one sex.

III. IMPORTANCE OF ADMINISTRATION

A study of administration is important for all individuals. A few of the more important reasons for such a study are listed here.

1. Administration is important in social, economic, political, religious, and educational affairs. It affects every person. The manner in which organizations are administered determines the course of men's lives. It affects their way of living, their goals, their ambitions, their happiness, and their achievements.

2. Administration will develop an understanding and an appreciation of a broad knowledge of the facts and practices which make up the science of administration as it is known today. Methods, techniques, devices, and procedures which are sound and in accordance with acceptable practice will be appreciated to a greater degree by all concerned.

3. A knowledge of administration will make it possible for the individual to recognize unsound practices in administration. Such a knowledge will help in restricting the exploitation of human resources and in furthering efficient management and organization.

4. A knowledge of administration will aid some individuals to decide whether or not to select this particular area on a career basis. It will aid them in evaluating their own qualifications for such work and help them to predict their own possibilities for success.

5. All administrative work is not confined to executives. Most employees and members of organizations outside the so-called executive or administrative group perform administrative duties. Even the head of a family group performs administrative duties in connection with household and family management. Therefore, it is essential that all individuals possess an understanding and an appreciation of this work so that they may efficiently carry out assignments. Furthermore, promotions and advancement often depend on one's knowledge of administrative technique.

6. Administration is fundamental in achieving joint purposes. Individuals are imbued with ideas which they want to see come to fruition. These ideas do not materialize unless there is planning and cooperative action. A knowledge of administration facilitates the achievement of such aims.

7. Administration helps to insure the continuance of organizations that have proved worth while to mankind and are needed in society. Its fundamental objective is to carry on that which has proved to be successful rather than to destroy the old and attempt a new and untried path.

8. A knowledge of administration furthers human relations. Good administration implies cooperating with one another, being able to overlook personal shortcomings, getting along with people in order to obtain utmost work output and efficiency, and possessing the ability to instill the feeling of "one big happy family."

Administration is fundamental in achieving joint purposes. (Courtesy of National Council, Y.M.C.A.)

Outstanding individuals in various walks of life have recognized the importance of administration. *Charles A. Beard,* a famous historian, refers to administration as the key science of the present day. *Henri Fayol,* French engineer and industrialist, stresses the great need for studying administration scientifically in that it is one of the most important elements in all vocations and professions. *Paul Pigors,* American sociologist, feels that the main contribution of administration is to preserve the status quo in society. *Brooks Adams,* American lawyer and historian, takes an almost opposite view from Pigors when he advocates administration as being most important because it can help in social change. *James Burnham,* American political philosopher, goes further and points to the fact that the chief administrators in present-day society have assumed so much power that the social revolution is already in evidence. *Charles E. Merriam,* American political scientist, contends that administration is another outcome of human technology which is making it possible for man to better adapt to his complex environment.

The evidence is ample that administration is rapidly becoming a science and that the study of this science is essential to everyone. A study of administration can result in a better ordered society, through more efficiently run organizations. Every individual belongs to formal organizations. Through a democratic approach to administration the individual can aid in carrying on what has proved to be good in the past and steer a course which will insure progress in the future.

IV. QUALIFICATIONS OF A GOOD ADMINISTRATOR

It is important that everyone recognize the qualifications of a good administrator. This is essential to help determine whether or not one should go into this important field of endeavor if the occasion arises. It will also help in evaluating the type of administration one is experiencing in his own organization, whether he be an administrator or hold another position.

The qualifications of an administrator are many. A list of some follows. There has been no attempt to list these in order of importance, although in the discussion of each, one may be able to discern the most essential and important qualifications.

A. Administrative Mind

Some individuals have a capacity which perhaps has been developed through training and experience, and which peculiarly adapts them to administrative work. These individuals are able to analyze situations objectively, have the ability to clarify generalizations, and possess the quality of administering in a constructive manner, rather than in an exploitative way. Such persons are sensitive to human relations and the important part they play in the successful functioning of any organization. These individuals think in imaginative terms. They are able to see into the future and plan a course of action with an open mind. They recognize problems in order of importance, are able to analyze a situation, develop various plans of action, and reach logical conclusions. They have ability to organize. This is what is meant by an administrative mind, and it is not characteristic of all individuals. Instead, it is a part of the qualifications of comparatively few people. The persons who seem to have this capacity for administration should be identified and persuaded to assume administrative responsibilities because they have one of the primary requisites.

B. Integrity

One of the most important qualifications of any administrator is integrity. Whether or not a leader can inspire the staff, have their cooperation, and achieve purposes of the organization, will depend to a great degree upon his or her integrity. Everyone likes to feel that an administrator is honest and sincere, keeps promises, can be trusted with confidential information, and is an individual in whom one has faith. Such confidence cannot emanate from administrators unless they have integrity. Failure to fulfill this one qualification will result in low morale and an inefficient organization.

C. Ability to Instill Good Human Relations

The ability to get along with associates in work is an essential qualification for an administrator. Only through cooperative effort is it possible for an organization to achieve its goals. This cooperative effort is greatest when the individuals responsible for coordination of human efforts have the welfare of the various members of the organization at heart. This means that an administrator must be able to convert the abilities of many individuals into coordinated effort. This is done in many ways. Some of these methods include setting a good example, inspiring confidence, selecting proper incentives, possessing poise, making the right decisions in tense moments, having an impersonal attitude, cooperating and helping others when necessary, and developing and practicing ethical standards. The administrator must be adept at the art of persuasion, which takes into consideration such important items as the points of view, interests, and other factors characterizing those to be perusaded.

There is very little associated effort without leadership. The administrator must be a leader and possess the attributes and qualities which people expect if they are to follow and contribute their best to achieve the purposes for which the organization has been established.

D. Ability to Make Decisions

The administrator must be able to make decisions when the situation necessitates such action. This presumes an understanding of what constitutes the important and the unimportant in the particular situation that is in question, the ability to foresee future developments and results of a decision, and a knowledge of what is reasonable and unreasonable. It also assumes knowledge as to what is in the best interests of the organization and what is not, and what has the best chance for success and what has the least chance.

Decision is essential in order to accomplish objectives at the most opportune time. The administrator should have the capacity and be willing to make a decision. Many times if a decision is not forthcoming it creates lethargy, suspense, and poor morale. The cooperative process depends upon decisions being made. It is absolutely necessary to insure decision throughout the entire organization so that one can experiment in new and better ways of doing things and adapt successfully to changing conditions. The administrator who procrastinates beyond a reasonable time, is afraid of making the wrong decision, thinks only of his or her own security, and is oblivious to the organization's needs should never hold such a position.

E. Health and Fitness for the Job

Good health and physical fitness are essentials for the administrator. Good health and physical fitness often have a bearing on making the right decisions. Socrates once said that people in a state of bad health often made the wrong decisions in regard to affairs of state. Jennings, the famous biologist, pointed out that the body can attend to only one thing at a time. Therefore, if attention is focused on a pain in the chest, a stomach ailment, or a nervous condition, it is difficult to focus it on the functions which an administrator must perform. Poor health may cause poor administration.

Vitality and endurance are essential to the administrator. They affect one's manner, personality, attractiveness, and disposition. Administrative duties often require long hours of tedious work under the most trying conditions. Failure to have the necessary strength and endurance under such conditions could mean inability to perform tasks which are essential to the welfare of the organization. Members of an organization have confidence in those administrators who watch over their interests under all conditions. It is possible for an administrator to obtain this confidence continuously only if he or she is in good health and physically fit to perform arduous duties.

When considering health and fitness for the job, it is important to recognize the many phases of health. The administrator should possess not only physical, but also mental, emotional, and social health. Emotional stability, especially, is a must.

F. Willingness to Accept Responsibility

Every administrator must be willing to accept responsibility. There are duties to be performed which greatly influence the welfare of many individuals. Plans have to be fulfilled if the purposes of the organization are to be accomplished. Action is required to insure production and render services. The person who accepts an administrative job is morally bound to assume the responsibility that is part and parcel of that position. A good administrator will experience a feeling of dissatisfaction whenever he fails to meet responsibilities.

G. Understanding of Work

The administrator will benefit from having a thorough understanding of the specialized work in which the organization is engaged. If it concerns a particular industry, it will be an advantage to know the production process from the ground up. If it is government, knowledge of related legislative, executive, and judicial aspects will help. If it is education, being thoroughly familiar with that particular field will be an asset. If it is a specialized field within education or other areas, it is necessary to have a knowledge of the particular specialty and also the part it plays in the whole process. It is difficult to guide purposefully and intelligently unless the technical knowledge is present, together with an understanding of its relation to the activities and situations with which it is concerned. One often reads about the Congressman who started as a page in the Senate, the railroad executive who once was a yard worker, the bank president who started as a bookkeeper, and the superintendent of schools who many years before started as a teacher. The technical knowledge and understanding of the total functioning of an organization are best gained through firsthand experience. An administrator will find that detailed knowledge of an organization's work is of great help in successfully guiding its operations.

H. Command of Administrative Technique

Administrative technique in many ways is similar to the first qualification listed, namely, "administrative mind." There is one essential difference. "Administrative mind" refers more to the "know how" and temperament of the individual, whereas "administrative technique" refers to the application of this knowledge and ability. It means that the individual can plan and budget his or her time and effort and also the time and work of others, in the most effective way possible. Time is not spent on details when more important work should be done. Tasks are performed in a relaxed, efficient, calm, and logical manner. Work is accomplished in conformance with established standards. Duties are effectively executed, including those which involve strong pressure and great amounts of time. Resources for performing the job are utilized.

It has been said there are three conditions which burn out an administrator in a short length of time: performing his own duties in a tense, highly emotional manner, performing too many details, and being part of an organization which is not considerate of its administrators.

I. Intellectual Capacity

Intellectual capacity in itself will not guarantee a good administrator. In fact, the so-called "intellectual" often makes a very poor administrator. Such traits as absent-mindedness and nonpunctuality are not compatible with acceptance of responsibility. The "intellectual" sometimes cannot make decisions because he visualizes so many sides of an issue. Furthermore, such an individual is often not interested in people, but in books, figures, or other data instead. This makes a poor leader since lack of interest in human beings results in poor followership.

However, one should not gain from this discussion that intellectual capacity should be disregarded. To be a good administrator one must be intellectually competent. One should be able to think and reason logically, to apply knowledge effectively, to communicate efficiently, and should possess other factors which are closely allied to the intellectual process. There have been many so-called "brains" who failed miserably as administrators, whereas most good administrators can usually be classified as at least average in respect to their intellectual capacities.

Space has not permitted a discussion of all the qualifications of the administrator. Others, such as courage and initiative, are also important. There is also the ability to be an "ambassador" for the organization. Liaison work with higher echelon groups in the organization and also with outside groups is important. It is necessary at times to stand up and fight for one's own department or division. To a great degree this will determine whether it is respected and on an equal basis with other administrative divisions.

V. DEVELOPMENT AND SELECTION OF ADMINISTRATORS

Many of the qualifications of administrators listed above cannot be developed through the formalized process of education, as this process is now understood. Such qualifications as administrative mind, human relations, decisiveness, health and fitness, responsibility, technical knowledge, command of administrative technique, and intellectual capacity are, with few exceptions, developed mainly with experience and as a result of exposure to concrete situations. Qualities of health, technology, and intellectual capacity probably lend themselves more to the educational process than do the others. Such characteristics as balance, perspective, decision, and understanding pertain to leadership acquired through experience in leading. Therefore, individuals interested in the area of administration should seek as many opportunties as possible to act as a leader. With the great number of volunteer positions open in all communities and with other opportunities available, this can be accomplished. One must recognize that there is no substitute for the experiences of leading an enterprise and encountering at first hand the many obstacles and interferences that present themselves. Individuals who have had such experiences are the ones who are sought to fill coveted positions.

The selection of administrators depends upon three things: the qualifications of the individual, the willingness of those under him to follow, and the conditions surrounding the position. All three factors should be taken into consideration. The individual should possess the qualifications that have been discussed in this chapter, the members of the organization should show willingness to follow, and the conditions surrounding this position should be compatible with the individual's experience, qualifications, and total personality. Of all the factors that are listed, the most important criterion is the degree of success the individual has achieved in comparable positions.

VI. MAJOR ADMINISTRATIVE DUTIES

Gulick and Urwick[1] have utilized the word POSDCORB to outline the functions of an administrator. This is based on Henri Fayol's work, *Industrial and General Administration*. An organization of duties under these major headings is apropos to the section under discussion. POSDCORB refers to the functional elements of (1) Planning, (2) Organizing, (3) Staffing, (4) Directing, (5) Coordinating, (6) Reporting, and (7) Budgeting.

A. Planning

Planning is the process of outlining the work that is to be performed, in a logical and purposeful manner, together with the methods that are to be utilized in the performance of this work. The total plan will result in the accomplishment of the purposes for which the organization is established. Of course this implies a clear conception of the aims of the organization.

In order to accomplish this planning, the administrator must have vision to look into the future and prepare for what he sees. He must see the influences which will affect the organization and the requirements that will have to be met.

B. Organizing

Organizing refers to development of the formal structure of the organization whereby the various administrative coordinating centers and subdivisions of work are arranged in an integrated manner, with clearly defined lines of authority. The purpose behind this structure is the effective accomplishment of established objectives. Organizational charts aid in clarifying such organization.

---

[1]Luther Gulick and L. Urwick. *Papers on the Science of Administration.* New York: Institute of Public Administration, 1937.

This formal structure should be set up in a manner which avoids red tape and provides for the clear assignment of every necessary duty to some responsible individual. Whenever possible, standards should be established for acceptable performance for each duty assignment.

The coordinating centers of authority are developed and organized chiefly on the basis of the work to be done by the organization, services performed, individuals available in light of incentives offered, and efficiency of operation. A single administrator cannot perform all the functions necessary, except in the smallest organizations. Hence, responsibility must be assigned to others in a logical manner. These individuals occupy positions along the line, each position being broken down in terms of its own area of specialization. The higher up the line one goes, the more general is the responsibility; the lower down the line one goes, the more specific is the responsibility.

C. Staffing

The administrative duty of staffing refers to the entire personnel function of selection, assignment, training, and providing and maintaining favorable working conditions. The administrator must have a thorough knowledge of the staff. He or she must select with care and insure that each subdivision in the organization has a competent leader and that each employee is assigned to the job where he can be of greatest service. Personnel should possess energy, initiative, and loyalty. The duties of each position must be clearly outlined. All members of the organization must be encouraged to utilize their own initiative. They should be rewarded fairly for their services. The mistakes and blunders of employees must be brought to their attention and dealt with accordingly. Vested interests of individual employees must not be allowed to endanger the general interests of all. The conditions of work should be made as pleasant and as nearly ideal as possible. Both the physical and social factors should be provided for. Services rendered by the individual increase as the conditions under which he works improve.

D. Directing

Directing is a responsibility which falls to the administrator as the leader. He or she must direct the operations of the organization. This means distinct and precise decisions must be made and embodied in instructions which will insure their completion. The administrator must direct the work in an impersonal manner, not become involved in too many details, and see that the organization's purpose is fulfilled according to established principles. Executives have a duty to see that the quantity and quality of performance of each employee are maintained.

The administrator is a leader. His or her success is determined by ability to direct others successfully toward established goals. Individuals of weak responibility and limited capability cannot perform this function successfully. The good administrator must be superior in determination, persistence, endurance, and courage. He must clearly understand his organization's purposes and keep them in mind as he guides and leads the way. Through direction, it is essential that faith be created in the cooperative enterprise, in success, in achievement of personal ambitions, in integrity of the leadership provided, and in the superiority of associated efforts.

E. Coordinating

Coordinating means interrelating all the various phases of work within an organization. This means that the organization's structure must clearly provide for close relationships and competent leadership in the coordinating centers of activity. The administrator must meet regularly with chief assistants. Here arrangements can be made for unity of effort, reports can be submitted on progress, and obstacles to coordinated work can be eliminated. Good coordination also means that all factors must be considered in their proper perspective.

The administrator must meet regularly with chief assistants. (Courtesy of Sacramento, California, City Unified School District.)

This duty requires the establishment of a faith which runs throughout the organization. Coordination can be effective only if there is faith in the enterprise and in the need for coordinated effort. It is the motivating factor that stimulates human beings to continue rendering service so that goals may be accomplished.

There should also be coordination with administrative units outside the organization where such responsibilities are necessary.

F. Reporting

Reporting is the administrative duty of supplying information to administrators or executives higher on the line of authority, or other groups to which one is responsible. It also means that subordinates must be kept informed through regular reports, research, and continual observation. In this respect the administrator is a point of intercommunication. In addition to accepting the responsibility for reporting to higher authority, he must continually know what is going on in the area under his jurisdiction. Members of the organization must be informed on many topics of general interest such as goals to be achieved, progress being made, strong and weak points, and new areas proposed for development. This information will come from various members of the organization.

G. Budgeting

As the word implies, budgeting refers to financial planning and accounting. It is the duty of the administrator to allocate to various subdivisions the general funds allotted to the organization. This must be done in a manner which is equitable and just. In carrying out this function, he must keep the organization's purposes in mind and apportion the available money to those areas or projects which will help most in achieving these purposes. It also means controls must be established to insure that certain limits will be observed, so-called "budget padding" will be kept to a minimum, and complete integrity in the handling of all the budgetary aspects of the organization will be maintained.

H. Fayol's Administrative Duties

A list of sixteen administrative duties in Gulick and Urwick's book, *Papers on the Science of Administration,* has been credited to Fayol, a specialist in administration. They are worthy of careful thought by all who are in or who covet administrative positions, since they reflect considered opinion of a few years back.

1. See that the plan of operations is carefully prepared and strictly carried out.
2. See that the human and material organizations are suitable for the objects, resources, and needs of the undertaking.
3. Establish a management which is competent and has a singleness of purpose.
4. Coordinate operations and efforts.
5. Make decisions which are clear, distinct, and precise.
6. Make careful selection of staff—each department has a competent and energetic head: each employee where he can be of most service.
7. Define duties clearly.
8. Encourage the desire for initiative and responsibility.
9. Reward men fairly and judiciously for their services.
10. Impose penalties for mistakes and blunders.
11. See that discipline is maintained.
12. See that individual interests do not interfere with the general interest.
13. Pay special attention to unity of command.
14. Ensure material and human order.
15. Subject everything to control.
16. Avoid red tape.[2]

----

[2]Ibid, p. 126.

The duties of the administrator that have been discussed above show how essential his work is to the maintenance and effectiveness of any organization. He or she has the responsibility of maintaining the organization by leading a group of individuals toward the accomplishment of specified goals.

VII. CODE FOR ADMINISTRATORS

Francis J. Curtis, Vice-President of the Monsanto Chemical Company, pointed out recently in a speech that administrators should be protected from overwork. He emphasized this point by stating that a man 47 years old who had started his business career at 22 at a salary of $3,600 and had advanced to the second echelon from the top management post and a salary of $40,000 was worth to the company, at the very least, $425,000. He laid down for executives ten requirements for membership in what he called the *Coronary Club*. These rules were as follows:

> 1. Your job comes first; personal considerations are secondary.
> 2. Go to the office evenings, Saturdays, Sundays, and holidays.
> 3. Take the brief case home on the evenings when you do not go to the office. This provides an opportunity to review completely all the troubles and worries of the day.
> 4. Never say no to a request—always say yes.
> 5. Accept all invitations to meetings, banquets, committees, etc.
> 6. Do not eat a restful relaxing meal—always plan a conference for a meal hour.
> 7. Fishing and hunting are a waste of time and money—you never bring back enough fish or game to justify the expense. Golf, bowling, pool, billiards, cards, gardening, etc., are a waste of time.
> 8. It is a poor policy to take all the vacation time that is provided for you.
> 9. Never delegate responsibility to others—carry the entire load at all times.
> 10. If your work calls for traveling, work all day and drive all night to make your appointment for the next morning.[3]

The value of the administrator to his organization should be recognized and the necessary measures provided to protect the investment. Mr. Curtis felt that able assistants, regular medical examinations, compulsory vacations, sabbatical leaves, retirement provisions, hobbies, and outside interests were some essential measures.

QUESTIONS AND EXERCISES

1. Why is a knowledge of administration necessary for every member of an organization?
2. Define the term "administration" in your own words and give an illustration to point out the various facets of your definition.
3. In a paragraph of not more than 250 words discuss the history of administration, giving special emphasis to the Greeks, Cameralists, and Woodrow Wilson.
4. Discuss the qualifications of a good administrator, giving concrete examples to support the importance of each qualification that is listed.
5. Prepare an organization chart for some department, school, or agency with which you are associated. Discuss significant aspects of the administrative setup of this organization.
6. What is meant by the statement, "Administration is a science"?

---

[3]"Business Advised On Human Assets," *New York Times,* March 29, 1954, p. 19.

7. List and discuss the major duties of the administrator. Tell how these apply to a specific organization with which you are familiar.

8. Prepare a rating sheet that could be utilized by students to determine the extent of their qualifications for the field of administration.

SELECTED REFERENCES

Barnard, Chester I. *Organization and Management.* Cambridge, Massachusetts: Harvard University Press, 1949.

Barnard, Chester I. *The Functions of the Executive.* Cambridge, Massachusetts: Harvard University Press, 1946.

Bender, James F. *The Technique of Executive Leadership.* New York: McGraw-Hill Book Company, Inc., 1950.

Cooper, Alfred M. *How to Supervise People.* New York: McGraw-Hill Book Company, Inc., 1941.

Fosbroke, G. E. *Common Sense Business Leadership.* New York: Duell, Sloan and Pearce, 1946.

Green, Philip. *Your Organization.* New York: Hastings House, 1943.

Gulick, Luther and Urwick, L. (Editors). *Papers on the Science of Administration.* New York: Institute of Public Administration, 1937.

Laird, Donald A. and Laird, Eleanor C. *Practical Business Psychology.* New York: Gregg Publishing Company, 1951.

Lepawsky, Albert. *Administration.* New York: Alfred A. Knopf, 1949.

Lincoln, James F. *Lincoln's Incentive System.* New York: McGraw-Hill Book Company, Inc., 1946.

Newman, William H. *Administrative Action.* New York: Prentice-Hall, Inc., 1951.

Ross, Donald H. et al. (Editors). *Administration for Adaptability.* 525 West 120th Street, New York: Metropolitan School Study Council, 1951.

Russell, John Dale, and Reeves, Floyd W. *The Evaluation of Higher Institutions,* Vol. VI, "Administration." Chicago, Illinois: The University of Chicago Press, 1936.

Tead, Ordway. *The Art of Administration.* New York: McGraw-Hill Book Company, Inc., 1951.

Tead, Ordway. *The Art of Leadership.* New York: Whittlesey House, 1935.

Urwick, L. *The Elements of Administration.* New York: Harper & Brothers, 1943.

Chapter II

ADMINISTRATION AND PERSONNEL POLICIES

The most important consideration in administration is personnel. The members of an organization determine whether it will succeed or fail. The administrator must take into account the factors that promote cooperation, principles of good human relations, fallacy of final authority, importance of decisiveness, need for good staff morale, principles to be observed in personnel management, incentives for promoting cooperative effort, and the communicating process.

I. PRINCIPLES OF COOPERATION

The individual determines to what organization he or she wants to belong. The choice is conditioned by such motivating factors as purposes, desires, and impulses. After associating with an organization, services and relationships will depend upon how one is respected as an entity. The function of administration comes into force for reconciling conflicting interests, ideals, conditions, and positions.

Cooperation is essential to the successful functioning of an organization. Cooperation is effective and necessary to perform tasks that require a combination of human powers and to accomplish work that must be performed in a minimum amount of time. It is also important where the physical endurance and other human characteristics of one individual are insufficient—where group thinking is needed, or where work must continue over an extended period of time.

To achieve cooperation implies that the specialties and unique abilities of individuals must be noted and utilized in situations where their services will be rendered under optimum conditions. The permanency of cooperation will depend upon the degree to which the purposes of the organization are achieved and individual motives are satisfied. The function of the executive is to see that these essentials are accomplished.

II. THE INDIVIDUAL AS A MEMBER OF AN ORGANIZATION

How may individuals be expected to react as members of an organization? This is a question that should be asked by all interested in administration.

An individual may act in many ways, depending upon his biological make-up. Action can be impulsive and unpremeditated, caused by certain drives or impulses. A response may be one of fear, anger, or joy. The action can be habitual, the result of learned acts performed under select conditions. It may be rational, a result of having several alternatives to follow. Under this circumstance, action is taken only after consideration of the various issues involved. Or action may be intuitional, based on a feeling that some specific action should be taken because of instinctive perception, rather than careful logical thought and reasoning.

Each individual is different and is made up of a combination of characteristics. The action that he takes will depend upon what he thinks will contribute most to the establishment of the ego.

Each individual wants to be recognized, have a feeling of belonging, and maximize his ego. The process that determines whether such goals are realized is social in nature. Everyone recognizes that group action is essential to the establishment of self. Therefore, membership in organizations is sought. Whether or not one is accepted depends upon what one has to offer in the way of service or specialized abilities. An organization's recognition of an individual's contributions results in satisfaction and self-esteem. The building of self or the development of ego can occur in all types of associated activity, whether it be at work, home, school, church, or in some other setting.

The associated efforts involved in the work experience of the individual should be satisfying. This is where most individuals spend a considerable amount of time. If the individual is not recognized, cannot grow and develop, does not feel that he belongs, he will look to other areas for these essential human needs. In so doing he may neglect his work and even become obtrusive in his efforts which, as a result, may affect many other persons. An organization's success depends upon each individual member's being an essential and important component of the total process.

The administrator in the capacity of leader must recognize the importance of each individual in the organization. Leaders who are trusted and friendly, who recognize importance of group goals, and who have respect and concern for each member of the group will motivate behavior which is happy and productive.

Every administrator should seek to imbue the organization with the theme that every individual has a stake in the enterprise. The enterprise can be successful only as all contribute to the maximum of their potential. With the success of the enterprise will come increased satisfaction to each individual. Above all, it must be recognized that submergence of self is necessary for the achievement of the organization's goals.

III. THE FALLACY OF FINAL AUTHORITY

The administrator is often envisioned as an executive who occupies a very high position with absolute power. He can hire and fire at will, he can issue orders covering a wide range of areas, and everyone in the organization is subject to his every whim and desire. He is looked upon as having the supreme and final authority over all his subordinates and their every act. The administrator is seen as a "Scrooge" who gives orders to various "David Cratchet's."

This idea of administration has come down through history from the ancient kings who possessed absolute authority over their subjects and from men in high positions who seized or inherited great power. Such powerful individuals still exist today in some of the Fascist and totalitarian states of the world. However, in this country where democratic principles pervade such authority is a fallacy.

Final authority in any one individual's hands is a dangerous weapon and should be permitted only in rare instances. As one author has stated, "Administrators hold power and where humans hold power there is temptation to tyranny; and where there is temptation, there is yielding." Francis Bacon said, "The one who has power thinks he can command the end, yet rarely has he patience to endure the means." Whitehead concurred when he stated, "The enjoyment of power is fatal to the subtleties of life." Prince Kropotkin is more direct in his answer when he says, "It is a commonplace of history that power is poisonous to those who exercise it."

Modern-day administrators must rely on the other members of their organizations for the achievement of their objectives. Decisions are reached only after several members, all of whom have interests bearing on the judgment, have deliberated. Many of the decisions are made by individuals who are subordinate to the administrator at the top. Plans are worked out, reports are made, and the spadework is often done by the lower echelons, leaving only a routine approval by the man or woman at the helm.

If the administrator takes the sole authority for making decisions without consulting others, many judgments will be wrong because of lack of information. Organizations function best when informed thinking is brought into play. President Eisenhower, upon taking office, pointed out that he was depending upon his various Cabinet members and other government officials to make many decisions, leaving only the most important issues for him to decide.

The authority that does exist belongs to the job and not to the person. The administrator should never feel powerful and all-important. Authority does not reside in one human being but in the best thinking, judgment, and imagination that the organization can command. Every individual has the authority which goes with his position and only that much. In turn this authority is conditioned by other members whose work is closely allied to his in achieving the objectives for which the organization exists. Authority comes from those who perform the more technical aspects of the organization's work as well as from those who, because of their positions, are responsible for the ultimate decisions. Department heads, foremen, and staff consultants issue reports interpreting the facts. Their judgments, conclusions, and recommendations contribute to formulation of the final decisions that are the responsibility of the administrator. If these interpretations, judgments, conclusions, and recommendations are not accepted, the organization may fail. Its best thinking has been ignored. Furthermore, individuals cannot be induced to contribute their efforts in an organization that has little respect for their thinking. Authority is not resident in one person. Instead, it permeates the entire organization from top to bottom.

Naturally, there has to be compliance by the members of the organization with orders that are handed down by administrators. This is essential for the efficient running of any organization. Most individuals will comply with such orders, provided they understand the communication, it is consistent with the purpose for which the organization exists, is compatible with their interests and incentives as members of the organization, and they are capable of complying. Administrators must keep these facts in mind in issuing communications. Sometimes it becomes necessary to issue orders which do not conform with the individual's wishes. In such cases there must be good reason for such action. In addition there should be some preliminary explanation and persuasion or an offer of inducements in order that the issue will be overlooked. Everything should be done to avoid denial of authority.

At times when there is flouting and disregard of authority, it becomes necessary to sever an individual's association with the organization. Attacking an organization or intentionally disregarding assigned duties should result in punitive action, even to the point of separation from service. Rules and regulations that exist grow out of practice and are made in the best interests of the organization. They help in the achievement of objectives. They must be adhered to.

IV. DECISIONS

The decisions an administrator makes determine his or her prestige and standing with other personnel in the organization. If a decision is not made at a time when one is needed, suspense and lethargy will develop. If the wrong decision is continually made, the staff and organization will lose faith. Good leadership requires that decisions be made which are right and in the best interests of the organization. This includes every member of that entity. Good leaders must be willing to decide important issues and be capable of doing so in the right way. This is essential from the standpoint of good personnel relations as well as organization efficiency.

A. When Do Decisions Have to Be Made?

Decisions have to be made in varying situations. They are necessary when directions are issued by a superior officer requesting that action be taken. If the president of a college tells a dean or department head that a reorganization of the subdivision is necessary, the administrator in charge of the lower unit has to make decisions in order to carry out the desire of the superior officer.

Decisions are necessary when subordinate members of one's own staff appeal to the administrator for action on certain proposals. Confusion may exist as to conflicting assignments or a feeling of discrimination on the part of a subordinate. In such cases the administrator must act. His or her perspective of the entire situation is better and the position demands that a decision be made to iron out the difficulty. Only confusion and poor morale will exist if the administrator hedges and does not act.

Decisions are often made on the administrator's own initiative. Many times long-term goals, plans, and thinking require that decisions be made without a request from either above or below. In many ways these decisions represent the effectiveness of an administrator. When President Roosevelt took office in 1933 he immediately closed all the banks in the country. This was a decision which was taken on his own initiative, demanded much courage and foresight, but later proved wise and contributed greatly to the financial stability of this country. Administrators may be questioned when they make decisions on their own initiative.

Therefore, they must be reasonably sure they are right before taking a stand. They are in a position to decide problems and issues better than any other individual. They have an obligation to perform this function. Decisions should not be premature or too late, but should be made when they are pertinent to the situation at hand. They should be made only if they will result in action which is effective and will contribute to the accomplishment of set goals. Furthermore, they should be made only if the administrator in question is the right individual to pass on such matters.

All administrators are human beings. They are subject to error. The best they can do is to use their fine powers of discrimination to estimate the wisdom of their actions in terms of future results. This means that before a decision is made all pertinent facts would be considered, which include past experience and knowledge with similar situations. Good personnel relations and good morale will ultimately result if such a procedure is followed.

B. Factors to Consider in Making Good Decisions

Since administrators are constantly required to make decisions which affect personnel in their organization, it is essential that they prepare themselves for this responsibility. They should continually be gathering data and materials on all important matters and on all individuals within the organization. Periodically, both the superior and the subordinate members of the organization should be informed of the facts and findings. Policies should be established which are clear and have the consent of the members of the organization.

Decisions should include a consideration of all the necessary aspects of the case or situation in question and should be applicable to the needs of the organization.

Decisions should be practicable and capable of feasible operation. In addition, they should be recognized by the personnel involved as being helpful to the accomplishment of organization's goals. They should improve morale rather than destroy it and should be received with a cooperative attitude.

Finally, it should be recognized by every administrator that effectiveness as an executive is derived fundamentally from a sharing of decision-making with the members of the organization. The associated thinking of informed colleagues is a firm basis for sound decisions.

V. STAFF MORALE

There are certain definite conditions which are known to contribute to staff morale. Some of the more important of these conditions will be discussed. Administrators should continually strive to create such conditions in their organizations. The degree of staff morale that exists will be in direct proportion to the degree to which such conditions are satisfied.

A. Leadership

It goes without saying that the quality of the leaders will determine staff morale to a great degree. From the top down, there should be careful selection of all individuals who act in leadership capacities. Other things being equal, individuals will contribute better service, produce more, have an over-all better morale, and have more respect for individuals who are leaders in the true sense of the word. This is also important from the standpoint of attracting the most out-standing persons to an organization. Human beings do more than brick and mortar and other material things to induce the best minds and the most qualified persons to join an organization.

There must be mutual trust and confidence between leaders and other per-sonnel. This is essential for obtaining the moral support that is so necessary to the establishment of good faith on the part of all. Furthermore, only as this good faith is established will the operating procedures be carried out in the most efficient and effective way possible.

B. Physical and Social Environment

Good physical and social environments are essential to good staff morale.

The health of the worker must be provided for. There must be good lighting to protect the eyes, good air to protect the lungs, and adequate safety precautions to protect the body. There must be provisions for mental health which include proper supervision, provision for advancement, provision for any emergency that may arise, and provision for intellectual improvement. Anything that is conducive to physical, mental, and emotional health is important to the morale of the individ-ual and in turn to his efficiency as a member of the organization.

The social environment is also an important consideration. The individuals with whom one works and the activities in which one engages can strengthen or dampen the spirit. An individual is the product of his interactions with others. Therefore, in order to improve oneself it is very important to associate with those who can contribute to this improvement. Since the working day represents, to a great degree, the majority of an individual's social relationships, it is important that these relationships be wholesome and conducive to individual improvement.

C. Advancement

Human beings like to feel that they are "getting ahead in the world." This is an important consideration in developing and continuing a high degree of staff morale. This consideration necessitates informing each member of an organization as to what is essential for progress. Opportunities should be provided for self-improvement in learning new skills, gaining new knowledge, and having new ex-periences. In addition, encouragement should be given those who are anxious to improve and are willing to devote extra time and effort for such a purpose.

Performance records should be available so that personnel can determine the degree to which they are achieving their goals, their weaknesses and strengths, and the requirements necessary for promotion. A broad program of in-service training should be established in every organization to provide adequately for this essential requisite to staff morale.

D. Recognition of Meritorious Service

Another requirement, similar to advancement, which is a requisite for staff morale, is recognition for outstanding contribution. As has been previously pointed out, all human beings have an ego which likes to be flattered. Those who make outstanding contributions to the organization should be recognized. This is very important to further greater achievements.

There should be provisions for material awards in the form of salary. This is one incentive that is used in American society as an indication of accomplishment. Therefore, in order to have good morale and also to compete with other organizations, this is necessary. There should also be provision for other incentives such as positions with additional prestige, commendation, and public acknowledgment. It is essential to acknowledge the progress that an organization is making and the contributions of the members who make such progress possible.

VI. PERSONNEL MANAGEMENT

There are certain principles that must be recognized in dealing with personnel. Every executive must understand such truths if he or she would administer wisely.

A. Level of Performance

It must be recognized that, over a long period of time, the level of performance of individual members of an organization will be determined by the performance of the individual who occupies the highest executive position. Individuals who are competent cannot seem to produce at their highest level for an extended period of time if they are encumbered by weak leadership. The leader sets the pace. An organization, to function at its highest efficiency, must have at the top a person who is also "tops" in efficiency. It is a fallacy to think that a weak leader can be surrounded with outstanding associates and produce great results. In time the poor leadership will reflect itself from the top to the bottom of the organization.

B. Selection and Dismissal of Personnel

The manner in which the administrator selects, keeps, and dismisses personnel will determine to a great degree his success as an executive.

Only the most competent individuals must be selected. The individuals who have proved themselves in their jobs should be retained. The administrator's ability to provide incentives and to use the power of persuasion will determine whether or not key personnel are kept. Finally, the way in which an administrator deals with incompetent and obtrusive individuals will determine in great measure the state of morale and efficiency of the staff.

C. Identifying the "Individual"

Every individual member of an organization wants to be a member of the team and feel that he is making a recognized contribution to the group effort. This implies that he wants to know what is going on, how his contribution is aiding in making progress, and that he belongs.

The administrator must recognize that the human being is the "end" and not the "means to an end." His or her job should provide for release of creative human talents in an associated enterprise. This demands the conception of personnel not as workers turning out a product or rendering a service for a master, but as a collection of individuals who are partners in the endeavor. Through such an approach there will be established a loyalty to group effort which will increase services and make production "hum."

Respect for the human personality must be the main consideration in all administrative action. The human element is the most valuable factor in all life. Hundreds of man-hours are utilized in the search for one person lost at sea. Untold wealth is spent to free a coal miner trapped in the ground. Similarly, in an organization, attention must be focused on the human being. The goals that are set in terms of inanimate things must first be evaluated in terms of the animate. Technology must give way to what is best for the human being. All policy and practice must reflect an emphasis on the individual in personal relations.

D. Obtaining Confidence of the Staff

In order to win the cooperation of their staffs, administrators must be cognizant of several requisites.

Administrators must *win* the confidence of their staffs. Regardless of the reputations they have when they take the posts, their success in being accepted and gaining the trust of their personnel will depend on what is done after they take over the "reins of authority."

To win the confidence and cooperation of staff members requires that administrators be honest and sincere. When they are wrong they should admit their errors. At times they must divulge unpleasant truths. They must never be sarcastic. To be insincere with an associate will result in loss of confidence. Individuals recognize that administrators are not perfect, but at the same time they expect an admission of error when it exists and a conscious and sincere desire to understand problems.

Administrators will gain the confidence of the members of their organizations only as their actions unfold from day to day on the job. They are the masters of their own destinies.

E. Welfare of Personnel

Administrators and organizations should recognize that in personnel management the welfare of the individual must be provided for. There must be adequate medical protection, pensions, recreation facilities, safety precautions, sickness benefits, and accident compensation. In addition, as has been pointed out, there must be good working conditions in respect to light, air, temperature, and sanitary conditions.

A point that is very important, however, in making provisions for the welfare of employees, is that good human relations cannot be purchased. Good working conditions are essential to human welfare but cannot be used as a substitute for the principles of cooperative effort and human relations that have been previously discussed.   They are details that should be attended to in the name of human decency and in order to provide the most favorable setting for productive effort. The administrator cannot take the attitude that "Now that I have given you all these things, I can order you around any way I would like and disregard good human relations as much as I wish."

F. The Money Motive

Those who deal with individuals must realize that money is not the only thing that motivates human beings.   They cannot have the attitude that since they have provided a large salary, they don't have to provide any further incentive.

Any administrator who makes such an assumption is due for a big disappointment.   An organization cannot exist on a purely economic motive.   It is a factor that should be considered, but it is limited in its potentials.   Individuals want something more than money out of a job.   An actual experience points this up.   One individual in a school position was given a thousand-dollar raise one year. The chairman of his department continually referred to the raise as the solution to any and all problems that existed in regard to this person.   However, there were many other factors in regard to that individual's welfare which the thousand dollars could not solve.   In fact he moved to another position the following year.

In addition to money, individuals want recognition, prestige, a faith in the leadership provided, and the knowledge that they are contributing to a worthy cause, are making others happy, and enriching their lives through their endeavors. In this day and age when so much stress is placed on material things, it is very important for administrators to recognize that a good raise and a large salary are not panaceas for every problem.

G. Individual Differences

An important principle of personnel management is the recognition of individual differences and different types of work.   Individuals differ in many ways— abilities, skills, training, physical, mental, and social qualities.   There are also various types of work which require different skills, abilities, and training.

These differences in individuals and types of work must be recognized by the administrator.   One of his or her main duties in respect to personnel should be to make sure that the right person is in the right niche.   An individual who is a "round peg in a square hole" does not contribute to his own or to the organization's welfare.   To be placed in a position which should be held by a person with lesser qualifications or vice versa is unjust and devastating in its results.

It is important for the administrator to recognize in some formal way individual differences that exist in the organization.   A system of status must exist for purposes of communication and orderly procedure.   Such systems of status must be readily understood, authoritative, and authentic.   These systems of status not only make for better communication but also provide the basis for personnel improvement and advancement within the organization.   Furthermore, they help to develop a sense of responsibility in the individual.   The status that is granted any one person should be in line with capacities and importance of the function. Many disruptive features can develop in status systems if there is not recognition of individual abilities, if the system is allowed to become an end rather than means to an end, and if proper incentives are not provided at each level.

VII. INCENTIVES

Individuals contribute services or produce goods because of certain motivating factors. These motivating factors can be called incentives. Energies are expended and efforts put forth because of incentives. Since individuals are the most important factor in an organization, it is very important that incentives be considered.

Newman points out various incentives, on which there is considerable agreement in management, to which most human beings respond.

1. Higher financial income
2. Social status and respect
3. Security
4. Attractive work
5. Opportunity for development
6. Worth-while activity
7. Personal power and influence
8. Treatment of each subordinate as an individual person
9. Voice in his own affairs for each man
10. Just and diligent supervision[1]

Man is motivated as certain incentives are brought into play, or on the other hand, as certain bad features of work are decreased. For example, if one's salary is increased, it acts as an added incentive, whereas if excessive working hours are decreased, that also acts as an incentive. There is also another consideration in viewing incentives. The individual's state of mind is very important. A person's attitude will determine whether certain incentives can act as motivating factors. This consideration is very important in the fields of religion and education where the desire to render a service and the desire to do good are attitudes of mind which motivate action.

A. Types of Incentives

There are many types of incentives which result in an individual's associating with an organization and thence contributing his energies to its success. Some of the more outstanding incentives are discussed below:

1. **Material Items.**—Some of the most attractive incentives in this day of interpreting values in terms of material possessions are such items as money and shelter. These serve as incentives for most people up to the subsistence level. However, beyond this point, most individuals need additional inducements.

2. **Nonmaterial Items.**—Such incentives as prestige in one's work, a position where one's power is felt, or where an individual is tabbed with the title of "man or woman of distinction" are very important to many people. Individuals will sometimes forego high salaries and other material possessions to gain these nonmaterial things.

---

[1]William H. Newman. *Administrative Action.* New York: Prentice-Hall, Inc., 1951, p. 449.

3. Optimum Physical Conditions.—It is important to most persons to work in an atmosphere and setting where there are good physical conditions such as light, heat, and fresh air in the immediate surroundings of one's endeavors. In addition, the general geographical section of the country plays a major part. Some desire a warm climate all year. Others like the mountains and still others like dry air. These represent incentives which motivate persons to select certain locations.

4. Satisfaction of Personal Ambitions to Do Good.—Individuals are frequently spurred on by personal desires to do good. The desire to serve one's family and one's neighbors, the desire to render a service to one's community, the desire to satisfy personal ideals, and the desire to produce a thing of beauty which will provide esthetic satisfaction to many—these are incentives which are very important in the lives of many individuals.

The geographical section of the country may be an incentive. (Courtesy Department of Physical Education, University of California, Berkeley.)

5. Belonging to An Attractive Organization.—Some individuals like to be associated with a recognized and well-known organization, or one that has certain features attractive to them personally. This may mean being on the faculty of an "Ivy League" College, associated with the National Broadcasting System, the Riverside Church in New York City, or Twentieth-Century Fox Studios. These are well-known institutions, and, for some, to be identified with an organization that is known is an incentive. Others find certain organizations attractive because of the persons or employees who work there. Attraction might be based on such conditions as freedom from racial hostility, a place for professional growth, or means of satisfying personal ambitions.

6. A Harmonious Pattern of Work.—Persons like to associate themselves with an organization where methods of work are familiar, attitudes are similar, and practices are known. Through years of experience the individual becomes set in his ways and in his thinking. He desires to associate himself with organizations that think and work along similar lines—ones which he knows and likes.

7. Mental Health.—Individuals prefer working conditions which are conducive to good mental health. Many desire such things as freedom from tensions and conflict, absence of highly competitive working conditions, security on the job, and absence of strain. They do not want to be tied down to their jobs to such an extent that they interfere with their family and community responsibilities. Many are willing to accept less pay and chance for advancement in order to have these conditions.

B. Persuasion

In many cases it is necessary for an organization to change the thinking of individuals so that the incentives which it has to offer will be attractive. This may be called persuasion. All administrators should possess the art of persuasion if they would surround themselves with the most competent individuals.

Men's and women's minds may be changed by coercion or by education. Some individuals join organizations because they have been coerced into joining. Slaves in pre-Civil War days were forced to work on certain plantations. Young men are drafted into the Army. Laborers are many times denied certain benefits unless they join the union. These are examples of coercion. Individuals are forced to cooperate. All will recognize that this type of persuasion is not the type that is most productive of goods and services.

Some individuals join organizations because they are persuaded that it is in their own interest and welfare to become a member and cooperate. People usually do not contribute and become members unless they are convinced it is worth while. Through education, it is possible to persuade individuals of the need for cooperating with certain organizations. The area of religion provides a good example of the individual's being educated from the time that he is very young, through adulthood. Through religious instruction and indoctrination the person develops a need for joining a particular church. Thus the individual has been persuaded through education to "belong." The art of persuasion can also be accomplished through an appeal to patriotism or the idea of service to a worthy cause.

The important item to remember when providing incentives is that all individuals cannot be treated alike. The administrator must recognize that different individuals are motivated by different incentives. What moves one person to action will not necessarily move another. Another point is that administrators are unable to offer all the incentives that are needed to get the cooperation that is necessary. Therefore, the thinking of some individuals must be changed through the art of the administrator's persuasion. Through a combination of incentives and persuasion the most competent individuals can be brought into an organization, where as members they will contribute the cooperation that is needed for successful accomplishment of purposes. Some incentives are necessary—some persuasion is also necessary. Through a balance of both, progress will be made.

VIII. COMMUNICATION AND PERSONNEL RELATIONS

Communication has been previously referred to as the lines of authority within the structure of a formal organization. A system of communication is essential in order to have an efficiently run organization. The system should be clearly understood by all personnel so that conflict will not ensue. This is essential to good personnel relations. The following are some important rules to keep in mind in regard to the system of communication.

A. Channels of Communication Should Be Known by All Members of the Organization

Through the use of organization charts, education, announcements, and other devices, the administrator should leave no doubt in anyone's mind as to each person's position in the system of communication. Official appointments should be made known, each individual should understand the nature and scope of his position, and the lines of authority should be definitely established.

B. The Importance of a Formal Line of Communication

All members of the organization should understand why it is important that every person be responsible to some one individual and why such formal relationship is necessary to efficiency. The administrator should explain these things to his staff if they are not already clearly understood. Individuals will cooperate more readily if they understand the need for such organization.

C. The Line of Communication Should Be as Direct as Possible

There will be less opportunity for misunderstanding if the line of communication is short and direct. Communications are given either orally or in writing and the greater the number of coordinating centers through which they have to pass, the greater is the chance for error. There is also the danger of a misinterpretation as the communication progresses through many individuals. The administrator should recognize this principle and, in setting up or revising the structure of the organization, should provide for only as many positions as are absolutely necessary for purposes of communication and coordination. If the administrative organization becomes too large, it becomes cumbersome, bureaucracy develops, red-tape ensues, and the efficiency of the organization breaks down. The lines of communication should be clear, logical, short, direct, and within the understanding of all.

D. The Line of Communication Should Be Used, Once It Is Established

With few exceptions, communications should pass through each coordinating center of the formal line of authority. Administrators should know what is going on. This is possible only if communications pass through them on the way up and on the way down. In addition to the importance of keeping key persons informed of various actions, this is also important from the standpoint of eliminating conflicting communications, having proper interpretation as the communication progresses through various levels, maintaining responsibility, and insuring that the prestige of executives is maintained. These important considerations will not be possible unless the system of communication is observed from top to bottom.

Under certain circumstances, individuals in the lower ranks of organization have business to transact directly with individuals in the higher echelons of authority. To provide for such a condition, there should be some provision for direct lines of communication to the top.

E. Competent Individuals Must Occupy the Positions of Authority

In order to insure a high degree of morale, efficiency of operation, and effective cooperation, it is essential that only competent persons occupy the positions of authority in the formal line of communication. Good communication exists only where there is respect, confidence, and trust in those individuals who have been assigned key positions.

F. Emergencies Must Be Provided For in the Communication System

When a key individual in an organization dies, when a chairman of a department is unexpectedly absent from work, or when some other emergency occurs, the lines of authority must continue to operate. An organization survives and accomplishes its objectives only if it has provided for continuous operation at all times. This is similar to the adage known in the theatre: "The Show Must Go On." Regardless of what may happen, the play must go on as scheduled. Similarly, in any organization, regardless of the nature of the emergency, provision must be made so that the responsibilities are fulfilled. One can readily imagine what would happen if the President of the United States were killed and there were no provision for a successor. It would make the country weak and vulnerable. The same thing could happen to any organization.

G. All Communications Should Be Valid and Authentic

Communications will be accepted only as they are authentic and valid. This means that the individual who issues the communication has authority to assume such a responsibility and that it is an official communication. The administrator should be careful not to exceed the authority and responsibilities of his office. This is essential to a recognition of and faith in any system of communication.

QUESTIONS AND EXERCISES

1. Discuss the implications for administration of the saying, "No man can live unto himself alone."

2. From your own experience, prepare a list of principles which you feel are essential to good personnel relations.

3. Prepare two skits, one dramatizing some aspect of good personnel relations and the other pointing up some poor practices in regard to such relations.

4. Write an essay discussing the role of the administrator in achieving cooperation from members of an organization.

5. What are the essential requisites for every individual in order to perform good work?

6. What is meant by the term, "fallacy of final authority"? Cite two illustrations to support the idea involved.

7. What are the factors that must be taken into consideration in making decisions?

8. List and discuss five essentials of staff morale.

9. Discuss and cite examples to prove the validity of five principles of personnel management.

10. Why is money not the only incentive which motivates an individual to join an organization? Discuss the various types of incentives.

11. What do we mean by the statement that the administrator should possess the "art of persuasion"?

12. What are some basic principles that should be observed in respect to channels of communication?

SELECTED REFERENCES

Barnard, Chester I. *The Functions of the Executive.* Cambridge, Massachusetts: Harvard University Press, 1946.

Bender, James F. *The Technique of Executive Leadership.* New York: McGraw-Hill Book Company, Inc., 1950. Chapter III.

Cooper, Alfred M. *How to Supervise People.* New York: McGraw-Hill Book Company, Inc., 1941.

Gittler, Joseph B. *Social Dynamics.* New York: McGraw-Hill Book Company, Inc., 1952.

Glover, John Desmond and Hower, Ralph M. *The Administrator—Cases on Human Relations in Business.* Homewood, Illinois: Richard D. Irwin, Inc., 1952.

Halsey, George D. *Handbook of Personnel Management.* New York: Harper & Brothers, 1947.

Halsey, George D. *Supervising People.* New York: Harper & Brothers, 1946.

Laird, Donald A. *The Psychology of Selecting Employees.* New York: McGraw-Hill Book Company, Inc., 1937.

Lincoln, James F. *Lincoln's Incentive System.* New York: McGraw-Hill Book Company, Inc., 1946.

Newman, William H. *Administrative Action.* New York: Prentice Hall, Inc., 1951.

Parker, Willard E. and Kleemeier, Robert W. *Human Relations in Supervision.* New York: McGraw-Hill Book Company, Inc., 1951.

Stowers, Harvey. *Management Can Be Human.* New York: McGraw-Hill Book Company, Inc., 1946.

Tead, Ordway and Metcalf, Henry. *Personnel Administration.* New York: McGraw-Hill Book Company, Inc., 1933.

Ward, Roswell. *The Personnel Program of Jack and Heintz.* New York: Harper & Brothers, 1946.

Webb, Ewing T. and Morgan, John B. *Strategy in Handling People.* Garden City, New York: Garden City Publishing Company, Inc., 1930.

Yoder, Dale. *Personnel Management and Industrial Relations.* New York: Prentice-Hall, Inc., 1948.

Chapter III

MANAGEMENT

Administration must concern itself with many important functions. These have been outlined in general in the preceding pages. The purpose of this chapter is to discuss various aspects of the structure of an organization and deal more fully with certain administrative responsibilities.

A research committee's report a few years ago, concerned with the advancement of management, listed qualities or traits for rating executives. These main items, on which administrators were rated, point up the importance of a knowledge of various aspects of management.

1. Does the administrator organize, plan, and delegate his work?
2. Does he or she learn new methods and procedures?
3. Does he assume responsibility in keeping with good judgment?
4. Is this man or woman thorough and reliable in work performance? Does he or she get results?
5. What is the administrator's attitude toward the job of organization?
6. Does he identify good subordinates and train and develop them for increased responsibility?
7. Does the administrator cooperate with and obtain cooperation from those above and below him?
8. Does this executive make decisions?
9. Does the administrator analyze data critically and give the proper emphasis to each factor?
10. Does he use imagination; visualize future possibilities?[1]

I. THE IMPORTANCE AND PURPOSE OF ORGANIZATION

An organization is created when individuals form a group and coordinate their efforts to accomplish definite objectives. These aims or objectives take on various aspects. There are *legal* aspects which are stated in a charter, constitution, or a simple statement of objectives. There are aims which are *social* in nature and are established in order to fill some definite need in society by providing goods or services. In some cases aims are involved with the *technology* of the enterprise and with *profit-making*. Some objectives are in the *personal interests* of those associated with the organization, such as obtaining prestige, power, and reputation. All aims or objectives, regardless of their nature, are designed to do for individuals as a group what cannot be accomplished as well by themselves.

In order to have an efficient organization and accomplish objectives, it is necessary to have a division of work. There are usually many individuals associated with an enterprise and the best results are obtained only as the work is efficiently and

---

[1]David W. Belcher. "The Technique of Rating Key Personnel," *Modern Management* 8: 4-6, August, 1948.

properly divided among these individuals. Furthermore, since human beings differ in such things as ability, skill, and nature, and since there are limits to what one person can do, subdivision of work becomes essential.

With subdivision of work come additional responsibilities in respect to the management of an enterprise. The most favorable type of organizational pattern must be set up; the line and staff arrangement must be clearly established; the aims and policies must be known by all; coordination must be effected; programming, research, public relations, office management, budget control, and other items concerned with routine management must be provided for. If such items are properly administered, there will be effective communication among the members of the organization, individuals will contribute their services willingly, and purposes will be accomplished.

II. ORGANIZATIONAL PATTERNS

Determining what type of pattern will best serve an organization is an important administrative consideration. The organization of a department or other administrative unit will have an important bearing on how it functions. Therefore, it is important to consider the various patterns very carefully. According to Newman the key factors in determining what type of organizational pattern to follow are the following:

1. Take advantage of specialization
2. Facilitate control (ease of supervision, etc.)
3. Aid in coordination
4. Secure adequate attention (recognition within the organization)
5. Recognize local conditions
6. Reduce expense[2]

According to some administrators there are four organizational patterns which an organization may use. These should be considered in the light of the above criteria and are discussed briefly in the following paragraphs:

A. Organization According to Purpose

When organization is according to purpose, the main functions of an administrative unit are brought together and the structure is arranged according to the main purposes or functions for which an organization exists. For example, a city form of government has such functions or purposes as education, police protection, health services, and maintenance of parks. The government has been established to provide these essentials for its constituents. These purposes are considered as separate or closely allied units in a vertical manner in an organization. (See chart, page 50.) Such an arrangement serves to bring together in a single unit those individuals who are associated with similar services.

Under the "purpose" type of organizational pattern, the units organized according to "process" cut across all the vertical "purpose" functions. (See chart, page 50.) Each of these "process" units is concerned with some particular specialized skill or profession. In the area of city government, for example, these might

---

[2]William H. Newman. *Administrative Action.* New York: Prentice-Hall, Inc., 1951. p. 132.

be finance, engineering, clerical, or secretarial work. All are essential to the proper functioning of city government and to the achievement of the various purposes for which the government exists. They service the "purpose" departments.

Some of the advantages of the "purpose" type of organization are that it helps in the accomplishment of particular functions which comprise an administrative unit. It brings together personnel who have similar interests. It focuses attention on the specialized purposes for which an organization exists. It is functional, practical, and can be easily understood by all concerned.

There are some disadvantages of this type of organization. Difficulty is sometimes involved in isolating the purposes for which an organization exists. Considerable overlapping makes such a procedure complicated. This pattern can result in insufficient stress being placed on minor purposes. The consultant services organized in the "process" organization may not be utilized sufficiently. Furthermore, the major purposes into which the organization is structurally patterned may become independent to the point where the over-all central purpose of the organization is not effectively accomplished.

B. Organization According to Process

When organization is according to process, individuals who have special skills or are members of a particular profession comprise the main units of the administrative structure. Using the city government again as an example, this could mean that all the engineers, teachers, lawyers, doctors, etc. would be organized into departments or other administrative units and located vertically on the organizational chart. Such functions as education, health, and police protection would not receive as much administrative emphasis.

Some of the advantages of this type of organization are that it brings together individuals who are specialists or professionals in certain fields of endeavor. It is conducive to high professional standards in specialized types of work. It places the emphasis on skill. It makes possible a better coordination of specialized work because individuals with similar specialties are in one unit rather than placed in many units. And it utilizes the specialized skills, abilities, and knowledges of individuals to the maximum degree.

Some of the disadvantages of this type of organization are that it may be impractical to isolate specialized functions. It places less stress upon purposes and may hinder their effective accomplishment. The heads of the various administrative units organized according to process are likely to be narrow in their thinking and thus hinder successful accomplishment of the over-all objectives of the larger administrative unit.

C. Organization According to Associated Materials or Persons

An administrative pattern which is prominent in stores is division according to particular products or materials. For example, Macy's, May's, and similar establishments are broken down into such departments as hardware, women's apparel, jewelry, cosmetics, books, and men's clothing. Their emphasis is upon the material rather than upon the purpose of the organization or the skill of the individual.

PURPOSE AND PROCESS SUBDIVISIONS IN ORGANIZATION*

Process Subdivision	Health Department DIRECTOR ASSISTANT DIRECTORS	Education Department SUPERINTENDENT ASSISTANT SUPERINTENDENTS	Police Department CHIEF ASSISTANT CHIEFS	Park Department COMMISSIONER ASSISTANT COMMISSIONERS	
Clerical and Secretarial Service DIRECTOR	Private Secretaries Stenographers File Clerks Clerks Messengers	Private Secretaries Stenographers File Clerks Clerks Messengers	Private Secretaries Stenographers File Clerks Clerks Messengers	Private Secretaries Stenographers File Clerks Clerks Messengers	
Finance Department DIRECTOR	Budget Officer Accountants Purchasing Officer Statisticians	Budget Officer Accountants Purchasing Officer Statisticians	Budget Officer Accountants Purchasing Officer Statisticians	Budget Officer Accountants Purchasing Officer Statisticians	Other finance activities including tax administration, continued accounts, etc.
	Personnel Manager Lawyer	Personnel Manager Lawyer	Personnel Manager Lawyer	Personnel Manager Lawyer	
Engineering Department DIRECTOR	Engineers Architects	Engineers Architects		Engineers Architects Landscape Staff	
	Repair Force Janitors	Repair Force Janitors	Repair Force Janitors	Repair Force Janitors	
	Physicians Dentists Nurses Psychologists	Physicians Dentists Nurses Psychologists	Physicians Psychologists		
	Bacteriologists Inspectors	Laboratory Assistants Gardeners Classroom Teachers Special Teachers Librarians Recreation Leaders Playground Supervisors Traffic Supervisor	Crime Lab. Staff Police School Staff Uniformed Force Detective Force Traffic Force Jail Staff Mounted Force Veterinarian Communications Staff	Plant Lab. Staff Gardeners Recreation Leaders Playground Supervisors Park Police Traffic Force Zoo Staff Veterinarian Switchboard Operator	
	Switchboard Operator	Switchboard Operator			
Motorized Service SUPERINTENDENT	Motorized Service	Motorized Service	Motorized Service	Motorized Service	

Vertical network—Purpose Departments
Horizontal network—Process Departments

*Luther Gulick and L. Urwick (Editors). *Papers on the Science of Administration*. New York: Institute of Public Administration, 1937.

There is also prevalent an organizational pattern which stresses the persons who will be served through an enterprise or organization. For example, homes for the aged, the Veterans' Administration, and institutions for the mentally disabled are organizations where all individuals working with a definite group of people or clientele are placed in one administrative unit regardless of their specialties.

D. Organization According to Setting

Another type of administrative pattern is concerned with organization according to geographical location. Some companies and newspaper offices are organized according to a particular area which they serve. Book companies have offices and directors serving such sections as the eastern, midwest, and western sections of the country. Large newspapers such as the *New York Times* have administrative offices in various sections of the world so that there is global coverage of world news.

GEOGRAPHICAL SUBDIVISIONS IN ORGANIZATION*

Health Department	Education Department	Police Department	Park Department
DIRECTOR	DIRECTOR	DIRECTOR	DIRECTOR
Assistant Director	Assistant Director	Assistant Director	Assistant Director
Headquarters Staff	Headquarters Staff	Headquarters Staff	Headquarters Staff
Technical Staff	Technical Staff	Technical Staff	Technical Staff
Downtown	Downtown	Downtown	Downtown
Regional Office	Regional Office	Regional Office	Regional Office
North Side	North Side	North Side	North Side
Regional Office	Regional Office	Regional Office	Regional Office
South Side	South Side	South Side	South Side
Regional Office	Regional Office	Regional Office	Regional Office
West Side	West Side	West Side	West Side
Regional Office	Regional Office	Regional Office	Regional Office

Vertical Network—Purpose Departments
Horizontal Network—Regional Departments
*From Luther Gulick and L. Urwick. *Papers on the Science of Administration.* New York: Institute of Public Administration, 1937, p. 18.

III. LINE AND STAFF

The line and staff type of organization was reputedly developed by the Army and utilized effectively by the Prussians in the campaigns of Gustavus Adolphus of Sweden in the seventeenth century. It is utilized in one form or another in the administrative structure of most organizations. Many of its features are essential to good administration.

The line organization can best be illustrated by using the Army as an example. It refers to the individuals and structure which are responsible for executing, as contrasted with those individuals and structures which are designed to plan, consult, and advise. In the Army the administrative structure has a major general leading a unit called an Army. There are many subdivisions starting with brigadier generals leading brigades, colonels leading regiments, lieutenant colonels or majors leading battalions, captains at the head of companies, and on down through platoons to the corporal and his squad. Each of these key individuals represents a step in the line organization from top to bottom in the Army. These are the lines of authority which pyramid from a private to a major general.

The staff organization is set up according to specialized functions. It does not execute. It acts in an advisory manner to line officers. For example, the engineer

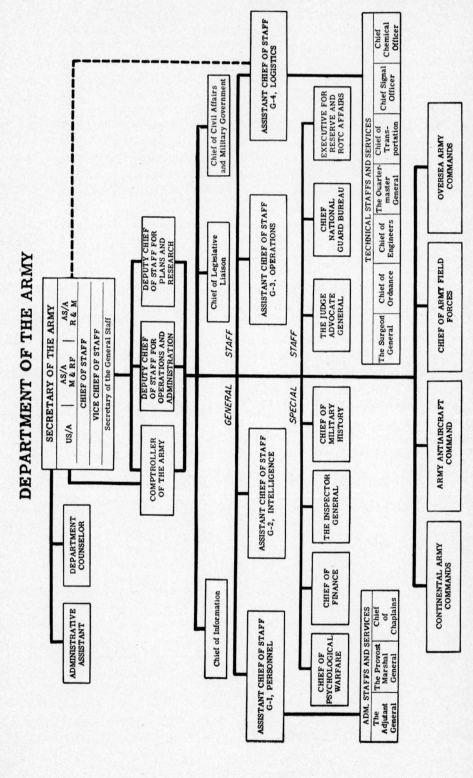

Line and staff. (*United States Government Organization Manual*, 1952-1953. Federal Register Division. National Archives and Records Service, General Services Administration, Washington, D. C., Superintendent of Documents, Government Printing Office.)

and quartermaster divisions represent staff functions. They do work for the whole Army. The main purpose of the staff is one of specialization. Any function which can be so labeled can become a "staff" function. Individuals in staff positions develop standards and plans and give specialized types of services which aid the line officers in executing planned operations.

It has been previously pointed out that every organization of any size must have some formal structure operating throughout its breadth and depth. The "line" and the "staff" are essential to this formal structure. Whereas the line officer's authority extends over all of the subordinate units under his jurisdiction, the staff officer's authority exists only within his own specialized department. As described by one writer, his authority over the line officers is an "authority of ideas." Through advice and consultation the line officers can be influenced by the specialized knowledge of the staff officers.

In this administrative structure all members, regardless of their specific responsibilities, must recognize that both line and staff persons have certain responsibilities for the success and accomplishments of an organization. The staff must recognize their responsibility is to give specialized information and advice. The line must recognize the important function performed by the staff and consider very carefully the ideas and information they dispense.

The difference between line and staff is very important. Individuals associated with each phase must stay within the limits of their responsibilities. Administrators must recognize, however, that although this plan of organization is useful and effective for the assignment of duties and responsibilities, at the same time it can become too rigid and formal. If this is allowed to happen, the initiative and creativeness of many individuals will be lost. The staff may logically and reasonably give commands to the line and the line may perform many of the functions formally designated for staff. The procedure cannot be fixed. The talents of all individuals must be utilized. New types of organization should be developed which break away from many of the unfavorable, undemocratic features of line and staff structure. In all cases the major need is to have proper balance so that the energies, abilities, skills, and thinking of *all* individuals, regardless of their specialities, may be utilized most effectively for the good of the organization. At the same time, an organizational structure should exist which does not permit overlapping, confusion, conflict, and chaos.

IV. ADMINISTRATION AND COORDINATION

Since an organization of any size requires subdivision of work, coordination becomes essential. All individuals engaged in a process must closely coordinate their efforts so that the established goals may be accomplished.

Coordination may be achieved by interrelating the various individuals with their different types of work through an organizational structure which has key individuals located at strategic points. These individuals, through effective communication, coordinate their own and the work of other members of the enterprise.

Coordination may also be achieved by developing in the members of the organization a desire to unite and achieve. As a result of such dominance of purpose, each member will actively attempt to fit particular specialties and efforts into the total, integrated scheme.

If coordination is to be achieved through organization, a system of authority must be established which is sound, practical, and recognized by the members. Organization which has good coordination depends upon centralization of authority that has an effective network of channels of communication through which the efforts of all may be controlled. Several factors should be taken into consideration if effective coordination is to be provided for:

1. The job to be done should be clearly defined. This implies that the facts must be known and informed opinion sought.

2. There should be a head of the enterprise so that adequate leadership and direction will exist.

3. The number of individuals necessary to carry out the work of the organization as it is planned must be determined. Along with this there must be a clear allocation of responsibility for all of the work units into which the total organizational structure has been divided.

4. The formal structure of authority, with its various subdivisions, must be perfected. There must be agreement if assignments are to be carried out. Effective communication has to be established so that there will be an informed opinion from the top to the bottom of the organization. The organization must be so developed that the director, chairman, leader, or whatever he or she is called can coordinate all the various aspects of work with the result that goals are achieved.

5. There should be continuous review and appraisal of results. New problems with new developments will continually occur. Only by continually being conscious of the necessity for making changes in line with new conditions, will the most effective organization be developed.

Coordination is best achieved when all members of an organization are active in new plans and actions that are taken. Members, in order to coordinate their efforts and minds, must participate in the planning and in making decisions. They must be recognized as important to the efficient functioning of the enterprise. The administrator must always keep in mind the importance of continually striving for a good *esprit de corps*, team play, and unity of purpose among *all* members of the organization.

V. ADMINISTRATION AND REORGANIZATION

It has been pointed out under the preceding heading of "Coordination" that the best type of organization is essential to good coordination. Furthermore, the necessity for continuous appraisal of the organizational structure and workings of the members of the enterprise in order to insure success has been stressed.

The administrator, in order to insure that he or she has the best type of organization, should periodically ask the following questions:

1. Is the organization divided into as few work units and as few subdivisions of authority as possible? This is essential to avoid an organizational structure that is cumbersome with great amounts of "red-tape." Other things being equal, few work units and subdivisions of authority make it easier to coordinate an enterprise. Fewer management levels result in less delay, with less handling of important details.

2. Is the basis for making decisions as near as possible to the place where action originates? It is important that those who supply the answers to questions which involve particular specialties be informed persons who know the facts. The judgment of those who are nearest to the situation and best informed should be the basis for making decisions.

3. Does the system of communication provide for translating detailed information from the lower echelons into more general information as it progresses to higher echelons of authority? Those higher in the scalar organization can devote less time to detail. Therefore, the organization should provide that decisions be made, minor details be accomplished, and only the information that is essential to a broad perspective of the enterprise reach the top leader in the enterprise.

4. Does the organizational structure clearly show the purposes for which each subdivision exists? As an organization develops and as progress is made, it should become increasingly clear why each subdivision of authority and each work unit exists. Each should be a distinct and recognizable area of responsibility. Each should be important as a separate entity which is related to, and an important subdivision of, the total task to be accomplished. Each should require the services and efforts of a properly qualified individual who is responsible for this link in the total process.

5. Does the organizational structure provide for a close relationship among the various work units and subdivisions of authority? Each unit or subdivision should have a clear working relationship with others in the organization. The responsibility of each should be recognized, but, in addition, the dependence of one upon the other for the successful accomplishment of purposes should also be recognized. The jurisdiction of each should be clear as well as its obligation to the total effort of the entire project.

6. Are the problems that are being faced caused by a weakness in the organizational structure or by procedures that have been developed? This question of structure or procedure must be determined. A change in procedure should usually be the first recourse.

7. If a change is made, what will be its effect upon such things as coordination, administrative control, and member morale? The administrator and staff should be very sure when a change or reorganization takes place that it is going to be in the best interests of all concerned. It may be that good member morale under a structure which has some weak spots is better than poor member morale under a structure which is strong. Of course, it must also be recognized that the art of persuasion should be utilized in most reorganization processes.

8. If there is reorganization, what will be the effect upon materials? What will be the effect upon man power? Will there be better cooperation? Will better services be performed? Will production be increased? Will clientele be increased? These are a few more questions that should be asked before any reorganization takes place. Reorganization that is major in nature should be done only after complete consideration of all the facts.

The good administrator does not look upon an organizational structure as one that is infallible, permanent, and fixed. Neither does he look upon it as something that should be changed every time the wind blows in another direction. Too much change, or change which has not been thought through carefully and is needless, will only create problems of employee morale and confusion.

Administrators should make it a policy to have periodic meetings with their key subordinates, who previously have met with their subdivisions. In these conferences management problems, organizational structure, assignment of duties and responsibilities, long-term plans, progress, methods used, and other similar items should be discussed at length. In this way problems are clearly seen, weaknesses are identified, plans are made, morale is raised, and all members of the organization participate in the enterprise. Under such circumstances changes can be brought about which will be accepted willingly because the reason behind them is clearly understood.

VI. BUDGETING AND FINANCIAL CONTROL

Budgeting is the formulation of a financial plan in terms of the work that is to be accomplished and services that are to be performed. All of the expenditures should be closely related to the objectives which the organization is trying to achieve. As such, the administrator plays a very important part in the budgeting process.

Budgets should be planned and prepared with a thought to the future. They are an important part in the administrator's three-, five-, or seven-year plans and the program of accomplishment that has been outlined for a period of time. Projects of any size should be integrated progressively over many years. Thus the outlay of monies to realize such aims requires long-term planning.

Financial control and budgeting provide the necessary administrative machinery and operations to request funds, to make them available to areas and individuals, and then to exercise control to the extent of seeing that they are used in a right and efficient manner. In the last analysis, the administrator is responsible for carrying out the above. It is a major duty. It is one that requires special qualities such as integrity, foresight, wisdom, and firmness.

Fiscal management reflects the administrator's program. It shows where the emphasis is, what is considered important in long-term planning, and the activities that need developing. The administrator must therefore closely coordinate programming with budgeting. The two go hand in hand.

Formulation and preparation of the budget is a joint enterprise in many respects. It is based on reports and information that have been forwarded through the various subdivisions of the organization. These reports must contain information on such things as programs, projects, obligations that exist, funds that have been spent, and monies that have been received from various sources. Administrators must have the total picture of the entire enterprise at their finger tips. They must be cognizant of the work being done throughout the establishment, work that should be done, needs of every facet of the organization, and of a hundred and one other items that must be considered in the preparation of the budget. The larger the organization, the larger should be the budget organization under the administrator. The efficiency of the enterprise depends upon expert judgment in fiscal matters.

Richard G. Mitchell, an expert in finance, writing on "Administrative Planning" in the *Recreation* magazine, discusses the importance of "making the budget worth every dollar." He points out that the budget portrays what is to be done. It is told in fiscal terms. He lists five important considerations in budget preparation. These are:

1. *What was planned last year?* This means a tying together of last year's budget with the one proposed, to show how the over-all short- and long-term planning fits into the picture.
2. *What was accomplished last year?* This points up the important accomplishments of last year and the progress that has been achieved toward realizing the organization's objectives.
3. *What can realistically be accomplished this year?* In this section the various projects and purposes that can be accomplished this year are discussed.
4. *What needs to be done?* Here can be stated the absolute-minimum activities that are in need of accomplishment this year. With this information, a comparison can be made

to see the relationship between what has to be done and what has been incorporated in the planning. Fixed and other expenses which cannot be avoided would be listed here.

5. *How is it to be done?* In this section will be pointed out such essential information as the needs in regard to staff, salaries, and other necessary items.[3]

In a strict interpretation of the word, the "budget" is merely a record of receipts and expenditures. As used here, however, it reflects the long-term planning of the organization, pointing up the needs with their estimated costs, and then insuring that a realistic program is planned which will fit into the estimated income.

VII. PLANNING

Abraham Lincoln once said, "If we could first know where we are and whither we are tending, we could better judge what to do and how to do it." This is essential regardless of whether it is planning in national government or in the department of a school. One has to be well acquainted with the past and present history of the organization and have some definite idea as to the direction one should go if planning is to be done intelligently.

Planning for the future involves the element of risk. Most administrators, however, who have made a name for themselves assume the risk and rise or fall on the basis of their judgments and decisions. One cannot live today without taking some risk. Whenever one walks across the street, rides in an automobile, flies in an airplane, or goes swimming, the element of risk is involved. This is also true of administrators in their work. Whenever they make a decision, whether it is to develop a new program or build a new building, there is an element of risk that the project will not materialize, at least as it has been planned. The funds may not be available as expected, personnel may be lacking, a shortage of materials may exist or some other unforeseen development may occur. All administrators must take risks. The important thing to remember is that risks should not be taken without careful consideration of the problem at hand. However, if a plan has been carefully made, if informed opinion has been consulted, if the future looks favorable for its development and if certain reasonable precautions have been taken, one should "jump in and get both feet wet." This is a responsibility of the administrator. As one individual has said, "To try and fail is at least to learn; to fail to try is to suffer the inestimable loss of what might have been."

Planning can involve two areas. One area is concerned with the particular specialty with which the organization is dealing. This might be manufacturing nylon stockings or turning out trained teachers of elementary education, selling insurance or selling good human relations, dispensing knowledge or dispensing pills. This particular area of planning requires research. Necessary facts must be assembled. Alternative plans must be considered. Expert advice must be utilized. Resources must be taken into consideration. Pilot studies may have to be conducted to determine the soundness of an idea or plan. The needs of the consumer must be examined. These and many other considerations must be thought through. Only after considerable research will the logical answer be determined and plans

---

[3]Richard G. Mitchell, "Administrative Planning—Its Effective Use," *Recreation*, 44, January and February, 1951.

laid for the future. If an organization can maintain a research division, one of whose main responsibilities is to do continuous research along these lines, it will aid tremendously in making sound plans for the future.

The other area which involves planning is that of developing a sound organization. This has been considered to some degree in a previous section, "Administration and Reorganization." Planning must be done in areas of the organization. Additional staff members must be considered, procedures must be examined, and practices scrutinized. The direction and coordination of the enterprise must be studied. Plans must be made in regard to future development. Some of the questions that must be asked are: Where does the organization want to expand? How can the organization become more efficient? How can better coordination be worked out among the various subdivisions? How can staff morale be improved? How can abilities and skills of members be better utilized? These and many other problems must be examined when making plans for developing a sound organization.

The administrator cannot do all of this planning. The best thinking should be utilized in those areas where planning needs to be done. Planning staffs should be established. They should have the responsibility of studying various lines of action and recommending plans. They should establish priorities. Such staffs should gather the facts, study and organize them, and recommend certain directions that should be taken on the basis of suitability and desirability. They have the responsibility for advising, not executing. Their advice should indicate ways and means of attaining the objectives which have been established for the organization. They must work very closely with the various administrators as well as with those individuals in the organization who can give them informed opinion. The staff should be directly responsible to the chief administrator and should represent the best interests of the organization. Vested interests should be consulted but judgments must be made and plans formed on the basis of impartiality and an impersonal approach. It must further be recognized that planning on the administrative level is meaningless unless there is also planning on the sublevels into which the organization is divided. Many of the ideas, facts, judgments, and even decisions should flow from the lower echelons. If the organization is large, a planning staff should be working full time. In this way trained individuals may be utilized. Also, these individuals can be generalists as opposed to specialists who may have some particular vested interest which they wish to promote. Planning is an important function of any organization. The administrator should provide for such a responsibility if his organization is to thrive and succeed.

Newman[4] points out six essential features of analytical planning.

1. *Clarify the problem.* Make sure that such essential factors as goals to be achieved and obstacles and problems confronting the accomplishment of the plan are known.

2. *Determine the alternatives.* The various courses of action should be determined, the advantages and disadvantages of each listed, and essential facts concerning each gathered.

3. *Get the facts.* Facts should be obtained through analysis, studies, interviews, questionnaires, and other methods that are effective.

---

[4]Newman. *op. cit.*, p. 88.

4. *Analyze the facts.* Determine what the important and significant ones are.

5. *Decide on the action to be taken.* Decision will rest on the basis of facts.

6. *Arrange for execution.* Timetables should be established, authorizations prepared, and essential plans laid.

VIII. RESEARCH

The administrator who doesn't recognize the importance of research as an aid is working an injustice on the organization. It is essential that all administrators keep up to date in respect to the operations of their enterprises and similar fields of endeavor apart from them. Data are very important tools in many emergencies and in planning for the days and years ahead. Facts speak for themselves and in order to place oneself and one's organization in a defensible position, research must be done to prove the effectiveness of an organization.

Researchers say that anything that exists at all can be measured. It is important to measure what one is doing. The administrator must know what various subdivisions are accomplishing, what the public reaction to the organization's product or service is, and what the effect of changes will be. It is important to keep up with latest developments in the field, with social, economic, and political issues, and with the "hundred and one" things that develop from day to day on the job.

The administrator who fails to continually accumulate pertinent data through the utilization of various statistical and other techniques plus planned research, cannot do an effective job. This is an essential in a complex society where everything from international relations to technological development greatly affects various phases of one's work.

IX. PUBLIC RELATIONS

Administration must recognize the importance of good public relations. No organization can live unto itself alone. As long as this situation exists, it is important that a good relationship exist between any organization and the public, which in the long run determines the worth of the enterprise. The organization's work, in order to be satisfying to the associated members, must be accepted and recognized by the public. The products it turns out or the services it supplies must be recognized for the important way they contribute to enriched, meaningful or enjoyable living. Good will is built; it does not just happen. It may take months and years for the public to understand the contribution that an organization is trying to make. It is therefore very important to inform the public in as many ways as possible as to the work that is being accomplished. In addition to dispensing information, it is also important to serve the public in a manner which will be satisfying. This means being informed about public opinion as to likes and dislikes, suggestions and grievances, attitudes and opinions. Administrative responsibility does not stop once a good relationship with the public has been established. Instead, good public relations are developed only as they are continually taken into the thinking and planning of the enterprise. This requires constant vigilance and attention. A major administrative responsibility is to see that the consumer of the product or service is informed and satisfied. This is something that must be provided for in administrative planning. It cannot be dealt with in a "hit-and-miss" fashion. Public relations are dealt with in more detail in a later chapter in this book.*

X. OFFICE MANAGEMENT

Office management is an important administrative consideration. If not dealt with in a wise fashion it can absorb all of the administrator's time as well as result in inefficient management. There is always an enormous amount of detail concerned with administration. Reports have to be made, budgets prepared, inventories taken, correspondence attended to, filing done, telephone calls made, visitors welcomed, appointments arranged, and many other items handled that are essential to the functioning of any administrative office.

There are two essentials to insure that these details will be handled efficiently. The first is a very efficient secretary. A secretary often can make or break an administrator. If she is efficient she will not have to be told to take care of many minor tasks; she will do them automatically. Letters that are dictated will not have to be proofread. Filing will be done so that materials and information can be procured at a moment's notice. Callers on unimportant business will be cared for without disturbing the administrator. Appointments will be arranged in accordance with the best interests of the administrator. When the executive is away the office will be properly covered. Phones will be answered with a cheerful greeting. Courtesy and politeness will always be in evidence in dealing with associates and others. Confidential information will not be divulged. The office will be kept neat and clean. Arrangements for trips will be provided for. It has often been said that the administrator is not indispensable, but his secretary is. She is everything from a public relations expert to a connoisseur of the best restaurants in town. She can relieve the administrator of many details, headaches, and responsibilities. She should be one of the administrator's first considerations in connection with office management.

The second essential for the administrator who is in charge of an organization of considerable size is an administrative assistant. Through an administrative assistant, the administrator can be relieved of many office details, of doing "spadework" on budgets and inventories, and entertaining visitors. The administrative assistant can take charge of the office while the administrator is performing public relations duties and other assignments which are very important from the standpoint of the welfare of the organization. This assistant can also dictate much of the correspondence, fill many of the requests for special information that continually arise, and substitute for the administrator on speaking and other engagements which cannot be filled because of the demand on the executive's time. It is difficult to mention all the responsibilities of such an individual. The type of organization served would determine the nature and scope of his duties.

Other essentials for good office management include having personnel engaged in such work who are congenial and work well together. The office is many times the first place that a visitor sees. Impressions formed in such an environment often

*See Chapter XI.

are the basis for judging the entire enterprise.   There also should be adequate space, equipment, and supplies.   The basic tools for office work are essential.   Furthermore, the various health aspects of the office should be maintained.

QUESTIONS AND EXERCISES

1. What is meant by "subdivision of work" and why is it important?

2. What is the difference between organization according to "purpose" and organization according to "process"?   What are the advantages and disadvantages of each?

3. Prepare an organizational chart for some department, school, or agency with which you are familiar.   Discuss the various administrative aspects of the chart.

4. Discuss and illustrate the organizational pattern pertinent to associated materials or persons.

5. Discuss and illustrate the organizational pattern which is pertinent to setting.

6. What is meant by "line" and "staff"?   Diagram an organization with which you are familiar and discuss the responsibilities of "line" and "staff" personnel.

7. What are some essentials to consider in having good coordination in an organization?

8. What are some basic considerations before reorganizing an enterprise?

9. Prepare a budget for a health education, physical education, or recreation department, taking into consideration the principles set forth in this chapter.

10. Why is planning so important, and what two main areas can it involve?

11. To what extent is a research program important to an organization?

12. Draw up a list of procedures that should be followed in order to ensure efficient office management.

SELECTED REFERENCES

Barnard, Chester I.   *Organization and Management.*   Cambridge, Massachusetts: Harvard University Press, 1949.

Forsythe, Charles E. and Duncan, Ray O.   *Administration of Physical Education.*   New York: Prentice-Hall Inc., 1951.   Chapter VI.

Given, William B., Jr.   *Reaching Out in Management.*   New York: Harper & Brothers, 1953.

Heyel, Carl.   *Human Relations Manual for Executives.*   New York: McGraw-Hill Book Company, Inc., 1939.

Laird, Donald A.   *The Psychology of Selecting Employees.*   New York: McGraw-Hill Book Company, Inc., 1937.

Nash, Jay B., Moench, Francis J., and Saurborn, Jeannette B.   *Physical Education: Organization and Administration.*   New York: A. S. Barnes and Company, 1951.   Part IV.

Newman, William H.   *Administrative Action.*   New York: Prentice-Hall, Inc., 1951.

Tead, Ordway.   *The Art of Administration.*   New York: McGraw-Hill Book Company, Inc., 1951.

Voltmer, Edward F., and Esslinger, Arthur A.   *The Organization and Administration of Physical Education.*   New York: Appleton-Century-Crofts, Inc., 1949.   Chapters IV and XIII.

Chapter IV

DEMOCRATIC ADMINISTRATION

Democratic administration is essential if the American way of life is to continue and become a permanent feature of this culture. It is of especial importance during this day and age when freedom is being challenged from all sides, when men cannot work and fight for their beliefs without fear of investigation, when guilt by association is commonplace, and when education is under fire.

I. EDUCATION AND GROUP PROCESS

Education is frequently under attack. Schools are often accused of not teaching the three R's, allowing subversives to infiltrate the ranks of teachers, being Godless, using discipline that is too rigid or too lax, and conducting experiences where not enough facts are mastered. Probably those who claim that educators are not democratic are more justified in their attack than many others.

Although education is moving more and more along democratic lines, there is still ample evidence that democratic procedures are not widespread. The consumer of the product does not have much to say as to what he should be taught; boards of education prevent certain textbooks from being used in the class room; many teachers are barred because of race, color, or religious faith; the problems of segregation have not been finally settled; and some administrators rule autocratically.

Public school education in the United States is deeply rooted in democratic principles. The schools should be a place where democracy flourishes. School is a place to learn, make mistakes, experience social control, develop initiative, and become creative and productive. Schools should teach individuals how to develop responsibility and self-reliance, and to understand their fellow-men. Authoritarian practices prevent such development and education. President Griswold of Yale University defines democracy as ". . . a political society in which the greatest possible measure of justice implicit in the phrase 'equal opportunity' is combined with the greatest possible measure of freedom and encouragement for the individual to develop his own talent, initiative, and moral responsibility." This is a goal for all educators.

Administrators must recognize and believe in these democratic essentials in order to direct organizations in a manner which can be truly labeled "democratic." They must have greater knowledge of the learning process, of such things as how learning takes place, the effects of coercion, the importance of sympathetic guidance and social interaction, individual differences, and desirable goals. Autocratic ad-

62

ministrators will determine the policies, make the decisions, and literally "run the show." If administrators go to the other extreme and believe in a laissez-faire or "hands off" policy, they do not furnish the necessary guidance and leadership which is their responsibility. Instead of following either of these two extreme approaches, they should try to give that type of democratic leadership which provides for participating as a member of the group and arriving at policies and decisions through group thinking rather than unilaterally.

Democratic administrators must have good human relationships. They must have faith in people and in their ability to do constructive thinking. They must understand human beings in order to recognize those who do and those who do not contribute to group goals. They must be able to motivate all to communicate and participate. Furthermore, they must help in the in-service training of staff so that they, too, will critically evaluate scientific evidence and personal opinion.

The administrator should recognize certain steps in the democratic process of a staff and organization working together in order to accomplish group goals. Some of the steps that should be considered are as follows:

1. Goals should be developed through the group process. The goals that are set should be attainable, challenging, and adapted to the capacities of the members.

2. Good morale should be developed among the entire staff. This is an essential to constructive group action. A permissive climate must be established in group deliberations. All must feel a sense of belonging and recognize their important contribution in the undertaking. A feeling of "oneness" should pervade the entire group.

3. Group planning must be done in a clearly defined manner. A stated procedure should be followed. It should be a cooperative undertaking, based upon known needs and flexible enough to allow for unforeseen developments. The fulfillment of plans should bring satisfaction and a feeling of success to all who participated in their formulation and accomplishment. All should share in recognition for a completed job.

4. In staff meetings and other group discussions the administrator must encourage utilization of democratic principles. Each member's contribution must be encouraged and respected. Differences of opinion must be on a "principle" basis rather than on a "personal" basis. The organization's objectives and purposes must be continually kept in mind. All members must be encouraged to facilitate the group process by accepting responsibility, alleviating conflict, making contributions, respecting the opinions of others, abiding by the will of the majority, and promoting good group morale.

5. There must be periodical evaluation of progress. The group should evaluate itself from time to time as to its accomplishments, in terms of the organization's goals, and the effectiveness of the group process. Each individual must evaluate his own role as a member of the organization in respect to contributions made to the group process and the accomplishments of the group.

II. THE IMPORTANCE OF DEMOCRACY IN OUR SOCIETY

The furtherance of democratic principles is essential to society. These recognize the right of all individuals to have a say as to how their lives should be governed. As such, it is important for every person to see that these principles are observed in all organizations to which they belong.

Democratic principles help to prevent greedy and strong individuals from usurping more and more power. On the other hand, they provide for the advancement of society by allowing the best ideas and the most constructive thinking to be considered. An "authority of ideas" prevails, rather than an "authority of individuals."

The end toward which society must strive is to develop and promote what is best for the individual. This means that individuals should not be used as means to an end by unscrupulous human beings. All have heard of individuals who have become powerful by sacrificing human lives to their own personal benefit. This applies to an army officer on the field of battle who needlessly exposes his men to attack and equally as well to the administrator who carves a name for himself by utilizing his staff to struggle and slave so that he can become greater in the eyes of the public at large.

A democratic society and democratic organizations must strive to improve the welfare of all their members. They must provide for such freedoms as speech, assembly, and publication, and for such democratic essentials as group planning and associated effort in the accomplishment of worthy goals.

Democratic administration must recognize that true democracy depends upon the degree to which members of the organization participate in the making of decisions. The administration should ask such questions as: Is the democratic process providing a sound program for the management of the organization? Is there sufficient cooperation, coordination of effort, and subordination of vested interests to reach decisions which are best for the entire organization? The answers to such questions will determine the effectiveness of the democratic process.

III. PROBLEMS ASSOCIATED WITH THE DEMOCRATIC PROCESS

Application of the democratic process to the functioning of an organization does not solve all problems. Instead, many situations and difficulties arise because of elements that are inherent in the application of democratic principles. It is important to recognize these problems and cope with them as they arise. Despite such dilemmas, the advantages of the democratic process far outweigh the disadvantages.

A. The Problem of Divided Opinion

In a democratic organization, it is assumed that the wishes of the majority prevail. There is a question that often arises in this connection: Is the majority always right? Very often an important issue will be determined by one vote. Students of history remember that during post-Civil War days Andrew Johnson failed to be found guilty by one vote. Every individual can recall similar situations within organizations where like results have occurred. Is this a weakness of democracy? Should important problems, plans, and issues, be decided by such a small difference of opinion?

It seems that the reasoning behind such a dilemma is clear. All who believe in democracy recognize the importance of having as much unanimity of thinking as possible. However, they also recognize that it is much better to have a majority make a decision than to have it made by one person who is an autocrat.

Also in this connection, there is the problem that individuals who have opposed an issue must conform to the will of the majority, if democracy is to exist. The solution is very clear. A democracy requires cooperative action on the part of all. Unless this follows, democracy deteriorates. There are numerous incidents familiar to all when opposing groups have failed to comply. Many who voted against the Eighteenth Amendment to the Constitution refused to comply. In the area of athletics many of the schools that were in the minority and voted against the so-called "sanity code" and other curbs on "big time" athletics, would not conform, and broke the rules. This cannot happen if democratic principles are to work. A functioning democratic organization or society depends upon compliance with the will of the majority. Only in this way can it survive.

B. The Problem of Subjective Personal Opinion as Opposed to Scientific Fact

In many democratic discussions it appears to some individuals that scientific evidence should dictate policies, and personal opinions must not become involved. On complicated issues situations develop where certain individuals are acquainted with scientific data which in themselves define the issue. Therefore, the conclusion is reached that discussion, voting, or other devices are useless since the course of action is very clear as indicated by known fact.

The answer to such a problem seems to be that there will be acceptance if individuals know and recognize the facts. Generally acceptance fails to materialize when evidence is not conclusive or when it has not been properly publicized. The democratic process can contribute immeasurably to such enlightenment. Through discussion, facts can be presented and understanding reached. Individuals with reasonable intelligence will accept scientific fact as against personal opinion, if the presentation is clear and the evidence is convincing. William Gerard Hamilton during the late eighteenth century made a statement which has a bearing on this point. "Two things are always to be observed; whether what is said is true in itself, or being so, is applicable. In general, things are partly true, and partly not; in part applicable, and in part not. You are careful therefore to distinguish; and to show how far this is true and applies, and how far not." The democratic process is the most effective method yet devised to show what is true and applies.

C. The Problem of Standards

A question that is often raised in connection with the utilization of the democratic process is: What does it do to standards of performance? There is a belief in some quarters that by allowing majority opinion and decisions to prevail, standards of performance are lowered to a "middle level." The individuals who have a low set of standards tend to pull down those with high standards. In effect, this results in a compromise on middle ground. The standards take on mediocrity rather than remain at a high level.

The answer to this problem is difficult. A democracy rests upon the worth of the individual. It has faith in the individual, in the goals that he will set, and the standards he wants to follow. The challenge presents itself to those whose standards are high to bring the rest up to their level, rather than to allow themselves to be relegated to a lower one. Such a process may take time. Results are not always immediate in a democracy. Nevertheless, the principles upon which it is based are sound. By utilizing such principles as freedom of discussion and assemblage, it is possible to educate and to elevate standards.

D. The Problem of Time

Democratic discussions with their need for deliberation and agreement take time. Such delay often creates problems, sometimes with serious consequences. There is often too much delay between the need for action, decision, and execution. Democracy is based upon the necessity for individuals to see the need for a course of action and then after seeing this need, deliberate it, and finally see that the decision which they have made is put into effect.

It is true that this dilemma often works to the disadvantage of many individuals. However, it does not necessarily have to be this way. It has been seen how rapidly the Federal Government will act in case of emergency. For example, it did not take long for Congress to declare war after the attack on Pearl Harbor, or to vote the necessary supplies and help once our country was at war. The delay occurs when there is misunderstanding, a situation is not meaningful, and the course of action is confusing. Perhaps it is wise in many cases to have this lag of time. Hasty action also results in many mistakes.

The element of time is usually important in cases of emergency. Democratic organizations make provisions for action under such conditions. Members of an organization can vest such powers in qualified individuals when necessary. John Locke in his *Treatise on Civil Government* pointed out that sometimes it is inevitable that decisions be made quickly by the executive in charge. It would seem logical that the wise administrator and organization would provide for such emergency action.

E. The Problem of Discussion With Noninterested and Noninformed Individuals

Another problem which frequently arises in democratic deliberations is that some individuals who participate in group discussions are many times not interested or competent to discuss intelligently and constructively the subject at hand. Such a situation may be very helpful as an educational device. As individuals become better informed on various topics they contribute more. Many minds are better than one or two. Any group should welcome as much help as possible in solving problems.

F. The Problem of Authority

Criticism has often been directed against the democratic process from the standpoint that it results in confusion and poor direction. The authority for certain acts is not clearly established. Furthermore, it is conducive to a conflict of ideas, which results in indecisiveness.

It seems important to recognize the part that democratic principles play in such a problem. A democratic organization vests in its members the right to help determine policies, purpose, and methods. They want a "say" in these important factors which vitally affect their lives. At the same time, however, they vest authority for execution of policy and purpose in administrators who are responsible to the group for their actions. Any democratically run organization has to recognize clearly the definite lines that exist between policy forming and execution. If an individual has been placed in an administrative position, the wherewithal to perform duties effectively must also be granted. In a sense, all individuals have authority in their respective positions. Authority goes with the job and not with the individual. This is true from the top to the bottom of the organization. There is no "final authority" except as it exists in the entire membership. All organizations that are to be efficient and effective must clearly recognize these principles upon which the functioning of an organization rests.

G. The Future of Democracy

The problems that have been listed should not be used to deter the application of democratic principles to any organization. If one takes any other method of government, it would readily be found that problems of much greater magnitude and seriousness exist. Furthermore, the administrator as a leader can do much toward solving and alleviating the difficulties that are associated with democratic dilemmas. Outstanding leadership is essential to any democratic organization. High-quality leadership will stress the importance of group participation, freedom of action, good human human relations, and the importance of each individual member. This is important and far outweighs any advantages associated with systems that are not democratic.

IV. ELEMENTS OF DEMOCRATIC ADMINISTRATION

Democratic administration is essential for the most efficient and effective accomplishment of organization goals. This does not mean that all members in the organization have equal authority and responsibility. Instead, wherever there is associated effort there must be leadership with clear allocations of authority and responsibility.

The administrator of a democratic organization must be a leader. This means ability to guide, show the way, and lead. The following statement has many implications for administrators:

> The boss drives his men; the leader coaches them,
> The boss depends upon authority; the leader on good will,
> The boss inspires fear; the leader inspires enthusiasm,

The boss says, "I", the leader says, "We."
The boss assigns the task; the leader sets the pace,
The boss says, "Get here on time"; the leader gets there ahead of time,
The boss fixes the blame for the breakdown; the leader fixes the breakdown,
The boss knows how it is done; the leader shows how,
The boss makes work a drudgery; the leader makes it a game,
The boss says, "Go," the leader says, "Let's go,"
The world needs leaders; nobody wants a boss![1]

The administrator must keep in mind that every person in a democracy has certain inalienable rights, namely, "life, liberty, and the pursuit of happiness." It must also be remembered that in a democracy, the one who governs or administers, derives the powers which are exercised from the "consent of the governed."

The inalienable rights can be secured for all individuals whether they play the role of follower or leader. The extent to which they are secured when individuals are followers depends upon the nature of the leadership. The administrator or leader must always keep this in mind. Directions, guidance, motives, methods, and every action clearly demonstrate the degree to which these democratic principles are a part of his thinking and acting.

Robert J. Lavell in a recent article in *The Phi Delta Kappan* emphasized the preceding points on democratic leadership and in addition listed five principles which point up the democratic leader. These are:

1. The democratic leader is chosen either directly or indirectly by those whom he is to govern.
2. The democratic leader envisages more than the immediate goal.
3. The democratic leader points out the way to others.
4. The democratic leader convinces or induces others to follow toward the goal.
5. The democratic leader guides others on their way to a goal.

These five important points should be remembered. They imply that administrators will hold their positions only so long as they have the confidence of their staffs. Administrators keep long-range goals continually in mind and have been made leaders because of abilities to plan and proceed toward the accomplishment of these aims. As leaders they must also persuade others of the direction and methods that should be followed and used. Finally, they are administrators and leaders because they know how to do things, can accept and delegate responsibility, and possess qualifications to work in an associated enterprise where all are working together for definite goals. In all these things they recognize the wisdom in the words of J. S. Knox, "You cannot antagonize and influence at the same time." And also the words of Cavour, "He who trusts men will make fewer mistakes than he who distrusts them."

Some additional principles of democratic administration should be kept in mind:

1. The greatest production records are broken and valuable services performed when the members of an organization are working toward goals which they have established under wise and democratic leadership.

[1]Western Division Bulletin, Massachusetts, Girl Scouts in the book entitled "Thirty Years of Girls' Club Experience." Worcester Girls Club, Worcester, Mass.

2. The administrator can be appointed to a job but cannot be appointed to a position of democratic leadership. This label is gained only through actual experience and application of democratic principles to administration. The staff will decide when such a title is to be conferred. It must be gained through a winning of staff confidence.

The Educational Policies Commission has given some good advice to the administrator.

> An autocratic administrator gets the best advice he will ever get at the time he first takes office. From that point forward the quality of counsel he can command from his associates is destined to a steady deterioration. The subordinate who at first is bold enough to offer opinions and recommendations soon becomes one who presents only facts. No matter how closely his mental processes parallel those of the leader, occasions inevitably arise when his suggestions vary from what the leader thinks to be correct. If they vary too much, this variation is viewed as evidence that the counselor is incompetent. Whether he is liquidated, demoted, or merely ignored is immaterial. The important point is that he is forced out of the counseling picture as a maker of proposals, a suggester of policies.
>
> Some of the dictator's original suggestion-givers become fact-presenters. This job, too, is bound to degenerate. The fact-presenter becomes more and more a selector of facts which the boss will consider significant. Thus he moves closer and closer to the precipice over which he must eventually fall into the abyss of the yes-men, who make up facts to order. In a real dictatorship, moreover, even this submissive falsifier has not yet reached the depths of policymaking inefficiency. There remains at the lowest circle of the Inferno a place reserved for the only one whose counsels a thorough-going dictator can accept year after year—the head nodder—and even this doomed soul is forced to step up the energy of his nods until he is obviously an automaton which any self-respecting autocrat must despise.[2]

3. The worth of every individual must be recognized. Everyone in the organization, from the custodian to the highest officer should share a rightful place and be allowed and encouraged to participate. Individuals are not "expendable" in a democratic organization. All should have a sense of belonging and security. All should be respected and have a voice in their affairs.

4. All individuals want to achieve certain goals. At the same time, they recognize these goals cannot be achieved without the help of others. When several individuals are brought together to achieve goals, leadership is required. The administration and leader should not exploit this desire on the part of the members. The administrator should concentrate on the achievement of such goals so that all may share the results and satisfactions they seek.

5. The administrator or leader has considerable opportunity and potentiality for doing good. Through inspired leadership it is possible to change individual lives for the better, develop faith, have others recognize the importance of service, appreciate the importance of being associated with a great movement, and in some measure be responsible for a better world in which to live. One who serves in an administrative capacity should recognize this responsibility just as much as the responsibility for achieving material gains.

[2]Educational Policies Commission. *Learning the Ways of Democracy.* Washington, D. C.: The National Education Association, 1940. pp. 20-21.

6. Justice and fairness must be the rule in all personnel relationships. The golden rule must be applied to all the administrative workings of an organization. Not to abide by such a worthy and important principle will result in failure.

7. The administrator and leader is a morale builder. His role in many ways can be compared to that of a football coach. The members of the organization or team must be selected with care in order to achieve the greatest ends. The administrator or coach must demonstrate preachments and actions which are compatible. Both the leader and the team must stay within the framework of the rules which have been arrived at democratically. Team play is an absolute essential; all must feel a part of the team. There should be frequent conferences and huddles to make plans and iron out problems. It is important to know the score at all times, and all should clearly recognize the benefits that come from cooperative effort and a job well done. If these items are taken into consideration and followed, the morale of the group will be good and goals will be accomplished. The key individual is the administrator or coach.

A fitting close to this section is a quotation from the Funeral Oration of Pericles which was translated and quoted by Walter R. Agard: "What Democracy Meant to the Greeks."

> Our government is called a democracy, because its administration is in the hands, not of the few, but of the many. Yet, although all men are equal in the sight of the law, they are rewarded by the community on the basis of their merit; neither social position nor wealth, but ability alone, determines the service that a man renders. Our citizens are interested in both private and public affairs; concern over personal matters does not keep them from devoting themselves also to the community. In fact, we regard the man who does no public service, not as one who minds his own business, but as worthless. All of us share in considering and deciding public policy, in the belief that debate is no hindrance to action, but that action is sure to fail when it is undertaken without full preliminary discussion. Consequently, we show the utmost initiative in what we do and the utmost deliberation in what we plan.[3]

V. EDUCATING DEMOCRATIC ADMINISTRATORS

The elements of democratic administration suggest certain considerations for the education of administrators who wish to become more fully aware of the importance of adapting democratic principles to their fields of endeavor.

One requisite that stands out from the previous discussion is the factor of human relations. The administrator in order to be democratic must be a master in the art of dealing with people. There must be an appreciation of individual difference. The importance of such things as tact, diplomacy, sympathetic understanding, interest in the affairs of others, and consideration of the feelings of others are attributes which should stand out in the administrator's make-up. Furthermore, a deep faith in people, a sensitivity to group interaction, sincerity, and an understanding of the incentives which motivate individuals are essential. This suggests that in addition to the wide experiences that help to develop such characteristics, there should be broad training in sociology, psychology, and other sciences.

[3]Selected from pp. 60-62. Reprinted by permission of the University of North Carolina Press, Copyright 1942, University of North Carolina press.

A second important item that should not be overlooked is that administrators should have broad interests. It is important for them to take a broad view of their position. They represent the organization's interest and as such they should not only understand the nature of the interests which comprise its total activities but also have an understanding of a wider sphere. This has implications for local, national, and world understanding. Furthermore, in their dealings with others, they will come in contact with interests which are wide in scope and important in nature. It is essential that administrators be conversant enough with such interests to carry on an intelligent conversation, to say the least. Such an asset has implications for the success of their organizations.

A third item of importance is the necessity for administrators to express themselves well. Whether it is in a staff meeting or speaking to a public gathering, administrators are presenting not only their own but also their organization's views. It is important that they be presented clearly, accurately, effectively, and intelligently. This does not mean that they have to be orators.

A fourth factor that is important is that administrators should recognize all the facets of the democratic process. The history of various democratic undertakings should be studied. The trials and tribulations which individuals undergo to further democratic principles should be appreciated. The story of the Greeks and the notable democratic example which they set, together with other historical settings for government by the constituents should be understood. A detailed history of how democratic principles were brought to this country should be known. Through an appreciation and understanding of past democratic experiences, it may be possible to eliminate some of the mistakes that have been committed by others. Furthermore, it should give further insight into the possibilities and worth of applying democratic principles to administration.

It can readily be seen that a great amount of responsibility falls upon the shoulders of the administrator. The desire, technical knowledge, drive, and other qualifications which often come to mind first should not disillusion one into thinking that it is possible to be a good administrator without the knowledge or intent of utilizing democratic principles. The administrator's success in the long run will rest upon his ability to lead a democratically organized and functioning organization.

QUESTIONS AND EXERCISES

1. What is meant by the term "Group Process"? Why is it essential?
2. What is the relationship between education and democratic administration?
3. List and discuss some important steps which must be recognized by the administrator for the accomplishment of group goals.
4. Prepare two skits, one illustrating an autocratic administrator and one a democratic administrator.
5. Compare the advantages and disadvantages of various types of government including democracy, fascism, and totalitarianism.
6. List and discuss some of the disadvantages of the democratic process. How can the disadvantages be overcome?
7. Prepare an essay of 250 words on the subject, "Principles of Democratic Administration."

8. What implications does the Funeral Oration of Pericles have for democratic administration?

9. Discuss some of the essential features that should characterize the training of administrators, if they are to be democratic.

10. Discuss some actual situations with which you have been associated, pointing up the various organizational aspects which were or were not conducive to democratic administration. To what extent were they justified, if they were not democratic in nature?

SELECTED REFERENCES

Briggs, Thomas H. and Justman, Joseph. *Improving Instruction Through Supervision.* New York: The Macmillan Company, 1952.

Chase, Stuart. *Roads to Agreement.* New York: Harper & Brothers, 1951.

Educational Policies Commission. *Learning the Ways of Democracy.* Washington, D. C.: The National Education Association, 1940.

Fosbroke, G. E. *Common Sense Business Leadership.* New York: Duell, Sloan and Pearce, 1946.

Given, William B., Jr. *Reaching Out in Management.* New York: Harper & Brothers, 1953.

Green, Philip. *Your Organization.* New York: Hastings House, 1943.

Halsey, George D. *Supervising People.* New York: Harper & Brothers, 1946.

Heyel, Carl. *Human-Relations Manual for Executives.* New York: McGraw-Hill Book Company, Inc., 1939.

Kellett, E. E. *The Story of Dictatorship.* New York: E. P. Dutton & Compay, Inc., 1937.

Koopman, G. Robert, Miel, Alice, and Misner, Paul J. *Democracy in School Administration.* New York: Appleton-Century Company, 1943.

Kozman, Hilda Clute (Editor). *Group Process in Physical Education.* New York: Harper & Brothers, 1951.

Laird, Donald A., and Laird, Eleanor C. *Practical Business Psychology.* New York: Gregg Publishing Company, 1951.

Maier, Norman. *Principles of Human Relations.* New York: John Wiley & Sons, 1952.

Miller, Ward Ira. *Democracy in Educational Administration.* New York: Bureau of Publications, Teachers College, Columbia University, 1942.

Poston, Richard. *Democracy Is You.* New York: Harper & Brothers, 1953.

Stiles, Lindley J., and Dorsey, Mattie F. *Democratic Teaching in Secondary Schools.* New York: J. B. Lippincott Co., 1950.

Story, M. L. "Controversial Issues and School Administration," *The Journal of Educational Sociology.* 25, May, 1952.

Tead, Ordway. *The Art of Administration.* New York: McGraw-Hill Book Company, 1951.

Tead, Ordway. *The Art of Leadership.* New York: Whittlesey House, 1935.

Tead, Ordway, and Metcalf, Henry. *Personnel Administration.* New York: McGraw-Hill Book Company, 1933.

Webb, Ewing T., and Morgan, John B. *Strategy in Handling People.* Garden City, N. Y.: Garden City Publishing Company, Inc., 1930.

Whyte, William H., Jr., et. al. *Is Anybody Listening?* New York: Simon and Schuster, 1952.

Wiles, Kimball. *Supervision for Better Schools.* New York: Prentice-Hall, Inc., 1950.

Chapter V

GOVERNMENTAL ASPECTS OF
EDUCATIONAL ADMINISTRATION

Education is closely tied up with government at federal, state, and local levels. The teacher and administrator, consequently, must be familiar with various governmental relationships if they are to conform with the law, utilize governmental agencies and resources in their work, and promote education to the greatest degree. The trend toward increased government participation in education makes such knowledge even more important. Furthermore, it must continually be kept in mind that government *is* "the people." It is established for the welfare of its constituents. Government should serve education in a way which is best for all the people. Educators in general and administrators in particular should see that this goal is accomplished.

The government plays an important part in all phases of education, including health education and physical education, through legislation that it passes, monies that it provides, services that it renders, and limitations that it sets up. It is therefore very important that all engaged in these fields of education and administrators especially know something about federal interest, state function, and community responsibility in these undertakings. Only by having this knowledge will it be possible to plan intelligently and wisely.

I. PURPOSE OF EDUCATION

The purposes for which education exists have been set forth by many individuals and many organizations. One group of purposes reflects the social-economic goals for education as presented in ten characteristics which are desired for the individual American. These characteristics were stated in 1937 by a committee that included a philosopher, a lawyer, a sociologist, a superintendent of schools, and two secretaries of state education associations. These characteristics are:

1. Hereditary strength
2. Physical security
3. Participation in an evolving culture
   a. Skills, technics, and knowledges
   b. Values, standards, and outlooks
4. An active, flexible personality
5. Suitable occupation
6. Economic security
7. Mental security

8. Equality of opportunity
9. Freedom
10. Fair play

Also included in the report of this committee, which included John Dewey and Willard E. Givens, were statements that "education must be universal in its extent and application, universal in its materials and methods, and universal in its aims and spirit." When analyzing and studying this list, one cannot help but realize the great implications each of the items has for the fields of school health and physical education.

In 1938 the Educational Policies Commission also set forth certain purposes of education which they felt included a summarization and enlargement of statements that had been published previously by various committees and individuals representing the National Education Association. These purposes were (1) the objectives of self-realization, which are concerned with developing the individual to his fullest capacity in respect to such things as health, recreation, and philosophy of life, (2) the objectives of human relationship, which refer to relationships among people on the family, group, and society levels, (3) the objectives of economic efficiency, which are concerned with the individual as a producer and a consumer, and (4) the objectives of civic responsibility, which stress the individual's relationship to his local, state, national, and international forms of government.

School health and physical education, as phases of the total education process, contribute in great measure to each of these objectives. This is very much in evidence when analyzing each of the statements closely. This report by the Educational Policies Commission also sets forth other facts which have a direct bearing on these specialized fields. It is made clear that education is not confined to the formalized institution called the school. Instead, it takes place everywhere and is coextensive with life. It is concerned with the periods of infancy and youth as well as the period of adulthood. It is a continuous process. Furthermore, it is not concerned merely with knowledge. It is concerned also with such things as the human body and ethics.

II. GROWTH OF EDUCATION IN RELATION TO GOVERNMENT

English common law had its effect upon education in the United States. Under English common law the parent had complete control over the education of the child. The school was also closely related to the Church in England. Therefore, it is not surprising to note that in the southern part of the United States, where the Church of England had considerable influence, public education was regarded to a great degree in a charitable sense for orphans and children who came from poor families. Those children who came from more fortunate homes attended church and private schools. Some of the more fortunate had private tutors. In the middle colonies, parochial schools developed, sponsored by Lutherans and Catholics. During this early period the schools in the New England colonies, as well as in other sections of the country, reflected the religious influence. However, as time went on a system of common schools, secondary Latin schools, and colleges was developed for civic as well as religious purposes.

It was in the New England section that the American public-school system had its beginnings, namely, in the Massachusetts Bay Colony. A Colonial law in 1647 provided that every town of fifty families support a primary school and every town of one hundred families a grammar school, where students could receive the necessary training for college. The law provided that parents should pay for their children's education, if at all possible. If this was impossible, the town was to pay the fees. These schools were supported through public taxation. The Massachusetts law set a precedent for state participation in education. This, together with development of the concept that control of public education is a community enterprise, and the fact that other liberal educational ideas were being voiced, started the development of public education in the United States.

In the late eighteenth century several bills were passed which had a marked effect upon educational development in this country. The Ordinance of 1785, concerned with the sale of land in the West, provided that part of the land in every township should be reserved as a gift for the maintenance of public schools. This was the beginning of federal grants for public education. The Ordinance of 1787 stated in part, "Religion, morality, and knowledge, being necessary to good government and the happiness of mankind, schools and the means of education shall forever be encouraged." This ordinance dealt with the Northwest Territory which land speculators were anxious to develop at the time. By placing such a provision in the ordinance, the national government encouraged and gave moral support to educational progress.

Prior to the adoption of the Federal Constitution, six states (North Carolina, Pennsylvania, Georgia, Vermont, Massachusetts, and New Hampshire) had made provisions in their own constitutions for education. The Federal Constitution contained no direct reference to education. However, the Tenth Amendment reserves to the respective states, or to the people, the powers not delegated to the United States nor prohibited to the states. Thus public education was regarded as a legal function of each state.

The struggle for a free, state-supported system of public education was assured by the middle of the nineteenth century, but the system needed more development and enlargement. From the end of the Civil War to the end of the nineteenth century, the school system was improved considerably. The school population increased rapidly. The public high school became an integral part of the educational process. The Kalamazoo case in Michigan, 1870-1872, established the legality of public taxation for the support of the high school. The number of teacher training institutions increased. The cost of all public education skyrocketed over 400 per cent during the last forty years of the nineteenth century.

The constitutions of the various states reflected their interest in education. Each established a system of public schools which provided for the education of the population within its boundaries. The actual execution of education was delegated by the state to school districts through which the people exercised control over the educational offerings.

Much progress was made in the construction of school buildings. New administrative units such as kindergartens, vocational departments, and physical education departments were included. Colleges and universities increased in great numbers.

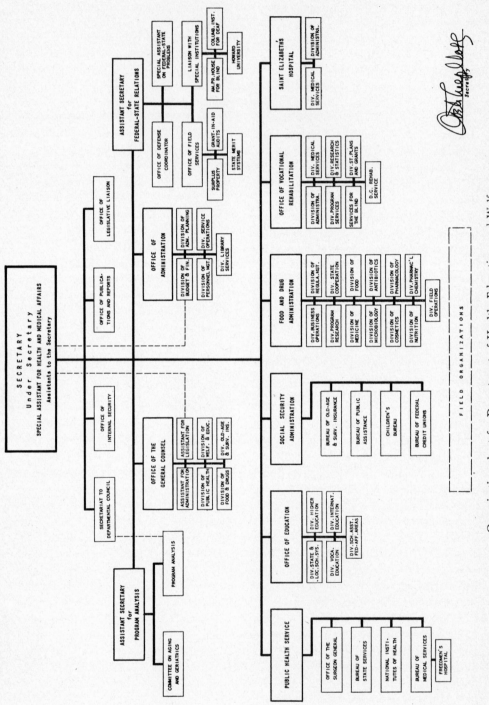

Organization chart for Department of Health, Education, and Welfare.

There were only 246 colleges founded by 1860, but there were nearly 500 by 1900. In chartering state universities, the South became the leader. Georgia set aside land and passed legislation authorizing a state university in 1784. North Carolina chartered a state university in 1789. Tennessee chartered its state university in 1801. Also about this time, Thomas Jefferson procured a charter from the Virginia State Legislature for the University of Virginia. In addition he helped develop the courses of study and the design of buildings and campus.

Federal aid to education increased with the passage of the Morrill Acts in 1862 and 1890. These acts provided for large grants of land and annual money grants for a college of agriculture and mechanic arts in each state.

During the post-Civil War period, the office of state superintendent of public instruction, or some similar position, became generally established as a permanent office in most of the states. At the beginning, in many states, this was a political office to which men without professional training were appointed or elected. This situation has been changed, however, with the adoption of better methods of selection and the recognition of the need for greater authority in the administration of the state system of public education.

The position of superintendent of schools in cities has assumed an important role in city school administration. In 1870 there were fewer than 30 city superintendents in the entire United States, and they were found in only 13 of the 37 states; but by 1876 this number had been increased to 142. In 1890 there were 380 superintendents in cities of over 5,000 population and by 1920 there were 15,892. County and larger community systems of education also made great progress.

Some interesting legal cases have evolved in connection with government and education. In the Nebraska case in 1919, the state legislature passed a bill which forbade the teaching of foreign languages in public or nonpublic schools to children below the eighth grade. Upheld by the Supreme Court of Nebraska, it then was appealed to the United States Supreme Court. This court ruled that it was unlawful to prohibit the teaching of foreign languages in private schools, because as implied in the Fourteenth Amendment it was depriving foreign language teachers from engaging in their chosen work and prevented the right of parents to engage such teachers for their children.

In the Oregon case in 1922, a statute was passed requiring the attendance of children between ages of eight and sixteen in public schools. Such a statute would have required all children to attend public as against nonpublic schools. The United States Supreme Court ruled that the legislation was not in order because it interfered with the right of parents to educate their children in whatever way they felt was the best.

There have also been many cases in regard to providing equal educational opportunities for everyone regardless of race, color, or creed. This has been under discussion in recent years with the courts ruling that equal educational opportunity must be provided for all. In 1954 the United States Supreme Court ruled unanimously that segregation was prohibited in public schools.

A significant recent change in the educational setup at the national level has been the creation of a Department of Health, Education and Welfare, with full

Cabinet status, fashioned out of the old elements of the Federal Security Agency. The basic pattern of the Federal Security Agency which has been retained in the new Department consists of three major services: Social Security Administration, Public Health Service, and Office of Education. Mrs. Oveta Culp Hobby, former Director of the Federal Security Agency, became the first Secretary of Health, Education and Welfare. This change came about despite the fact that school groups had long advocated and tried to promote the Office of Education as an independent agency operating under a lay board of education, appointed by the President and confirmed by the Senate. This board in turn would appoint the United States Commissioner of Education, and exercise policy-making rights. It would have authority in the federal government similar to that exercised by state boards of education in relation to the state commissioners of education in such states as Colorado, Connecticut, Maine, Minnesota, New York, and Texas. The relation of education to government is constantly changing and to think that its legal status is fixed or permanent would be a fallacy.

III. INTEREST OF FEDERAL GOVERNMENT IN EDUCATION

Federal interest in education began with the formation of the United States in 1783. This interest has continued over the years and has reflected itself in such ways as land grants, conditional grants in aid, emergency grants in aid, and federal appropriations.

In the Declaration of Independence, Americans pointed out that all men are born free and equal and are entitled to the rights of life, liberty and the pursuit of happiness. It was felt that if these rights were to be forthcoming, if Americans were to participate wisely in government, make good use of their natural and other resources, and be competent leaders in government as well as in their particular fields of specialization, education must be provided. Therefore, as soon as independence had been won people started talking about education. Robert Coram, a recognized leader of the day, drew up a document "The General Establishment of Schools throughout the United States," and James Sullivan, another leader, drew up one entitled "National System of Education." Noah Webster, of dictionary fame, called attention to the importance of education in contributing to world changes. Among other things he wanted to develop "an American Language" and to unite all Americans in a scheme for "universal improvement." He advocated public schools supported from tax funds because he felt private schools favored aristocratic tendencies.

Persons in high federal government circles generally agreed that schools were important in educating people for the practical things they do in day-to-day living. They felt that schools should be tax-supported. It was generally felt, however, that education was a state function. By failing to provide specifically for public education, the Constitution left it to the various state governments or to the people. At the same time they felt that the Preamble of the Constitution which states that one of its purposes is the promotion of public welfare, authorizes some direction over education.

During the early days of the Republic, several leaders favored the creation of a national university. President Washington urged Congress to make an appropriation and even left some money on his death for this purpose. Congress refused to heed the advice, however, and consequently no national university was founded.

The Ordinances of 1785 and 1787, previously referred to, indicate the role of the federal government in setting up definite parcels of land in the West for purposes of education. When Ohio was admitted to the Union in 1802 there was provision for one section of each township to be devoted to schools for the inhabitants. This provision was extended to other states which were rapidly joining the Union. Some of the states that came into the Union shortly after Ohio were Indiana, Mississippi, Illinois, and Alabama. There were only three states admitted after 1802 which did not receive land grants for public schools. These were Maine, which was a part of Massachusetts and not of the national domain, Texas, which when annexed in 1854 was a sovereign state, and West Virginia, which seceded from Virginia during the Civil War. The total land gifts to the states by the federal government have been estimated to be in the neighborhood of 75,155,075 acres with an estimated value of nearly a billion dollars.

In addition to the land grants, certain special grants have been made by the federal government to the states. Some of these are as follows: The Ohio and Indiana grants contained certain saline lands from which sales-proceeds were added to the educational fund. Louisiana and other states were granted title to swamp lands, with their revenue in the main to be used for education. By a Congressional act of 1908, 25 per cent of the income derived from federal forests is paid to the states in which these forests are located and that income in part is used for public schools. There have also been special grants for advanced education.

Some conditional grants were made through the Morrill Acts of 1862 and 1890 which represented grants to the states of public lands and money. These grants were for the establishment of state colleges in agriculture and mechanics and set forth certain conditions, such as teaching military science and tactics. The Hatch Act in 1887 established agricultural experiment stations in connection with land grant colleges and contained certain specific controls. The Smith-Lever Act of 1914 and other similar acts which followed provided aid for "the diffusion among the people of useful and practical information on subjects relating to agriculture and home economics, and to encourage the application of the same." A condition imposed by the federal government in these acts was that the states match the federal appropriations, dollar for dollar.

It can readily be seen how the federal government, beginning with modest grants, has gradually extended itself through the Morrill and Smith-Lever Acts to the point where federal contributions have amounted to millions of dollars annually. Furthermore, the federal government has increasingly had more say in the expenditure of this money.

In recent years the federal government has made more conditional grants to education. The Smith-Hughes Act provided for aid in the area of vocational education. The George-Deen Act of 1937 authorized additional appropriations for vocational education with certain stipulations. There has also been legislation giving aid to rural schools, aid to needy students through the establishment of the National Youth Administration, and aid for school building construction and the teaching of various subjects through the Works Progress Administration. In recent years there have been increased federal expenditures for schools for those areas of the country where government projects have caused conjested conditions. Also, the Veterans' Rehabilitation Act, G.I. Bill of Rights, and Veterans' Readjustment Assistance Act of 1952 are indications of participation in education by the federal government. The federal government has progressively had more to say about education in this country.

In order to have a leadership agency at the federal level in the field of education and also a clearinghouse for information, the United States Office of Education was created in 1867. Until 1939 the Office of Education was under the Secretary of Interior, from 1939 to 1953 it was in the Federal Security Agency and in 1953 it became a part of the newly created Department of Health, Education and Welfare with full Cabinet status.

The federal government through Congress and other agencies that are under federal control is responsible for the operation of the public schools of the District of Columbia and those in the territories and possessions of the United States such as Alaska and Puerto Rico.

There have been many attempts to increase federal aid to the states to correct the inequalities that exist in ability to pay for educational programs. Most individuals recognize the need for federal assistance to the states in the field of education. Vast numbers of children receive no elementary education at all or at best a seriously-substandard one. In World War II, twelve per cent of the men found unfit for service were rejected solely for educational deficiencies. In one recent year it was estimated that about 4,000,000 children between 5 and 17 years of age attended no school at all. More than ten per cent of the teachers in public schools are serving under emergency or substandard certificates. Educators believe that federal aid should be an equalization measure. Such a state as Mississippi cannot afford to pay as much for education as New York. This discrepancy is not caused by a greater concern for education in New York than in Mississippi. "Inequality of educational opportunity is the result of economic inequality, not of inequality of will," one person has said. While a nominal allocation may be made to every state, the bulk of the appropriation must be distributed among the states in accordance with need. It is also felt that any legislation along this line must contain adequate safeguards against discriminatory treatment of minority groups and must be limited to tax-supported and publicly controlled educational institutions. However, legislation has consistently hit a snag in Congress with the church also demanding a share in such appropriations. This, with the increased appropriations for defense during the time of national emergency, has tended to divert public thinking from such federal aid at the present.

Federal-state relationships in respect to education is of vital importance. A proper balance must be maintained in community, state, and federal relationships in this important field. The state, by virtue of Constitutional provision, has complete control over the function of education within its geographic limits. In turn, it delegates to the community educational responsibilities. As viewed by many educators, the responsibility of the federal government is to equalize educational opportunity among the various states and individuals and to provide the leadership that is necessary to develop the best educational practices in every section of the country. In actual practice, the history of federal-state relationships shows an increased control over education on the part of the federal government. With increased grants to the states and various phases of education has gone increased control as to how programs will be conducted and operated. It is felt by many that authority over education should not be centralized in the national government because in a democracy such a potent force for good or evil should be kept close to the people.

IV. THE FUNCTION OF THE STATE IN EDUCATION

Education is a state function and the constitutions of the various states represent the law in respect to education. Where there is no Constitutional provision, state legislatures are practically free to develop educational policy as they see fit. The community, on the other hand, has no authority for education except as it is delegated to it by the state legislature.

As provided in the Tenth Amendment to the Federal Constitution, "The powers not delegated to the United States by the Constitution, nor prohibited by it to the states, are reserved to the States respectively, or to the people." This implies that education is a state function. The state legislature, as the designated representative of the people, has the authority to exercise all the powers that have been reserved to the states except where these powers have in part been specifically delegated to other agencies by the Constitution or when prevented by specific statement in the state constitution.

All the forty-eight state school systems, as organized administratively, derive their authority from the legislature and operate locally as school districts. The administrative setup in all of the states follows a similar general pattern but differs in details. The state legislature has the legal responsibility for education. There is also some form of state education authority, such as a state board of education, whose responsibilities include such things as providing leadership and guidance for the various state subdivisions; planning, interpreting, and appraising education programs; and acting as a certifying agency for the employment of various types of personnel engaged in the educational process. The execution of the state educational program resides in the local community where the constituents participate through their board of education.

Over the years state school codes have been developed by the legislatures. These codes represent the various laws governing education within the state. They provide the various regulations and rules under which education shall be conducted. They include the type of program required, the delegation of certain educational powers, or permissive laws which point out the activities that local school districts may carry on, and the circumstances and conditions surrounding this permission. Traditionally they grant broad powers to local administrative subdivisions, but at the same time are clear in their statement that the final authority for education resides in the state. If the state decides that such is necessary, educational organization within the state can be changed. Although the state legislature may develop and pass legislation affecting the educational system, school codes are not final until they have been reviewed by the courts in their relationship to the constitution of the state and to the powers reserved to the state. The courts, however, have been

ORGANIZATION CHART FOR A STATE DEPARTMENT OF EDUCATION

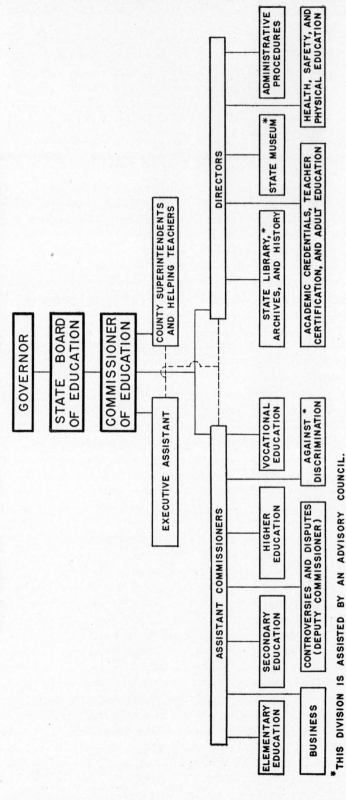

*THIS DIVISION IS ASSISTED BY AN ADVISORY COUNCIL.

consistent in pointing up that education is a state function and the state has the right to require uniform school programs within its geographic boundaries.

The state has the right to require compulsory attendance. This has been upheld in the courts on several occasions. The school code of the state has been found to be superior to any regulation or ruling passed by a local board of education.

Each state has made provision for a person who is the chief state educational executive. This individual is commonly called the state superintendent of public instruction or the commissioner of education. Each state also has some type of state board concerned with education. The responsibilities of such boards vary from complete supervisory control over all education in the state to very limited control. Boards of education may be classified into those concerned with such items as general education, vocational education, higher education, state retirement funds, libraries, textbooks, and art.

More than one-half of the states vest in the governor the authority to appoint members of state education boards. In other states they are either elected by the people, appointed by the legislature, appointed by the state superintendent with approval of the governor, or they are of the *ex-offico* type, composed in the main of persons who hold elective office in the state.

The average size of a state board is seven members, with the range in most states running between five and nine members. However, there are some with as few as three or as many as twelve members. In some states it is possible to change the composition of the board entirely, such as when a new governor takes office. However, in most states the tenure of members is staggered so as to assure continuity of policy.

The office of state superintendent of public instruction or state commissioner of education has been in effect for a long time. This position varies greatly from state to state. In some states he is the supreme educational officer, while in others he is the state board's professional executive officer. In others he occupies a position which is coordinate in power with the state boards. The duties of such a position range from supervision of all public and private schools, colleges, universities and other educational institutions to enforcing educational laws, auditing accounts, making rules and regulations for various educational subdivisions, and arranging teacher institutes.

The chief state educational officer is elected by popular vote in most states and in the others is appointed by the governor or the state board of education. The qualifications for such a position range from no academic requirements to a college degree. Some states require experience and in others candidates must meet certification requirements. Most individuals filling such jobs have a term of four years with others being re-elected every two years. A few have indefinite tenure.

The staff that operates the state department of education varies from state to state. Specialists in various specialized fields and activities plus clerical and other help comprise such divisions. Many such positions have little security with low salaries. In many cases positions are filled with individuals in payment of political debts.

The state's function and role in education during recent years has been to concentrate more and more power in the hands of the state education authority.

HOW A BILL BECOMES LAW IN NEW JERSEY
PROCEDURE FOR BILL STARTING IN ASSEMBLY
(SENATE BILLS FOLLOW SIMILAR COURSE)

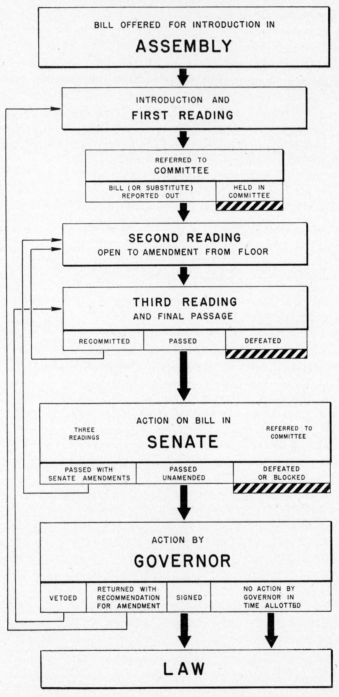

How a bill becomes law in New Jersey. (The Syllabus Committee. New Jersey State and Local Government. Curricular Syllabus No. 2. Trenton, New Jersey, State Department of Education.)

This trend toward concentration of authority goes hand in hand with the increased financial aid being given by the state for local schools. Despite the concentration of more power in the state education authority there is still a great diffusion of power among many boards and agencies with little coordination in the total state plans.

V. COMMUNITY RESPONSIBILITY IN EDUCATION

Education is a function of the state. As such, it is possible for the state legislature, except as limited by the Constitution, to determine the ways and means by which educational activity will be organized and carried out within its boundaries. The state legislature has the right to create one school district for the whole state, or it may create literally thousands of districts. In addition, each district may be different in respect to delegated power. The state also has the prerogative of requiring the local civil authorities to perform certain duties in respect to education.

An examination of the various states will show that the legislatures have not exercised unusual powers in the organization of their school districts. They seem to have followed an evolutionary pattern which developed as the needs of their constituents changed. The desires and needs of the community in most cases have played an important part in the changes that have taken place. In some cases, however, there has been an over-all change in the school districting for the entire state. For example, in 1915 reorganization in the state of Utah resulted in the consolidation of all existing districts into 40 school districts. This also occurred in West Virginia in 1933 when the legislature reduced the 398 small school districts to 55, with the county as the basic administrative unit.

In some states school districts and incorporated cities have the same boundaries. However, from the legal aspect, the city and the school district are two separate corporate entities, and each has separate and distinct functions to perform. The city differs from the school district in that it is concerned primarily with local matters, whereas the school district is an agent of the state and performs a specialized state function which transcends local matters. There can be no consolidation of the two functions from a local point of view. They are separate corporate entities.

A school district is the unit of local government with which many individuals have their first contact. All districts exist for essentially the same purposes. They provide the necessary land, buildings, and teachers and levy and appropriate the necessary taxes for maintenance of elementary and secondary schools. Each district has a school board, school committee, or board of education, which is usually elected by popular vote in the smaller communities, but in larger cities is often appointed. This board or committee generally selects a clerk or secretary, a treasurer, and a school superintendent, if the community is of sufficient size.

The following criteria represent an ideal school district:[1]

A Properly Organized School District

    1. Contains at least one well-defined community or a number of inter-related communities; ·

---

[1]*The Forty-eight State School Systems.* Chicago: The Council of State Governments, 1949, pp. 51-52.

2. Has the pupils and the resources to offer a comprehensive program of education from the kindergarten through the high school, and to make provision for post-high school and adult education at reasonable unit cost;

3. Is able to procure capable educational leadership;

4. Is able to maintain a competent, well-balanced staff of teachers, supervisors, and specialists;

5. Can finance its school program without unduly burdensome taxes;

6. Locates schools with due regard to

    a. bringing together enough children in each age group to make good instruction possible at reasonable cost, while

    b. placing schools in neighborhood or community centers, and

    c. holding the time spent in transportation to a maximum of one hour each way for high school children and less for younger children;

7. Is of such size and so organized that all the people of the district can exercise a voice in

    a. choosing the school board

    b. developing programs for all age groups, and

    c. other phases of planning and policy making.

A question has been raised in respect to the advisability of a close alignment of the school district with the local government. Many educators feel that if this policy is followed, the municipal government will in time consider education as merely another duty which it performs. The ideal school district should represent an administrative unit which grows out of the natural social, economic, and educational interests of the people and is designed to serve all individuals from the cradle to the grave.

Under the state administrative setup for education, the school district is the local administrative unit which carries out the educational activity for the various geographical sections of the state. It has been pointed out that within each district there is a board of education, school committee, school directors, trustees, or inspectors who administer the local unit. The board of education has the responsibility for administering educational affairs within the school district in conformance with state legislation and in the interests of the constituents. Although the board of education is the legal administrative authority for the school district, it still has to delegate part of the executive functions to professional personnel in the persons of superintendents of schools or other school officers. The functions of local boards of education and of professional personnel will be discussed in the next chapter where school and community organization and administration are dealt with more in detail.

VI. GOVERNMENTAL RELATIONSHIPS

All levels of government are interested in education. The federal government, the state government, and the local government all have parts to play if the educational activities within this country are to be carried out in an efficient and sound manner. There should, however, be certain principles which underlie the role that each should play. The federal government has been interested in and has contributed to education within the various states since the time of its inception. Education is a state function and the various states are autonomous in respect to educational activity within their boundaries. In conformance with the broad program established by the state, it has, to a large extent, delegated the right to administer educational affairs to the people in the local school districts. These relationships can be defined a little more in detail.

The federal government should be concerned mainly with equalizing educational opportunities within the various states and among all individuals. Inequalities exist at the present time because of economic limitations. Furthermore, the federal government should provide through its various agencies the leadership that is necessary at the national level, the research to aid in developing high educational standards throughout the country, and the information and guidance that will indicate the progress that has been made, the weaknesses that have been detected and the directions that the nation should take.

The functions of the state government are many. It is important that it supply the essential leadership; establish standards which maintain and improve the level of education within its boundaries; provide education to all its constituents regardless of economic, racial, and other factors; and aid the local administrative units financially, legally, and in any other way which will insure an adequate educational program.

The function of the local administrative unit is to put into operation the best type of educational program that is possible within the legal framework of the state. This implies that everything possible should be done to determine what is best in educational practice and what the needs of the people are. Then, within the framework of the state's delegation of powers, it is the responsibility of the local administrative unit to develop the program that accomplishes these things.

VII. GOVERNMENT AND HEALTH

The health of the populace has always been of concern to the government at the federal, state, and local levels.

A. Federal Level

The "general welfare" clause of the Constitution has provided the legal basis for the various health activities in which the federal government has been engaged over the years. Most of the health work of the federal government has been carried on through three agencies. The best known of these is the Public Health Service which until 1939 was a bureau in the Treasury Department. It then was transferred to the Federal Security Agency, and is now located in the new Department of Health, Education and Welfare which has Cabinet rank. The other agencies are the Children's Bureau of the Department of Labor and the Food and Drug Control in the Department of Agriculture.

The federal government has also broadened its activities in the field of health through legislation that has been passed in recent years. Some of this legislation included the Social Security Act of 1935 which provided for an annual appropriation to improve state and local health services and help the Public Health Service with a research program. The National Cancer Act of 1937 provided for the establishment of a National Cancer Institute concerned with research. The Vene-

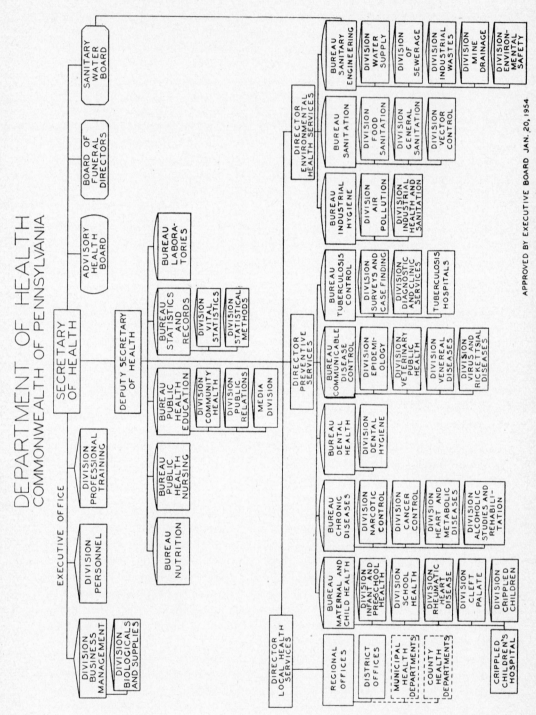

real Disease Act of 1938 placed additional responsibility on the Public Health Service in the prevention and control of venereal disease. Other acts such as the Hospital Survey and Construction Act of 1946, National Mental Hygiene Act of 1947, and the Water Pollution Control Act of 1948 gave the federal government a bigger stake in the health of its people.

The Public Health Service contributes immeasurably to the health of the nation. It has four main divisions. These are the Office of the Surgeon General, which includes such sections as Office of Vital Statistics and Dentistry; the National Institute of Health which as part of its responsibility conducts investigations in medical sciences; the Bureau of Medical Service which as part of its load is responsible for the administration of hospitals and clinics; and the Bureau of State Services, concerned with federal-state relationships in the field of health.

The federal government is also directly concerned with maritime quarantine, medical supervision of immigration, interstate quarantine in times of emergency, control of biological products, vital statistics, and other health problems having national implications.

In the field of health education, the federal government in its Office of Education has the same relationships it does with other special areas of education.

B. State Level

As in matters of general education, the various states are sovereign in respect to health matters. As a result, the records that are kept and practices that are followed are not uniform from state to state. Model registration forms for vital statistics and other uniform record keeping and practices, however, have been urged by the Public Health Service and other health agencies with some success. Another factor that has helped to promote uniformity of procedure among the various states is the Annual Conference of State and Territorial Health Officers.

As a general rule, each state has a department of health. The head of such a division may carry the title of commissioner of health or board of health. In some states the board of health draws up and enacts all laws pertaining to health, while in other states this is done by the state legislatures. The chief health officer in some states is appointed by the governor and in other states by the health board.

The responsibilities of the department of health in the various states are quite similar. They cover such areas as water supply, sewage disposal, food and drugs, industrial hygiene, milk control, and communicable disease prevention. A few states place some of these areas under other departments such as water supply under the state engineering department and industrial hygiene under the state department of labor.

Most state health departments delegate the administration of local health affairs to local health officers. These officers see that the state health laws are followed throughout the state. There are exceptions to this procedure in some states where such items as water and milk supply, laboratory services, and vital statistics are kept under the direct control of the state.

The field of health education at the state level has been the concern of health departments as well as education departments. In a few states the health and education departments have been combined, resulting in better public education in health areas. In some quarters, coordinating bodies composed of health and education personnel have also been developed with success.

Some excerpts from state laws regarding school health programs are as follows:

Georgia: Health and hygiene, the nature of alcoholic drinks and narcotics . . . shall be taught in the common or public schools as thoroughly and in the same manner as other like required branches, and the board of education of each county and local system shall adopt proper rules to carry the provisions of law into effect.

Michigan: It shall be the duty of boards of education in all school districts having a population of more than 3,000 to engage competent instructors of physical education and to provide the necessary place and equipment for instruction and training in health and physical education; and other school boards may make such provision: Provided, That nothing in this chapter shall be construed or operate to authorize compulsory physical examination or compulsory medical treatment of school children. The board of education of any school district may provide for the teaching of health and physical education and kindred subjects in the public schools of the said districts by qualified instructors in the field of physical education: Provided, That any program of instruction in sex hygiene be supervised by a registered physician, a registered nurse, or a person holding a teacher's certificate qualifying such person as supervisor in this field: Provided, however, That it is not the intention or purpose of this act to give the right of instruction in birth control, and it is hereby expressly prohibited to any person to offer or give any instruction in said subject of birth control or offer any advice or information with respect to said subject: Provided further, That any child upon the written request of parent or guardian shall be excused from attending classes in which the subject of sex hygiene is under discussion and no penalties as to credits or graduation shall result therefrom.

Nevada: Hygiene to be taught. Physiology and hygiene shall be taught in the public schools of this state, and especial attention shall be given to the effects of stimulants and narcotics upon the human system.

New Jersey: Teaching nature of alcohol and narcotics and effects thereof. The nature of alcoholic drinks and narcotics and their effects upon the human system shall be taught in all schools supported wholly or in part by public moneys as thoroughly and in the same manner as other like branches shall be taught, by the use of graded textbooks in the hands of the pupils when other branches are thus taught and orally only in the case of pupils unable to read. In the textbooks on physiology and hygiene the space devoted to the consideration of the nature of alcoholic drinks and narcotics and their effects upon the human system shall be sufficient for a full and adequate treatment of the subject. The failure or refusal of any district to comply with the provisions of this section shall be sufficient cause for withholding from such district the state appropriation.

C. Local Level*

The local health officer in the city or community has responsibilities which fall in categories similar to those found in the state department of health. It is very

*See also Chapters VI, XII, XIII, XIV, and XV.

important that there be continual vigilance at the local level in order to improve health conditions where needed. Unfortunately the local health officer is frequently a political appointee who spends only part of his time in this job and many times does not have the proper training in the field of public health.

The type of community, whether it is rural or urban, industrial or agricultural, determines in great measure the nature and scope of health work. Other influencing factors are available health facilities and money, and the needs of the people. In the past it was generally agreed that funds should be made available for health use equal to one dollar per capita of the population. This formula, however, with rising costs and increased services needed, is outdated and there should be financial outlays in excess of this amount.

VIII. GOVERNMENT AND PHYSICAL EDUCATION

The governmental relationships to physical education are similar to what they are for education in general. Physical education is an integral part of the total educational offering and as such has been influenced by governmental action in the same way as other phases of education.

A. Federal Level

At the federal level the main official connection that this specialized field has with government workings is in the Office of Education where it has specialists who act in an advisory capacity. They contribute to professional growth by dispensing literature pertinent to various aspects of the program, and by traveling throughout the country and meeting with various professional groups in an attempt to raise standards. Since physical education is related to health, it has received an impetus several times from various governmental agencies which are especially interested in seeing a strong and fit populace. Physical education has been aided by government bureaus which have developed and maintained national parks and are interested in the conservation of national resources. The profession has also been greatly affected by federal legislation which has been passed periodically. Legislation establishing land grant colleges, youth programs such as the Civilian Conservation Corps, the Works Progress Administration, and other similar legislation has had its effect directly or indirectly on physical education personnel, facilities, and programs. For example, some centralized schools that were built with the aid of WPA funds were required to combine their auditorium and gymnasium. The government also shows its concern with such things as the number of football games to be shown on television each fall, various aspects of professional baseball and other sports, and other items which affect the public's general welfare.

B. State Level

Since education is a state function, so also is physical education. Most states are concerned with physical education to the point where they have incorporated a division within the state department of education to help in carrying out this specialized function. Although the relationship between the state education department and the local school district is mainly advisory in nature, a great amount of help is rendered by state personnel. States perform such services as publishing syllabi and acceptable lists of curriculum materials; recommending standards for programs of activities, facilities, and equipment; conducting surveys; and sending out specialists to give advice and to consult with local leaders. They also play a prominent part in state professional associations.

The state department of education also sets up certification requirements which must be met by anyone who desires to teach in this special field within state boundaries. In many states it prescribes the extent of physical education in terms of time that must be devoted to this subject in the various school programs. In some states it sets up requirements as to sports programs, specifying the length of seasons and the number of interscholastic games that can be played in each sport. The state can require conformance with the regulations it sets up by withdrawing financial aid in the event of noncompliance with school codes.

It is interesting to examine the school codes of various states to determine the purpose and objectives of physical education as defined within these codes. An example of some of these follow:

Examples of Objectives:

> To develop organic vigor; to provide neuromuscular training; to promote bodily and mental poise; to correct postural defects; to secure greater co-ordination, strength and endurance; to promote desirable moral and social qualities; to promote hygienic school and home life; to secure scientific supervision of sanitation in school.

> To secure the health, vigor, and physical soundness and to inculcate a love for and a disposition to serve the country.

> To promote correct physical posture and bearing, mental and physical alertness, self-control, disciplines, initiative, sense of patriotic duty, and spirit of co-operation under leadership.

Examples of Time Requirement:

> Not less than twenty minutes each school day and not less than two hours each school week.

> Not less than thirty minutes each day for health instruction, physical exercise, and recess play.

> Not less than one hour weekly during the whole of the school year.

Examples of Age and Grade Limit:

> Every pupil, except kindergarten pupils, of all public schools.

> All pupils of all elementary and high schools, except the physically disabled.

> All pupils of all public common schools and all educational institutions supported wholly or in part by money from the state.

Examples of Credit and Graduation Regulations:

> Completion of course is a requirement for graduation.

Physical education in both elementary and high schools is credited and forms a part of the requirement for promotion and graduation.

Credits and penalties shall be applied for success or failure in physical education courses.

Examples of Provisions for Local Supervision:

A county, city, town or district may appoint a physical director for the locality, under the direction and supervision of the state director and paid by local school fund.

When number of pupils of a district or municipality is sufficient, a competent supervisor and special teachers of physical education shall be employed.

Each county, city and town school board employing 30 or more teachers may employ a supervisor of physical education whose qualifications for service shall be established by the State Superintendent of Public Schools, and who shall participate in all periodic physical examinations for all children.

C. Local Level*

The relationship of physical education to government at the local level is the same as that of general education. Physical educators have the responsibility of carrying out a program which is in the best interests of the consumer and meets the various state standards. Most state standards in physical education are insufficient, however, and, where they have been established, represent the minimum rather than the desirable. Therefore, each local physical education program should be broadened so that its potentialities are realized, not only for developing the physical aspects of each individual, but in addition, the social and mental aspects. The real job in physical education is done at the community or "grass roots" level. This is where the leadership must be exceptionally good, facilities adequate, and standards high. Educators in general and physical educators in particular must recognize their responsibility and their potentialities for enriching human lives through this medium in which individuals have a natural drive to engage. Whether or not physical education is an integral and important part of the total educational offering will be determined by the work that is performed at this level.

QUESTIONS AND EXERCISES

1. Why is it important for educators to understand the governmental aspects of their work?

2. Write a letter to your national and/or state government asking for literature and information regarding their relationship to your specialized field.

3. What are the purposes of education in American democracy? How can the government aid in achieving these purposes?

4. Prepare a research paper which points out some of the significant contributions of government to education since 1800.

5. What are the implications of the new department in the President's organization which gives Cabinet rank to such an essential function as education?

---

*See also Chapters VI, VII, XVI, XVII, and XVIII.

6. Trace the relationship of the federal government to education since 1783.

7. What are the arguments for and against federal aid to education?

8. Why is education referred to as a state function?

9. What are some characteristics of the administrative organization of education in the forty-eight states?

10. What is the community's responsibility in regard to education?

11. What is the purpose of the school district?

12. What has been the history of government at each level as related to health?

13. What has been the history of government at each level as related to physical education?

SELECTED REFERENCES

Bolduan, Charles Frederick, and Bolduan, William. *Public Health and Hygiene*. Philadelphia: W. B. Saunders Company, 1949, Part V.

Boyd, William. *The History of Western Education*. London: Adam and Charles Black, 1952.

Counts, George S. *The Social Foundations of Education*. New York: Charles Scribner's Sons, 1934.

Cubberly, Ellwood P. *Public Education in the United States*. New York: Houghton Mifflin Company, 1947.

Hadley, Arthur Twining. *Education and Government*. New Haven: Yale University Press, 1934.

Hjelte, George. *The Administration of Public Recreation*. New York: The Macmillan Company, 1948, Part I.

Knight, Edgar W. *Twenty Centuries of Education*. New York: Ginn and Company, 1940.

Meyer, Harold D., and Brightbill, Charles K. *Community Recreation*. Boston: D. C. Heath and Company, 1948, Section II.

Moehlman, Arthur B. *School Administration*. New York: Houghton Mifflin Company, 1940. Parts IV and V.

Monroe, Paul. *Founding of the American Public School System*. New York: The Macmillan Company, 1940.

Russell, John Dale, and Judd, Charles H. *The American Educational System*. New York: Houghton Mifflin Company, 1940.

Smillie, Wilson G. *Public Health Administration in the United States*. New York: The Macmillan Company, 1951, Part IV.

Chapter VI

SCHOOL AND COMMUNITY
ORGANIZATION AND ADMINISTRATION

The administrator, teacher, and leader must be cognizant of the administrative structure of the school and of the municipal government. In the previous chapter the stress was on the relation of government to education at federal, state, and local levels. The local or "grass roots" level in the fields of health and physical education needs further discussion. The community level is where most of the members of these professions participate, the bulk of the work is accomplished, the consumers of their products are located, and close professional relationships need to exist.

I. SCHOOL STRUCTURE

Under "School Structure" will be discussed the roles of the board of education, superintendent of schools, principal, and lay groups, and the place of health and physical education within this framework.

A. Board of Education or School Committees*

The board of education is the legal administrative authority created by the state legislature for each school district. The responsibility of the board is to act on behalf of the residents of the district it represents. It has the duty of appraising and planning the educational program on a local basis. It selects executive personnel and performs duties essential to the successful operation of the schools within the district. The board develops policies that are legal and in the interest of the people it serves. It devises financial means within the legal framework to support the cost of the educational plan. It keeps its constituents informed of the effectiveness and needs of the total program.

Some of the more specific powers of boards of education include: purchasing property, planning school buildings, determining the educational program, securing personnel, levying taxes for school purposes, approving courses of study, determining the school calendar, and providing for the school census. The powers of boards of education are fixed by state statutory enactment.

The qualifications for board members are very few. There are usually general requirements which specify citizenship, age, residence, and sometimes ownership of property. In many communities women as well as men are playing very prominent roles. According to surveys that have been conducted, boards of education

---

*The term "Board of Education" is used in this discussion although "School Committee" is used in some sections of the country.

Boards of education participate in the planning of school buildings. General George W. Wingate High School, Brooklyn, New York.

LOS ANGELES CITY SCHOOL DISTRICT

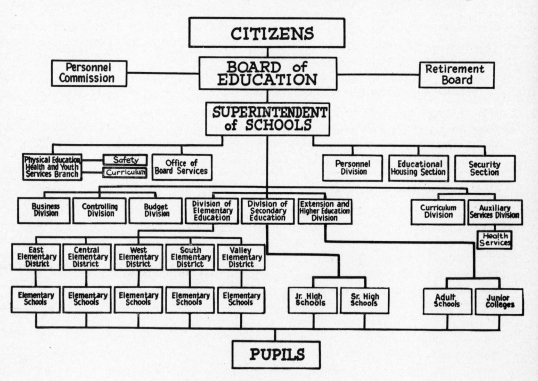

Los Angeles City School District.

usually include individuals who are past middle age, have been successful in their community, and are conservative in nature. There has been an improvement in recent years in the organization and composition of boards of education. The addition of women and individuals who are nonpartisan in their outlook, the organization of smaller and less cumbersome boards, and provisions for longer terms of office are resulting in a more stable educational policy.

Boards of education vary in size. There is the usual three-member board in the common-school district which represents the independent one- or two-room school setup. Township boards of education range from five to nine members, county boards from three to fifteen, and city boards from three to sixteen. The trend is toward small boards of education.

Boards of education members are appointed in some cases, and in others they are elected.

B. General Administrative Personnel

The administrative personnel that will be discussed includes the superintendent of schools, principal, and staff.

1. Superintendent of Schools.—Within a large school system where many schools are involved there is a superintendent who has over-all charge of the school program. Associate or assistant superintendents are in charge of technical detail, management, or various phases of the program such as secondary education. There is also a superintendent's position associated with smaller schools. These officers are known as district superintendents. They are responsible for many schools extending over a wide geographic area.

The superintendent's job is to carry out the educational policies of the state and the board of education. He acts as the leader in educational matters in the community. He also provides the board of education with the professional advice it needs as a lay organization. From an executive standpoint, he appraises the entire educational program over which he has control, working closely with the board of education to eliminate weaknesses and establish a strong system of education. Any large organization needs leadership. So does the educational system of any community.

The qualifications for the position of superintendent vary in different communities. In some villages and cities the individual must be a resident and in others this is not necessary. The educational requirement varies a great deal. Some communities require a doctorate and others require a minimum of professional training. There is a trend, however, in the direction of increased training. Most superintendents of schools have their bachelor's and master's degrees and an increasing number have taken work beyond the master's. Many have their doctorates. Both teaching and administrative experience are frequently listed as requirements.

2. Principal.—The position of principal is very similar to that of the superintendent. It differs mainly in respect to the extent or scope of responsibility. Whereas the superintendent is usually in charge of all the schools within a particular community, the principal is in charge of one particular school. The duties of the principal include responsibility for executing educational policy as outlined by the superintendent, appraising the educational offering, making periodic reports on various aspects of the program, directing the instructional program, promoting good relationships between the community and the school, and supervising the maintenance of the physical plant.

In many school situations, principals teach in addition to their administrative responsibilities. Some conduct extracurricular activities such as leading the band or coaching a varsity athletic team. Some principals have responsibilities on only one school level, but where various levels are combined in one structural unit, this responsibility may extend from the high school level down through the junior high school and even to the elementary school.

The qualifications for the position of principal vary. There is in evidence a trend toward increased training for such positions. Some communities feel that the principal should have more training than the teachers.

Boards of education must select school administrators from the individuals available. The prestige, money, security, and other factors that the position offers play an important part in determining the quality of individual that can be secured.

3. Other General Administrative Personnel.—In addition to the superintendent of schools and the principal, there are other administrative staff members. These include the supervisors over various specialties in the instructional program such as art, music, health and physical education; heads of departments who coordinate the various fields of the educational program such as English and mathematics; directors of various specialized services such as guidance and health; individuals in charge of grounds and other physical facilities; and many lesser administrative officers. All play a part in insuring the efficient running of the educational program.

C. Lay Groups

The general public is participating more and more in the work of the schools. Parent-teacher associations, citizens' councils, and study groups are a few of the organizations which express the lay opinion of the community in regard to educational matters. This interest on the part of the public should be encouraged and helped in every way possible. There are approximately 8,000,000 members of parent-teacher associations alone throughout the country. The public school program should reflect what the public wants and thinks is best for their children. This can be accomplished only through active "lay" participation. Administrators and other school personnel should make sure that the citizens of the community are adequately informed in respect to educational matters so that the best type of program may be developed.

D. Health Within the School Structure*

The superintendent and principal have the main responsibility for the school health program. The attitude they have toward health and the degree to which

---

*See also Chapters VII, XII, XIII, XIV, and XV.

they recognize the importance of achieving professional objectives will determine the success of the school health program.

Administrators must recognize certain important principles in regard to health in order that it may have an important place in the total school program. Some of these principles are: Health in the school should be an important and integral part of the over-all educational program. All teachers and other school personnel should understand and appreciate the importance of promoting health and the contributions they can make through their own work toward realizing such a goal. There should be individuals on the staff who have had special training in this field so that they may take the leadership in developing and promoting an adequate program.

Superintendents and principals have important responsibilities for promoting health within the school. Chandler Street Junior High School, Worcester, Massachusetts.

There should be coordination of the various instructional aspects of the educational program to insure adequate coverage of health information and to avoid unnecessary overlapping. There should be provision for concentrated health teaching. Adequate facilities, time, money, and personnel should be provided to properly carry on this special work. A close working arrangement with the community should be recognized as an essential to a well-developed program. There should be a statement of policies in regard to health which is clear and understood by all.

1. Terminology for the School Health Program.—The following definitions were drawn up by the Committee on Terminology which represented the American

Association for Health, Physical Education and Recreation and the American School Health Association.[1]

a. *School Health Program.*—The school procedures that contribute to the understanding, maintenance, and improvement of the health of pupils and school personnel, including health services, health education, and healthful school living.

b. *School Health Services.**—The school procedures which are established to (a) appraise the health status of pupils and school personnel; (b) counsel pupils, parents, and other persons involved, concerning appraisal findings; (c) encourage the correction of remediable defects; (d) help plan for the health care and education of handicapped children; (e) help prevent and control disease; (f) provide emergency care for the sick or injured.

c. *Health Appraisal.*—That phase of school health service which seeks to assess the physical, mental, emotional, and social health status of individual pupils and school personnel through such means as health histories, teachers' and nurses' observations, screening tests, and medical, dental, and psychological examinations.

d. *School Health Counseling.*—The procedures by which nurses, teachers, physicians, guidance personnel, and others interpret to pupils and parents the nature and significance of a health problem and aid them in formulating a plan of action which will lead to solution of the problem.

e. *School Health Education.*†—The process of providing learning experiences for the purpose of influencing knowledges, attitudes, and conduct relating to individual and group health.

f. *Healthful School Living.*‡—A term which designates the provision of a a safe and healthful environment, the organization of a healthful school day, and the establishment of interpersonal relationships favorable to the best emotional, social, and physical health of pupils.

g. *Health Coordination.*—The process of developing relationships within the school health program and between school and community health programs which contribute to harmonious action in the solution of problems relating to pupil health.

h. *School Health Council.*—A representative group of persons organized for the purposes of study, planning, and action aimed at the identification and solution of school health problems.

i. *School Health Educator.*—A person specially qualified to serve as a teacher, consultant, coordinator, or supervisor of health education in an individual school or a school system.

2. Essential Aspects of the School Health Program.—Health within the school structure will be discussed under three headings: health education, health services, and healthful school living.

a. *Health Education.*§—In the area of health education, scientific knowledge is imparted and experiences are provided so that students may better understand the importance of developing good attitudes and health practices. Information concerning such things as nutrition, communicable disease, rest, exercise, sanitation, first aid, and safety is presented. On the elementary level the responsibility for such health education rests on the shoulders of the classroom teacher, although in some school systems trained specialists are provided as resource persons. On the

---

[1]Report of the Committee on Terminology in School Health Education. *Journal of the American Association for Health, Physical Education and Recreation* 22: 14, September, 1951.
*See Chapter XV.
†See Chapter XIV.
‡See Chapters XII and XIII.
§See also Chapter XIV.

secondary level, it is recommended that individuals who have had special training in health education be responsible for concentrated health instruction. This is not always the case. Sometimes, in the absence of a trained specialist, the teacher of physical education, home economics, or science, or some other teacher is given the responsibility. A concentrated course in health education should be required of all students at least for one and preferably two years at the secondary level. Health educators should teach such courses and these subjects should be given the same credit and time allotments as other important ones in the curriculum. Again, this recommendation is not followed in many schools because of the lack of trained personnel, the fact that other subjects are given a priority listing, and the lack of an appreciation on the part of school administrators of the importance of health education. Many schools incorporate health education in the physical education class. When this is the case, it quite often becomes a "rainy day" proposition. Some feel that it is adequately cared for in other subjects such as science and home economics. Correlating health instruction in various subject-matter areas is to be encouraged. However, this in itself is not sufficient.

Healthful school living. Chandler Street Junior High School, Worcester, Massachusetts.

The emphasis in health education at the primary grade level should be on how to live healthfully, at the intermediate grade level on *why* certain types of health practices are important, and at the secondary level, on personal and community health. It should be reiterated that although there is a place for concentrated teaching at the secondary level, at the same time it is important for all subject-matter areas to recognize their possibilities and responsibilities for also teaching health.

The possibilities for health education should also be recognized in the various experiences the child has in school. When the school physician gives the medical examination, the dental hygienist examines the child's teeth, an emergency concerned with health exists in the community, or the curiosity of the child is aroused; "teachable moments" for imparting health information are presented. This type of health education often leaves a greater impression upon young minds than the more formal classroom type.

b. *Health Services.** —The health services phase of the school health program includes health appraisal, health counseling, correction of defects, provision for the exceptional child, prevention and control of communicable disease, and emergency care of injuries.

In this phase of the school health program it is important to recognize concern for mental, emotional and social, as well as physical health. In providing health services which include all these phases of health, several persons in addition to the health educator play prominent parts.

The classroom teacher has an important responsibility in health services. He or she is probably closer to the child than any other person on the staff and therefore can detect deviations from the normal. The teacher also is in a position to give good advice, provide first aid when necessary, administer certain screening tests, and oversee the general welfare of the child.

The school nurse plays a prominent role in the administration of the school health program. Through counseling, acting as a resource person for other staff members, developing close relationships with parents, helping physicians, and other responsibilities peculiar to her profession, the nurse is a key person in the school.

The school physician has the potentials of playing a very important part in the school program. Through such things as medical examinations, health guidance, protection of children from communicable diseases, development of health policies, and consultations with parents, it is possible for this person to exercise a great force for good in the health of the children and parents with whom he comes in contact. It has been the observation of many educators, however, that the physician often does not realize the educational implications of his role in the health program. As a result, he does not take advantage of "teachable moments" which occur whenever a child is being given a medical examination or when conferences are held with parents.

Dentists and dental hygienists play an important role wherever their services are provided. These specialists appraise the dental needs of students. Here again there is an unlimited opportunity to educate the student and the parent on the importance of proper oral hygiene.

Psychologists, psychiatrists, social workers, guidance counselors, speech correctionists, and others are increasingly being brought into school health services programs. All have an important part to play and contribution to make to the total health of young people who attend the schools in this country.

c. *Healthful School Living.*†—Healthful school living is also an important part of the total school health program. In addition to a healthful physical environ-

*See also Chapter XV.
†See also Chapters XII and XIII.

ment, a wholesome emotional environment must also be provided. Both are important to the health of the child.

The physical environment of the school should provide an attractive, safe, and wholesome place for students to congregate. This implies that such important considerations as lighting, ventilation, heating, location, sanitary facilities, play space, equipment, and other essentials are adequately provided for in the buildings and areas that are used for school purposes. It also means there is proper maintenance by the custodial staff and includes any other factors which influence the physical arrangements of the school plant.

The physical environment of the school should provide an attractive, safe, and wholesome place for students. Worcester, Massachusetts, public schools.

The emotional environment is just as important to the child's health as the physical one. To insure a wholesome emotional environment such things as proper rapport must exist between the teacher and pupils and among the pupils themselves; educational practices pertinent to such things as grades, promotions, assignments, schedules, play periods, attendance, class conduct, and discipline must be sound, and the teachers themselves must be well adjusted.

3. **Other Phases of Health Administration.**—There are two other aspects of the school health program that need special attention. They are the School Health Council and the Health Coordinator.

a. *The Health Council.*—Every school and every school system should have health councils or committees to help insure a desirable and adequate health program. This means there should be a health council for each school and one central health council for all the schools in a particular school system. The number of members comprising such councils may vary from three or four persons in a small school to fifteen or sixteen in a larger school. Potential members of such councils are school principal, health coordinator, nurse, psychologist, guidance person, custodian, dental hygienist, physician, dentist, physical education teacher, science teacher, home economics teacher, classroom teacher, teacher of handicapped, nutritionist, students, parents, public health officer, mayor, clergymen, and any other individual who is particularly related to the health of the school or community and has something to contribute.

Health councils are responsible for coordinating the entire health program of the school. This would include such things as determining subject matter to be taught, resources to be utilized and experiences to be provided; providing a healthy environment in which to live; arranging in-service training for teaching personnel; encouraging closer school-parent relationships in respect to such important health procedures as medical examinations; promoting sanitary conditions; providing for safety of children; and distributing health literature.

Representatives from various community and school groups which are interested in health can accomplish much when sitting around a conference table discussing their problems. A spirit of cooperation and "oneness" will aid in developing procedures and taking action which will promote better health for all.

b. *Health Coordinator.*—Health affects many subject-matter areas, the school plant, educational practices, and practically every aspect of school life. It is important, therefore, to have coordination. This means responsibility must be fixed in one person. By having someone responsible it is possible to integrate health into the total education program and the total community health program.

As a result of the need for coordination of the various phases of health, many schools have appointed health coordinators. In some places this individual is known by another title such as "health consultant" or "health educator." This person, in most cases, is appointed by the administration and has particular qualifications for the job.

The responsibilities of the health coordinator include such things as integrating and correlating the various phases of health education in the subject-matter areas, channeling health information to staff members, keeping records, preparing reports periodically on pertinent health matters, providing leadership for health councils, seeing that established health policies are carried out, appraising and evaluating the total health program, arranging special health examinations when needed, counseling students on health problems, aiding the school physician in the performance of his duties, helping in the maintenance of a healthful environment, organizing safety and other programs which promote health, and helping in furthering school-home relationships.

E. Physical Education Within the School Structure

Physical education is an integral part of the total education process and has as its aim the development of physically, mentally, emotionally, and socially fit citizens through the medium of physical activities which have been selected with a view to realizing these outcomes.

Physical education is increasingly occupying a more important role in the school offering. During its early history, physical education was regarded by general school administrators as a fad, an appendage to the school program, or a necessary evil to be tolerated. In recent years, however, it has been viewed by an increasing number of school people as an integral part of the total educational offering with many potentialities for contributing to enriched living.

1. **Terminology in Physical Education.**—Components of the school physical education program are characterized by many and varied terms. Since there has been no committee established to work out descriptive terms for the various phases of the program, as in the case of the school health program, there is lack of uniformity within the profession. The author would like to suggest that the three components of the school physical education program, into which it logically divides itself, be called (1) the required class (service) program, (2) the intramural and extramural program, and (3) the interschool program.

Physical education within the school. (Department of Physical Education, University of California at Berkeley.)

The *required class program* is the provision of physical education for all students, and is characterized by instruction in such things as the rules, strategies and skills of the various activities that comprise the program.

The *intramural and extramural athletics program* is voluntary physical education for all students within one or a few schools. It is characterized by such things as competitive leagues and tournaments and play and sports days, and acts as a laboratory period for the required class program. In the intramural program activities are conducted for students of only one school, while in the extramural program students from more than one school participate.

The *interschool athletics program* is designed for the skilled individuals in one school who compete with skilled individuals from other schools in selected physical education activities.

2. **Organization.**—The various school departments of physical education throughout the country have many different plans of organization. A few years ago it was quite common to see such titles as Department of Physical Culture or Hygiene. The term "physical training" was also used as a descriptive term for the work performed in this special area.

Today, one also sees a variety of titles associated with physical education work. In some schools it is the "physical education department," in others the "health and physical education department," and in others it is the "health, physical education and recreation division." Camping and safety are also included.

The titles that are given also show to some degree the particular work that is performed within these phases of the total program. In some schools physical education is organized into a separate unit with the various physical activities, intramural extramural, and interschool athletics comprising this division. In other schools, health and physical education are combined in one administrative unit. In some cases, although the word "health" is used, there is little evidence of the particular specialized type of school health work as it is known today. This is also true where the word "recreation" is used in the title. In the discussion to follow, the term "physical education" will be used.

There is usually a person designated as head or chairman of the physical education department. The title of director of physical education is also used. In smaller schools, it is quite common to have just one man and one woman on the physical education staff, each acting as the head of his or her separate division.

The duties of the head of a physical education department include coordinating the activities within his particular administrative unit, requisitioning supplies and equipment, preparing schedules, making budgets, holding departmental meetings, teaching classes, coaching, hiring and dismissing personnel, developing community relations, supervising the intramural, extramural, and interscholastic programs, evaluating and appraising the required class program, representing department at meetings, reporting to principal, and over-all general responsibility for the activities carried on.

3. **The Required Class Program.***—The required class program refers to the instructional program. In some states this phase of the program is required by state law and in others it is governed by a local regulation. In a few schools participation is not required but voluntary. Classes are scheduled in much the same way as other subjects. Students, however, are too often assigned on the basis of administrative convenience rather than homogeneously. Physical education people have advocated assigning students to classes in a way that would result in their realizing

*See also Chapter XVI.

the greatest physical, social and other benefits pertinent to this field of work. However, very few schools have followed these recommendations. The emphasis in the class program is instructional and various games and activities are offered at different levels in the school program. On the elementary level, rhythmic activities and low organized games are stressed, whereas on the secondary level there is a change to more highly organized games and sports.

A survey of the country will show many inferior programs of physical education, if they are compared to the standards that have been set for the profession. In many communities, the required class program, although serving the entire student body, is hampered by lack of time, facilities, and leadership. Stress on varsity sports and lack of administrative support have also been influential factors. The leadership that is found in many physical education programs is not resourceful, dynamic, and capable of promoting a sound program.

Where good required class programs of physical education exist they have been developed on the basis of the physical, social, mental, and emotional needs of the students. A broad and varied program of activities, both outdoor and indoor, progressively arranged and adapted to the capacities and abilities of each student is offered.

4. **The Intramural and Extramural Program.***—The goal of the intramural and extramural program is to provide competition in games, sports, and other physical activities, for the rank and file of the student body. This program is in addition to the required class program. Whereas the required class program is designed to be largely instructional in nature so that basic fundamentals for playing various activites can be learned, the intramural and extramural program is designed to provide an opportunity for students to utilize these learned skills in actual competitive situations.

There is a place in the intramural and extramural program for all students, regardless of degree of skill, strength, age, or field of specialization. It offers an opportunity for friendly competition between groups from the same school. Sometimes "sports" and "play" days are also included. These special events involve students from one or many schools who are invited to participate. Teams are composed of students from the same school and from many different schools.

As many as ninety or ninety-five per cent of the students participate in the intramural and extramural programs of schools where there is an active interest. Since these programs are conducted on a voluntary basis, this indicates the amount of enthusiasm and interest that can be generated through a well-organized program. Good attendance in such a program usually reflects a broad offering of activities with leagues or some other unit of competition, organized in a manner that appeals to the interest and needs of the students.

In small schools, intramurals and extramurals are usually conducted by one or two persons who are also in charge of the required class program. This places an additional load on such individuals and consequently some fail to develop the type of program that could be offered if more personnel were available. In larger

---

*See also Chapter XVII.

schools it is quite common to have a director of intramural athletics. This places the responsibility on one person and usually results in a better-organized and more effective program.

Close coordination should exist between the required class and intramural and extramural programs. Furthermore, department members, student managers, and interested faculty members should be encouraged to help in the conduct of the program. For the best administration of intramural and extramural programs, most schools also give careful consideration to units of competition; a program of fall, winter, and spring activities; eligibility requirements; provisions for medical examination; preliminary training periods; scheduling; variation in types of tournaments; coaching; and awards.

5. The Interschool Athletics Program.*—The interschool program in athletics is designed for the individuals most highly skilled in sports. It is one of the most interesting and receives more publicity than the other two phases of physical education in the school setup. The reason for this is not that it is more important or renders a greater contribution. Instead, it is largely the result of its popular appeal. The fact that sports writers and others discuss it in glowing terms and that it involves competition which pits one school or one community against another school or another community also increases its public appeal. A spirit of rivalry develops. This seems to be characteristic of American culture.

The interschool athletics program has probably had more difficulties attached to it than any of the other phases of the program. The desire to win and to increase gate receipts has resulted in evil practices. Large stadia and sports palaces have been constructed which require large financial outlays for their upkeep.

For many years there has been much controversy over whether or not girls should engage in interscholastic sports. Some advocate such activities for the girls because they feel they should also be offered the advantages that accrue to boys. On the other hand, others feel that physiological and social implications indicate that girls should not participate in such activities. As a result of this controversy, many schools have dropped interscholastic competition for girls and in their place have stressed "sports" and "play" days. Some states have even prohibited interschool competition.

In some schools the interschool phase of the program comes under a director of athletics. It is his responsibility to arrange the schedules; make the necessary arrangements for athletic events, such as securing officials; make the necessary ous details essential to a well-organized program. For many schools, smaller in size, the individual or individuals who administer the required class and intramural and extramural programs also administer the interschool phase of the total physical education program. Since all are closely related, utilize the same personnel in most cases, share the same facilities, and are interested in achieving the same objectives, it is important that they all come under the jurisdiction of the same department. Such an organization makes it possible for all to accomplish their purposes under the leadership of an individual who recognizes the value and place of each in a well-rounded program.

---

*See also Chapter XVIII,

In connection with financing athletic programs, many schools have what is called a general organization, which is in charge of the finances not only for the athletic program but also for other school activities such as dramatics and music. This has been used with success in some schools and takes the financial responsibility out of the physical education department and places it in an impartial organization.*

Other items of particular importance that should be provided for in the administration of athletics are provision for medical supervision and an accident plan. Both should be carefully considered by any school desiring to have a sound athletic program.

II. COMMUNITY STRUCTURE

It is important to understand not only the structure of the school, but also that of the larger community of which it is a part. If programs of health and physical education are to render the most valuable service at the community level, their leaders must clearly understand its structural organization. This important level of government touches human lives to a great degree.

A discussion of community structure may be covered under "village" and "city" government.

A. Village Government

A village is an organized community which is usually smaller in size and has a less complex form of government than those places with larger populations which are called cities. In some cases these smaller units of organizations are known by other terms, such as towns or boroughs. For purposes of convenience, the word "village" is used in this discussion.

When a sufficient number of people live in a concentrated geographical area and need to have cooperative effort in order to provide a public water supply, street lights and other essentials, the state provides they may form a government separate from the country or township. This makes it possible to have representative officials to conduct their affairs, levy and collect taxes and provide the conveniences essential to modern-day living.

The state prescribes the conditions under which a community may be incorporated as a village. These conditions usually include such items as specifications for population and geographic area. When these conditions are satisfied, the state may be petitioned. In return the village is given such powers of self-government as provided by that state. Incorporated villages have the usual powers to provide water, lights, sewers, fire protection, police protection, sidewalks, and other essentials to their welfare. Each incorporated village has a legislative body usually known as the council or the board of trustees. This body varies in number from three to nine and the customary length of term is one or two years. This legislative group can determine the tax rate and make appropriations within limitations set by the state. It usually has the power to levy special assessments, although most villages must submit the question of a bond issue to the constituents. The power to pass ordinances varies from state to state. The council or board of trustees can

---

*See also Chapter XVIII.

usually select certain village officers, control public services owned by the village, require licenses for peddlers and other business, and perform those minor functions peculiar to a village.

The main executive officer of a village is usually called the mayor and in most cases is elected for one or two years. This officer presides over the village legislative body, executes the ordinances passed by this group, and in some cases acts as a police justice. In addition to the mayor, villages frequently have such officers as a clerk or recorder, a treasurer or collector, police officer, street commissioner, justice of the peace, commissioners for public services such as health and fire, assessor, attorney, and, if in a separate school district, school officers. Officers are elected by the voters in some villages and in others are appointed by the council.

FORMS OF GOVERNMENT OF AMERICAN CITIES (OVER 30,000 POPULATION)

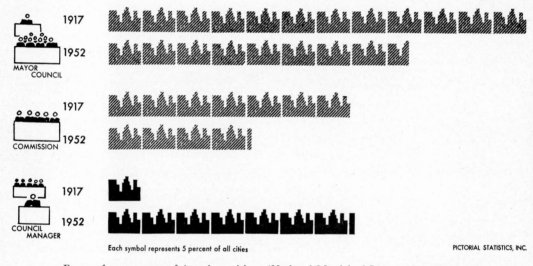

Each symbol represents 5 percent of all cities

PICTORIAL STATISTICS, INC.

Forms of government of American cities. (National Municipal League, New York.)

B. Municipal Government

A city is a governmental unit which has been created under state provisions and usually has a greater population and more powers than a village. There was a rapid growth of cities as a result of the industrial revolution with the concentration of manufacturing concerns in strategic geographical locations.

1. Types of City Government.—Cities are characterized in the main by three types of government. These are the council-mayor type, the commission type, and the city-manager type.

a. Council-Mayor.—The council-mayor type of city government is the oldest and the most common. It generally consists of a council to legislate and a mayor to see that the laws are enforced.

Some cities have mayors with strong powers and some do not invest much power in their chief executive. In the strong-mayor type of government, which has proved efficient in several situations, the mayor appoints the principal city officials, has a small council with which to work, and is given broad powers in directing the administration of the city. Where the mayor is just a nominal head, he has few powers, an unwieldly council with which to work, and commissioners or boards who are elected independently. Under such conditions it is very difficult to attain efficiency.

You Were Saying Something About Taxes?

—*Reprinted by permission of New York Herald Tribune Syndicate*

One reason for understanding your city government.

Some cities have two chambers, a board of aldermen and a common council. However, such a practice is becoming obsolete and a single-chamber council is becoming more popular.

The council, elected by the voters for terms varying from one to four years, has as its responsibility legislating city ordinances, determining tax rates, making appropriations, and usually controlling to some degree the various administrative departments such as police, health, and recreation. Many times, however, such departments are directly responsible to the mayor.

The mayor is elected by the voters for terms ranging from one to four years. Under him are usually the heads of the various departments such as police, fire, parks, recreation, and health. Sometimes the officers who head these departments are elected, but in most cases they are selected by the council or appointed by the mayor with or without the approval of the council. In many cities, the mayor presides at meetings of the council and usually has the right to veto ordinances passed by the council, which then can become law only if passed by a two-thirds or other majority of the council.

I. MAYOR-COUNCIL FORM

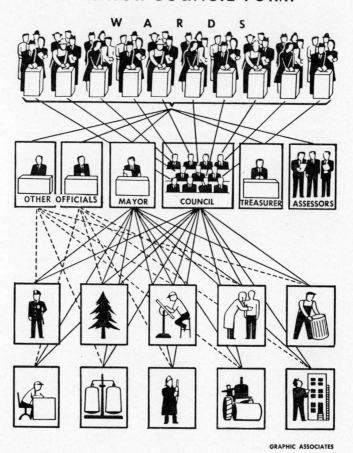

GRAPHIC ASSOCIATES

Mayor-Council form of city government. (National Municipal League, *The Story of the Council-Manager Plan.*)

The school affairs in a city are usually the responsibility of an independent board of education.

b. Commission.—The commission type of city government was first tried in Galveston, Texas, in 1901, as a result of an emergency caused by a tidal wave. This type of government is characterized by a few elected officers. The usual number is five. These officers comprise a commission which exercises the legislative and executive powers and is directly responsible to the voters. The commissioners are usually elected for a term of two years, enact all city ordinances, and grant permits or franchises for public services. As an administrative body, they exercise all the administrative authority which in mayor-council cities is shared by the mayor, administrative departments, and council. Each member of the commission

2. COMMISSION FORM

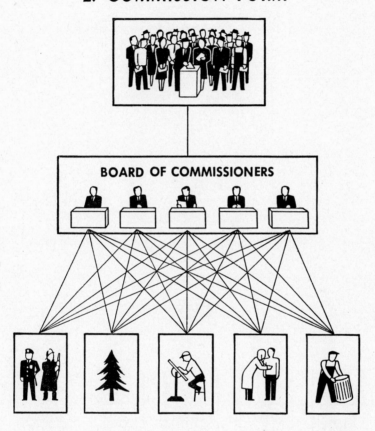

GRAPHIC ASSOCIATES

Commission form of city government. (National Municipal League. *The Story of the Council-Manager Plan.*)

is assigned to serve as the head of one of the five departments into which the administrative work is usually divided: finance and revenue, waterworks and sewage, police and fire, streets, and public improvements. The commission appoints the subordinate officials, unless their selection has been left to individual commissioners or to a special civil service commission. This type of government brings together the legislative and executive functions of city government and places these responsibilities in the hands of a small group of officials.

c. City-Manager.—The city-manager type of city government is the fastest growing type of the three that are discussed. There are about 1200 city and local governments, or about 40 per cent of all communities in the United States, using this type of organization. It is also considered by many to be the best and most efficient. It usually consists of a council of three to five members who determine the policy and a manager who is an expert in city government who administers the affairs of the city. Many times the manager is chosen by the commission or council for an indefinite term. He can be recalled by the commission or the voters.

3. COUNCIL-MANAGER FORM

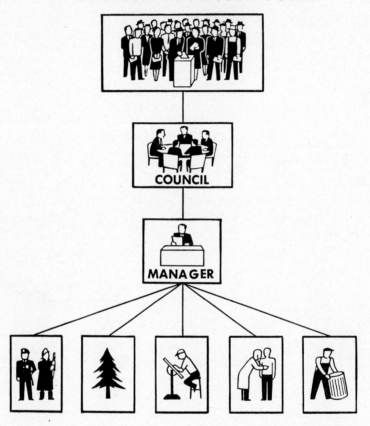

GRAPHIC ASSOCIATES

Council-Manager form of city government. (National Municipal League. *The Story of the Council-Manager Plan.*)

His duties usually include enforcement of city ordinances, hiring and firing of department heads, and advising the commission as to the needs of the city. The manager may be chosen from within or without the city and irrespective of political considerations. The powers and responsibility of city government are centered in one person. Thus, one individual can be held accountable. This form of organization makes the administration of city government a profession and in the numerous places where it has been adopted, it has increased efficiency.

2. Charter and Home Rule.—

a. Charter.—A city government has only such powers as it is granted by the state. These powers are usually stated in a charter which includes such facts as the name of the city, its boundaries and organization. At one time most states granted a separate charter to each city. However, this did not prove satisfactory because some cities were given special favors in accordance with the political pressure that could be brought to bear on the state legislature. Therefore, many states have circumvented this evil by grouping their cities into classes, according to population, and have enacted uniform laws for all cities that fall within each classification.

b. Home Rule.—In order to give cities more control over their own government, "home rule" provisions have been incorporated into the constitutions of many states. "Home rule" allows the city, within the framework of state laws and regulations, to frame their own charter.

A "home rule" charter may be developed and prepared by the city council, commission, group of interested citizens, or at a convention specifically designed for such a purpose. It is then submitted to the voters. Amendments are sometimes submitted by the council or initiated by petition and then submitted to the voters.

C. Public Health Organization at the Local Level

1. Health Department.—There are few, if any, local departments with more important functions than the health department. In spite of this, the amount of money set aside and the emphasis placed on this phase of government are usually less than that spent on many other areas such as for police or fire protection.

The department of health also works more closely with other branches of local government than most other departments. For example, it is closely related to bureaus having control of water supply and purification, garbage collection and disposal, sewerage and street cleaning, and police department enforcement of the sanitary code. It also works with officers in charge of education, especially in regard to medical and dental inspection of school children. Such essential relationships make it imperative to have a local health department which is efficient and functions properly.

In some cities governed by a commission, health is combined with police and fire administration to form a department of public safety. However, in most cities, especially the larger ones, there is a separate department of health. At the head of the health department in these larger cities there is usually a board of health or a commission, headed by a health commissioner. In a few cities the health activities are guided by a single commissioner, who is appointed by the mayor or city council.

In many cases small or medium-sized cities and villages do not employ full-time health officers, and the public health activities are cared for by a physician who devotes only part time to this work. Under such conditions, a health department in the full sense of the phrase does not exist and the public health activities are bound to be limited.

On some occasions, two or three small communities have felt the need for full-time health personnel and consequently have pooled their efforts and resources and have combined to develop a joint health administration with a full-time health officer. This has resulted in advantages to all communities concerned. It is hoped that this policy will be used to a greater extent by small villages, towns, and cities located within a short enough radius to make such a system practical.

The recognized, successful health departments in larger cities have boards of health presided over by a commissioner of health. These boards enact the sanitary code of the city, issue emergency health orders, and have been given broad powers in all health matters. In some emergency situations such a group has been given the power to imprison persons, destroy property, forbid traffic and perform similar duties to prevent the spread of disease.

The health department in larger communities is usually divided into certain specialized divisions, having control over various health aspects of the community. Some of these divisions are:

The *bureau of administration,* which coordinates all the various activities performed and serves as a central communication point with other city functions.

The *division of records,* which collects, preserves, and publishes vital statistics, issues burial permits, registers physicians, assists in enforcing child-labor and school attendance laws, and performs statistical work for the department.

The *sanitary division or bureau,* which has jurisdiction over sanitary conditions and looks into such things as reported nuisances and the sanitation of slaughter-houses and stables.

The *bureau of preventable diseases,* which is concerned with the prevention and control of communicable disease, holding of tuberculosis and other clinics, disinfecting of premises and goods, and supervising a staff of field nurses.

The *division of child hygiene,* which is concerned with child and infant care, eye and dental clinics, supervision of day nurseries, and placing and caring of dependent children.

The *food and drug bureau,* which has control over the food and drug supply in the city and inspects premises where foods are stored, handled, sold or prepared. It also is especially concerned with the persons who prepare or serve food in public eating places.

The *bureau of laboratories,* which carries on research work, maintains supply stations for diphtheria antitoxin and vaccine, and makes scientific studies of various diseases and combats them wherever possible.

The *bureau of hospitals,* which supervises the various hospitals which in large cities are maintained by the department for the care of individuals who have communicable diseases.

Last, but not least, there is the *bureau of public health education.* This bureau is gradually being added to more and more departments of health because it is becoming increasingly evident that individuals are not going to develop good health practices without an educational program. This bureau sends out various types of information concerning health matters, promotes cooperation between department officials and the public, publishes health literature for professional and lay persons, gives health lectures, and organizes exhibitions and other media for publicizing the importance of certain health practices.

The health department, as can be seen from the above description, provides many essential and important functions for a community. Unfortunately, many of the activities listed are not carried on by all cities. An analysis of the functions performed indicates a change of emphasis from that of merely eliminating nuisances and fighting epidemics, to one of prevention and providing information and services essential for good health.

2. Health Councils.—One of the best ways to insure that all the health resources in a community are being utilized effectively for the benefit of most people, is to have a community health council.

A community contains many groups and individuals who are interested in health. With so many interested in such an endeavor there is need for coordination and a clearinghouse for the solving of health problems. A council or committee which is composed of representatives of various community groups can serve a very useful purpose. Much progress can be made if representatives from such groups as voluntary and professional health agencies, schools, industry, merchants, and others interested in health meet to discuss health problems. Group discussion can take place, problems can be aired, plans can be made, and work can be done which would never be possible without some type of cooperative effort. The health council is a comparatively new organization, but has been found to be most helpful in promoting health in the community. As an agency through which many groups may cooperate to promote health, it has great possibilities for mobilizing public support for necessary health measures.

3. Voluntary Health Agencies.—Some voluntary health agencies usually exist in communities of any size. These are organizations concerned with health which receive their support from public drives for funds, gifts, membership fees, and donations. Some examples of these are the American Cancer Society, National Tuberculosis Association, National Committee for Mental Hygiene, American Red Cross, and the National Foundation for Infantile Paralysis. Voluntary agencies in the field of health take the leadership for solving particular health problems which affect great numbers of American people. Through voluntary contributions and work, these agencies attempt to meet the problems.

Many voluntary health agencies exist now and new ones are being formed periodically. The greatest need at the present time is to coordinate the work that all the various agencies for health, whether they be official, voluntary, or private, are doing. There is considerable confusion in the public's mind because of the numerous agencies that are asking for financial help and support. If the work were better coordinated and organized, the public would have a clearer picture of what is needed and consequently would lend greater support.

QUESTIONS AND EXERCISES

1. Draw a structural organization chart for your school showing the various administrative divisions. Discuss the responsibilities of each of the divisions. Give special attention to the health and physical education divisions.

2. Prepare an organization chart for your village or city governmental structure. Discuss the implications of this type of administrative organization for the specialized fields of health and physical education.

3. In regard to the board of education of the community in which you live, list the composition of the board, powers of the board, and qualifications of board members.

4. Discuss the role of the superintendent of schools, principal, and other administrators in a selected community.

5. Define each of the following: (a) school health program, (b) school health services, (c) health appraisal, (d) school health counseling, (e) school health education, (f) healthful school living, (g) health coordination, (h) health council, and (i) school health educator.

6. What part does a health coordinator play in the school health program?

7. Describe in detail the three main divisions of the total school physical education program.

8. Discuss the advantages and disadvantages of council-mayor, commission, and city manager types of city government.

9. Discuss the relationship of local government to school health. What administrative provisions have been made for these important considerations?

SELECTED REFERENCES

American Association of School Administrators. *Health in Schools. Twentieth Yearbook.* Washington: National Education Association, 1951.

Bolduan, Charles Frederick, and Bolduan, Nils William. *Public Health and Hygiene.* Philadelphia: W. B. Saunders Company, 1949, Chapter 45.

Boyd, William. *The History of Western Education.* London: Adam and Charles Black, 1952.

Counts, George S. *The Social Foundations of Education.* New York: Charles Scribner's Sons, 1934.

Cubberly, Ellwood P. *Public Education in the United States.* New York: Houghton Mifflin Company, 1947.

Cubberly, Ellwood P. *Public School Administration.* New York: Houghton Mifflin Company, 1922.

Cubberly, Ellwood P. *State School Administration.* New York: Houghton Mifflin Company, 1927.

Dudley, L. Leland. *The School and the Community.* Cambridge: Harvard University Press, 1933.

Educational Policies Commission. *School Athletics—Problems and Policies.* Washington, D. C.: National Education Association, 1954.

Engelhardt, Fred. *Public School Organization and Administration.* New York: Ginn and Company, 1931.

Hadley, Arthur Twining. *Education and Government.* New Haven: Yale University Press, 1934.

Hagam, Harlan L. *The Administration of American Public Schools.* New York: McGraw-Hill Book Company, Inc., 1951.

Hjelte, George. *The Administration of Public Recreation.* New York: The Macmillan Company, 1948, Parts I, II.

Kilander, H. F. *Health Instruction in the Secondary Schools—Its Organization and Administration.* Office of Education. Pamphlet No. 110. Washington: U. S. Government Printing Office, 1951.

Knight, Edgar W. *Twenty Centuries of Education.* New York: Ginn and Company, 1940.

Meyer, Harold D., and Brightbill, Charles K. *Community Recreation.* Boston: D. C. Heath and Company, 1948, Sections III, VI.

Moehlman, Arthur B. *School Administration.* New York: Houghton Mifflin Company, 1940, Part III.

Monroe, Paul. *Founding of the American Public School System.* New York: The Macmillan Company, 1940.

Mort, Paul R. *Principles of School Administration.* New York: McGraw-Hill Book Company, Inc., 1946.

Patterson, Raymond S., and Roberts, Beryl J. *Community Health Education in Action.* Saint Louis: The C. V. Mosby Company, 1951, Chapter III, Appendices I, II, III.

Pfiffner, John M. *Municipal Administration.* New York: The Ronald Press Company, 1940, Chapters III, XIV.

Reed, Thomas Harrison. *Municipal Management.* New York: McGraw-Hill Book Company, Inc., 1941, Chapters II, XVIII, XIX.

Report of the Committee on Terminology in School Health Education. *Journal of the American Association for Health, Physical Education and Recreation* 22: 14, September, 1951.

Russell, John Dale, and Judd, Charles H. *The American Educational System.* New York: Houghton Mifflin Company, 1940.

Smillie, Wilson G. *Public Health Administration in the United States.* New York: The Macmillan Company, 1951, Parts III, IV.

Williams, Jesse Feiring, and Wetherill, Gloyd Gage. *Personal and Community Hygiene Applied.* Philadelphia: W. B. Saunders Company, 1950, Chapters 19, 22.

Chapter VII

ADMINISTRATIVE RELATIONSHIPS
AND OBJECTIVES OF HEALTH AND
PHYSICAL EDUCATION*

Health and physical education as professional fields of endeavor are closely allied, especially in respect to their administrative aspects. In many schools both come under one administrative head. They are concerned with the accomplishment of similar objectives. In many small communities both health education and physical education are taught by the same person. Professional preparation institutions usually incorporate both areas in the same schools or departments. In the American Association for Health, Physical Education and Recreation, they are linked together professionally. Individuals working in these specialized areas share facilities, personnel, funds, and other items essential to their programs. General school administrators feel they are closely related.

These are only a few of the reasons why a close administrative relationship should and must exist between these specialized fields. Although professional persons realize the place of each and the need for specialists in each area, at the same time they also recognize the importance of maintaining a close and effective working relationship. The administrator is a key person in seeing that such a relationship is maintained. In some quarters, there has been disunity and strained relations between these areas because the administrator did not assume his role of appeaser and unifier.

I. CLOSELY ALLIED BUT SEPARATE AREAS OF ENDEAVOR

In recent years educational thinking has been more and more cognizant of the place of health and physical education in the school program. Each is closely related to the other, but at the same time each is distinct. Each area has its own specialized subject-matter content, its specialists, and media through which it is striving to better the living standards of human beings. In the larger professional preparing institutions each has its own separate training program. There is continual agitation for separate certification of its leaders in the various states. Some sections of the country have recognized this need and have established state standards for employment of these specialized workers.

Although many educators and others feel that physical education has traditionally reflected the thinking and work of both areas, this is an erroneous belief. There

*See also Chapters V and VI.

119

is a definite need for the specialist in each of the areas of school health and physical education. Each can render a service to humanity. Each can make a contribution which is distinct and separate from the other's. Each has its own destiny.

A close relationship among teachers in these areas, however, is evidenced by the fact that, to a great degree, they use the same facilities, perform work in each other's area, work on committees together, and have professional books and magazines which cover the literature of both fields. Both are concerned with the total health of the individual. Both recognize the importance of activity in developing and maintaining good personal health. Both are concerned with the physical as well as the social, mental, emotional, and spiritual aspects. Both recognize the importance of developing good human relations as a basis for effective living in a democracy. Both are interested in promoting the total health of the public at large as a means to enriched living, accomplishment of worthy goals, and increased happiness.

II. OBJECTIVES OF SCHOOL HEALTH AND PHYSICAL EDUCATION PROGRAMS

The ultimate objectives of school health and physical education programs are similar. The essential difference lies in the fact that each area attempts to achieve its goals by utilizing different skills, media, and approaches. The objectives of each of the two areas are discussed in the pages to follow.

A. Objectives of the School Health Program

The long-term, over-all objective of a health program is to maintain and improve the health of human beings. This refers to all aspects of health including physical, mental, emotional, and social. It applies to all individuals, regardless of race, color, economic status, creed, or national origin. The school has the responsibility to see that all students achieve and maintain optimum health, not only from a legal point of view but also from the standpoint that the educational experience will be much more meaningful if optimum health exists. A child learns easier and better when in a state of good health.

Some specific objectives established for the School Health Program as stated by the Illinois Joint Committee on School Health are as follows:

Objectives of School Health Services and School
Health Education

To inspire the child with a desire to be well and happy;

To convey to the child a public and personal health ideal, designed to ensure for him the continuation throughout life of wholesome and effective living, physical and mental;

To educate the child, according to a definite plan, in the cultivation of those habits of living which will promote his present and his future health;

To impart health knowledge and attitudes to the child so that he will make intelligent health decisions;

To develop in the child a scientific attitude toward health matters, and an understanding of the scientific approach to health problems;

To maintain adequate sanitation in the school, the home, and the community;

To protect the child against communicable and preventable diseases and avoidable physical defects by providing effective public health control measures, both individual and social, throughout the school and the community;

To bring each child up to his own optimal level of health;

To extend the school health program into the home by obtaining family and community support for the program;

To discover early any physical defects the child may have, secure their correction to the extent that they are remediable, and assist the child to adapt himself to any residual handicap;

To provide healthful school living for the child;

To relate the school health program to the health program in the community so that it may deal with real, current, and practical problems;

To organize effectively not only the program of direct health instruction but the equally important indirect learning experiences of the child in the field of health.[1]

One objective of health education is the cultivation of those habits of living which will promote present and future health. Washington Irving Elementary School, Waverly, Iowa. (Picture furnished by Burnett and Logan, Chicago.)

Turner lists the major objectives of the school health program as the achievement of optimal pupil health through:

1. The correction of physical defects.
2. The reduction of communicable disease.

[1]Illinois Joint Committee on School Health: *Health Education and the School Health Program.* Springfield, Illinois: Illinois Department of Public Health, July, 1944, pp. 10-11.

3. The development of healthful school living.

4. The interpretation of the school health program to home and the development of home and school cooperation.

5. The development and maintenance of desirable health habits.

6. The development of health knowledge.

7. The development of desirable mental attitudes toward health, health practices, and life situations.[2]

The commonly mentioned objectives concerned with the development of health knowledge, desirable health attitudes, and desirable health practices, deserve further discussion.

1. Development of Health Knowledge.—In order to accomplish the health knowledge objective, health education must present and interpret scientific health data for purposes of personal guidance. Such information will help individuals to recognize health problems and to solve them by utilizing information which is valid and helpful. It also will serve as a basis for the formulation of desirable health attitudes. In the complex society that exists today there are so many choices confronting an individual in regard to factors that affect his health that a reliable store of knowledge is essential.

Individuals should know such things as how their bodies function, causes and methods of preventing disease, factors that contribute to and maintain health, and the role of the community in the health program. Such knowledge will aid the individual to live correctly, help to protect his body against harm and infection, and impress upon him the responsibility for his own health and the health of others.

Knowledge of health will vary with different ages. For younger children there should be an attempt to provide experiences which will show the importance of living healthfully. Such settings as the cafeteria, lavatory, and medical examination room offer these opportunities. As the individual grows older, the scientific knowledge for following certain health practices and ways of living can be presented. Some of the areas of health knowledge that should be understood by students and adults include nutrition, the need for rest, sleep, and exercise, protection of the body against changing temperature conditions, contagious disease control, the dangers of self-medication, and community resources for health.* If such topics are brought to the attention of persons everywhere, and if the proper health attitudes and practices are developed, better health will result.

There should also be an adequate knowledge of what constitutes healthful living and adequate health services.

Both the physical and nonphysical environment should be considered in healthful living. The physical aspects of school buildings, homes, and other places where people congregate should be clean, sanitary, well lighted and ventilated, provide ample space, and be adjusted to the various health needs of individuals. In addition, the importance of the nonphysical environment should be recognized. This environment reflects how teachers and pupils get along with each other, incentives, organization and administrative structure and procedures, and other items which greatly affect mental and emotional health.

---

[2]C. E. Turner. *School Health and Health Education.* St. Louis: The C. V. Mosby Company, 1952, p. 155.

*See also Chapter XIV.

Knowledge of what constitutes adequate health services should also be known and recognized. Such health services as health appraisal, health counseling, communicable disease control, education of the handicapped, and emergency care of injuries should be understood and appreciated by all. Only as this knowledge is imparted will the various services be utilized in a manner most conducive to the health of students.

2. Development of Desirable Health Attitudes.—Health attitudes refer to the health interests of the individual or the motives which impel him to act in a certain way. All the health knowledge that can be accumulated will have little worth unless the individual is interested and motivated to the point that he wants to apply this knowledge to everyday living. Attitudes, motives, drives, or impulses, if properly established, will result in the individual's seeking out scientific knowledge and utilizing it as a guide to living. This interest, drive, or motivation must be dynamic to the point where it results in behavior changes.

The school health program must be directed at developing those attitudes which will result in optimum health. Students should have an interest in and be motivated toward possessing a state of buoyant health, feeling "fit as a fiddle," being well rested and well fed, having wholesome thoughts free from anger, jealousy, hate, and worry, and feeling strong and possessing physical power to perform life's routine tasks. They should have the right attitudes toward health knowledge, healthful school living and health services. If such interests as these exist within the individual, proper health practices will be followed. Health should not be an end in itself except in cases of severe illness. Health is a means to an end, a medium which aids in achieving noble purposes and contributes to enriched living.

Another factor that motivates individuals to good health is desire to avoid the pain and disturbances that accompany ill health. They do not like toothaches, headaches, or indigestion because of the pain or distraction involved. However, developing health attitudes in a negative manner, through fear of pain or other disagreeable conditions, does not seem to be a sound approach.

A strong argument for developing proper attitudes or interests should center around the goals one is trying to achieve in life and the manner in which optimum health is an aid in achieving such goals. This is the strongest incentive or interest that can be developed in the individual. If one wishes to become a great artist, an outstanding businessman, or a famed dancer, it is greatly beneficial if he or she have good health. This is important so that the study, training, hard work, trials, and obstacles that one encounters can be met successfully. Optimum health will aid in the accomplishment of such goals. As Jennings, the biologist, has pointed out, the body can attend to only one thing at a time. If its attention is focused on a toothache, a headache, or an ulcer, it cannot be focused satisfactorily on some essential work that has to be done. Centering health attitudes or interests on life goals is a dynamic thing because they represent an aid to accomplishment, achievement, and enjoyable living.

3. Development of Desirable Health Practices.—Desirable health practices represent the application of those habits which are best, according to the most qualified thinking in the field, to one's routine of living. The health practices that an individual adopts will determine in great measure the health of that person. If practices or habits are engaged in which are harmful to optimum health, such as failure to obtain proper rest or exercise, overeating, overdrinking and oversmoking, and failure to observe certain precautions against contracting diseases, then poor health is likely to follow.

Knowledge does not necessarily insure good health practices. An individual may have at his command all the statistics as to the results of speeding at 70 miles an hour, yet, unless this information is applied, it is useless. The health of an individual can be affected only by applying that which is known. At the same time, knowledge will not usually be applied unless an incentive, interest, or attitude exists which impels its application. It can be seen, therefore, that in order to have a good school health program, it is important to recognize the close relationship that exists among health knowledge, health attitudes, and health practices. One contributes to the other.

Knowledge does not necessarily insure good health practices. Library at the new Clark Street Elementary School, Worcester, Massachusetts.

Another health objective that is sometimes listed is that of skill development. This refers to the development of such skills as those involved in first aid and safety. A mastery of such skills enhances good health.

B. Objectives of the School Physical Education Program[3]

A study of the individual reveals four general directions or phases in which growth and development take place, namely, physical development, motor develop-

[3]Charles A. Bucher. *Foundations of Physical Education.* St. Louis: The C. V. Mosby Company, 1952, Chapter VIII.

ment, mental development, and human relations development. Physical education plays an important part in contributing to each of these phases of human growth and development.

1. The Physical Development Objective.—This objective deals with the program of activities which builds physical power in an individual through the development of the various organic systems of the body. It results in the ability to sustain adaptive effort, the ability to recover, and the ability to resist fatigue. The value of this objective is based on the fact that an individual will be more active, have better performance, and be healthier, if the organic systems of the body are adequately developed and functioning properly.

The physical development objective. (Department of Physical Education, University of California at Berkeley.)

Muscular activity plays a major role in the development of the organic systems of the body. The term "organic" refers to the digestive, circulatory, excretory, heat regulatory, respiratory, and other systems of the human body. These systems are stimulated and trained through such activities as hanging, climbing, running, throwing, leaping, carrying, and jumping. Health is also related to muscular activity; therefore, activities which bring into play all of the fundamental "big muscle" groups in the body should be engaged in regularly. Furthermore, the activity should be of a vigorous nature so that the various organic systems are sufficiently stimulated.

Through vigorous muscular activity several beneficial results take place. The trained heart provides better nourishment to the entire body. The trained heart beats slower than the untrained heart. It pumps more blood per stroke, with the result that more food is delivered to the cells and there is better removal of waste products. During exercise the trained heart's speed increases less and has a longer rest period between beats. After exercise it returns to normal much more rapidly. The end result of this state is that the trained individual is able to perform work for a longer period of time, with less expenditure of energy, and much more efficiently than the untrained individual. This trained condition is necessary to a vigorous and abundant life. From the time an individual rises in the morning until he goes to bed at night, he is continually in need of vitality, strength, endurance, and stamina to perform routine tasks, be prepared for emergencies, and lead a vigorous life. Therefore, physical education aids in the development of the trained individual so that he will be better able to perform his routine tasks and live a healthy, interesting, and happy existence.

2. The Motor Development Objective.—The motor development objective is concerned with performing physical movement with as little expenditure of energy as possible and in a proficient, graceful, and esthetic manner. This has implications for one's work, play, and anything else which requires physical movement. The name "motor" is derived from relationship to a nerve or nerve fiber which connects the central nervous system, or a ganglion, with a muscle. As a consequence of the impulse it transmits, movement results. The impulse it delivers is known as the motor impulse.

Effective motor movement is dependent upon a harmonious working together of the muscular and nervous systems. It results in greater distance between fatigue and peak performance; it is found in activities which involve such things as running, hanging, jumping, dodging, leaping, kicking, bending, twisting, carrying, and throwing; and it will enable one to perform his daily work much more efficiently and without reaching the point of being "worn out" so quickly.

In physical education activities, the function of efficient body movement, or neuromuscular skill as it is often called, is to provide the individual with the ability to perform with a degree of proficiency. This will result in greater enjoyment of participation. Most individuals enjoy doing those particular things in which they have acquired a degree of mastery or skill. For example, if a child has mastered the ability to throw a ball consistently to a designated spot and has developed batting and fielding power, he will like to play baseball or softball. If he can swim 25 or 50 yards without tiring and can perform several dives, he will enjoy being in the water. If an adult can consistently serve tennis "aces" he will like tennis; if he can drive a ball 250 yards straight down the fairway, he will like golf; and if he can throw ringers, he will like horseshoes. A person enjoys doing those things in which he or she excels. Few individuals enjoy participating in activities in which they have little skill. Therefore, it is the objective of physical education to develop in each individual as many physical skills as possible so that interests will be wide and varied. This will not only result in more enjoyment for the participant, but at the same time will allow for better adjustment to group situations.

Physical skills are not developed in one lesson. It takes years to acquire co-ordinations, and the most important period for development is during the formative years of a child's growth. The building of coordinations starts in childhood, when an individual attempts to synchronize his muscular and nervous systems for such things as creeping, walking, running, and jumping. A study of kinesiology shows that many muscles of the body are used in even the most simple of coordinated movements. Therefore, in order to obtain efficient motor movement or skill in many activities, it is necessary to start training early in life and continue into adulthood. Furthermore, a child does not object to the continual trial and error

Developing skill in worth-while physical activities is an objective of physical education. Department of Physical Education, University of California at Berkeley.

process of achieving success in the performance of physical acts. He does not object to being observed as an awkward, uncoordinated beginner during the learning period. Most adults, however, are self-conscious when going through the period of learning a physical skill. They do not like to perform if they cannot perform in a creditable manner. The skills they do not acquire in their youth are many times never acquired. Therefore, the physical education profession should try to see that this skill-learning takes place at a time when a person is young and willing and is laying the foundation for adult years.

The motor development objective also has important implications for the health and recreational phases of the program. The skills that children acquire will determine to a great extent how their leisure time will be spent. One enjoys participating in those activities in which one excels. Therefore, if a child excels in swimming, a great deal of his leisure time is going to be spent in a pool, lake, or at the beach. If he excels in tennis, he will be found on the courts on Saturdays, Sundays, and after dinner at night. There is a marked correlation between juvenile delinquency and lack of constructive leisure-time activity. If we want children to spend their leisure moments in a physically wholesome way, we should see that skills are gained in physical education activities.

3. The Mental Development Objective.—The mental development objective deals with the accumulation of a body of knowledge and the ability to think and interpret this knowledge.

Physical activities must be learned; hence, there is a need for thinking on the part of the intellectual mechanism, with a resulting acquisition of knowledge. The coordinations involved in various movements must be mastered and adapted to the environment in which the individual lives, whether it be in walking, running, or wielding a tennis racquet. In all these movements the child must think and coordinate his muscular and nervous systems. Furthermore, this type of knowledge is acquired through trial and error. Then, as a result of experience, there is a changed meaning in the situation. Coordinations are learned, with the result that an act once difficult and awkward to perform becomes easy to execute.

The individual should not only learn coordinations but should acquire a knowledge of such things as rules, techniques, and strategies involved in physical activities. Basketball can be used as an example. In this sport a person should know such things as the rules, the strategy in offense and defense, the various types of passes, the difference between screening and blocking, and finally the values that are derived from playing in this sport. Techniques which are learned through experience result in knowledge that is also acquired. For example, a ball travels faster and more accurately if one steps with a pass, and time is saved when the pass is made from the same position in which it is received. Furthermore, a knowledge of followership, leadership, courage, self-reliance, assistance to others, safety, and adaptation to group patterns is very important.

Knowledge concerning health should play an important part in the program. All individuals should know about their bodies, the importance of sanitation, factors in disease prevention, importance of exercise, need for a well-balanced diet, values of good health attitudes and habits, and the community and school agencies which provide health services. This knowledge will contribute greatly to physical prowess as well as to general health. Through the accumulation of a knowledge of these facts, activities will take on a new meaning and health practices will be associated with definite purposes. This will help each individual to live a healthier and more purposeful life.

A store of knowledge will give each individual the proper background for interpreting new situations which confront him from day to day. Unless there is knowledge to draw from, he will become helpless when called upon to make important decisions. As a result of participation in physical education activities, an individual will be better able to make discriminatory judgments, by which knowledge of values is mentally derived. This means that he has greater power for arriving at a wise decision and that he can better discern right from wrong and the logical from the illogical. Through his experience in various games and sports, he has developed a sense of values, an alertness, the ability to diagnose a tense situation, the ability to make a decision quickly under highly emotionalized conditions, and the ability to interpret human actions.

In physical education activities one also gains insight into human nature. The various forms of activity in physical education are social experiences which enable a participant to learn about human nature. For all children and youth this is one of the main sources of such knowledge. Here they discover the individual's responsibility to the group, the need for followership and leadership, the need to experience success, and the feeling of "belonging." Here they learn how human beings react to satisfactions and annoyances. Such knowledge contributes to social efficiency and good human relations.

4. The Human Relations Objective.—The human relations objective is concerned with helping an individual make personal adjustments, group adjustments, and adjustments as a member of society. Activities in the physical education program offer one of the best opportunities for making these adjustments, if there is proper leadership.

Social action is a result of certain hereditary and derivative tendencies. There are interests, hungers, desires, ideals, attitudes, and emotional drives that are responsible for everything we do. A child wants to play because of his drive for physical activity. A man will steal food because of the hunger drive. America is opposed to totalitarian governments because of its desire for personal freedom. The response to all these desires, drives, hungers, and the like may be either social or antisocial in nature. They are social or antisocial, depending on whether the experience is pleasing or displeasing. The value of physical education reveals itself when we realize that play activities are one of the oldest and most fundamental drives in human nature. Therefore, by providing the child with a satisfying experience in activities in which he has a natural desire to engage, the opportunity is presented to develop desirable social traits. The key is qualified leadership.

All human beings should experience success. This factor can be realized through play. Through successful experience in play activities, a child develops self-confidence and finds happiness in his achievements. Physical education can provide for this successful experience by offering a variety of activities and developing the necessary skills for success in these activities.

If children are happy, they will make the necessary adjustments. An individual who is happy is much more likely to make the right adjustment than the individual who is morbid, sullen, and in an unhappy state of mind. Happiness reflects friendliness, cheerfulness, and a spirit of cooperation, all of which help a person to be content and to conform to the necessary standards which have been established. Therefore, physical education should instill happiness by guiding children into these activities where this quality will be realized.

In a democratic society all individuals should develop a sense of group consciousness and cooperative living. This should be one of the most important objectives of the physical education program. Whether or not a child will grow up to be a good citizen and contribute to the welfare of society will depend to a great extent upon the training he receives during his youth. Therefore, in various play activities, the following factors should be stressed: aid for the less-skilled and weaker players, respect for the rights of others, subordination of one's desires to the will of the group, and realization that cooperative living is an essential to the success of society. In other words, the golden rule should be practiced. The individual should be made to feel that he belongs to the group and has the responsibility of directing his actions in its behalf. The rules of sportsmanship should be developed and practiced in all activities that are offered in the program. Such things as courtesy, sympathy, truthfulness, fairness, honesty, respect for authority, and abiding by the rules will help a great deal in the promotion of social efficiency. The necessity for good leadership and followership should also be stressed as important to the interests of society.

The needs and desires which form the basis for people's actions can be controlled through proper training. This training can result in effective citizenship, which is the basis of sound, democratic living. Effective citizenship is not something that can be developed by artificial stimuli. It is something that is achieved only through activities in which individuals engage in their normal day-to-day routine. Since play activities have such a great attraction for youth, and since it is possible to develop desirable social traits under proper guidance, physical education should realize its responsibility. It should do its part in contributing to good citizenship—the basis of our democratic society. In this chaotic world with its cold wars, hot wars, hydrogen bombs, racial strife, imperialistic aims, human ambitions, and class struggles, human relations are more and more important to personal, group, and world peace. Only through a better understanding of one's fellow man, will it be possible to build a peaceful and democratic world.

III. THE ROLE OF THE ADMINISTRATOR IN PROMOTING OBJECTIVES AND COOPERATION

Good administration is an essential in the fields of school health and physical education if the goals which have been set for these professions are to be realized. There must be harmony among the various members of the staff, adequate facilities provided, the program planned and continually reevaluated, a public relations plan established, leadership provided, and many other essentials and details attended to with dispatch if the objectives are to be achieved.

The administrator is a key person. The administrator sets the pace. The administrator provides the leadership. If this individual does not assume the responsibilities which go with such a position, there will be apathy and indifference all along the line and consequently the aims for which the professions exist will not be realized. Administrators must continually keep in mind the goals toward which they are working. With these in mind they should gear their staff relationships, programs, and other factors in a way which will be most efficient and productive from the standpoint of realizing such goals.

Administrators frequently have both the areas of health and physical education within their administrative division. This affords opportunity to promote the kind of cooperation that is needed to achieve the aims of each. One cannot be promoted at the expense of the other. One cannot be recognized as being more important than the other. If such is the practice, progress will be obstructed. Administrators must recognize the important place that each area has in the total picture. All administrative policies must preserve this balance.

If the administrators have only one of these specialized areas within their division, this should not limit their relationship with the other. Both areas are closely allied and it is very important that they work closely together. Administrators will determine in large measure whether or not this becomes a reality.

QUESTIONS AND EXERCISES

1. Survey 10 schools in your area to determine the administrative relationship of health and physical education.

2. Why is it important for health and physical educators to work closely together?

3. Prepare a research paper on the reasons why health and physical education were incorporated in the national association.

4. Why are both health education and physical education specialists needed in the schools?

5. Define health and physical education.

6. List and discuss the objectives of both school health and physical education.

7. Interview or correspond with five health educators and five physical educators on the main problems which are confronting their professions.

8. To what extent are the objectives of school health and physical education being achieved today?

9. Define the term "School Health Program." Discuss the various aspects of the program.

10. Why are health attitudes so important?

11. What are the goals of physical education in addition to developing an individual physically?

12. What are some of the benefits to an individual that come from physical activity?

13. How can physical education contribute to the development of good citizenship?

14. Why must there be cooperation to achieve the objectives in health and physical education? What part does the administrator play?

SELECTED REFERENCES

American Association of School Administrators. *Health in Schools. Twentieth Yearbook.* Washington D. C.: National Education Association, 1951.

American Medical Association. *Physicians and Schools.* Donald A. Dukelow and Fred C. Hein, Editors. Report of the Fourth National Conference on Physicians and Schools. Chicago: The Association, 1953.

Bauer, W. W., "Teach Health, Not Disease," *Journal of Health and Physical Education,* **12:** 296, May, 1941.

Brownell, Clifford Lee. *Principles of Health Education Applied.* New York: McGraw-Hill Book Company, Inc., 1949.

Bucher, Charles A. *Foundations of Physical Education.* St. Louis: The C. V. Mosby Company, 1952, Chapters V, VIII.

Forsythe, Charles E. and Duncan, Ray O. *Administration of Physical Education.* New York: Prentice-Hall, Inc., 1951, Chapters I, III, XI, XIV.

Grout, Ruth E. *Health Teaching in Schools.* Philadelphia: W. B. Saunders Company, 1953.

Joint Committee of the National Education Association and American Medical Association. *The Physical Educator Asks About Health.* Washington, D. C.: American Association for Health, Physical Education and Recreation, 1951.

Joint Committee on Health Problems in Education of the National Education Association and the American Medical Association. *Health Education.* Charles C. Wilson, Editor. Washington, D. C.: National Education Association, 1948.

Joint Committee on Health Problems in Education of the National Education Association and the American Medical Association. *School Health Services.* Charles C. Wilson, Editor. Washington, D. C.: National Education Association, 1953.

Kilander, H. F. *Health Instruction in the Secondary Schools—Its Organization and Adminis-tration.* Office of Education. Pamphlet No. 110. Washington, D. C.: Government Printing Office, 1951.

Langton, Clair V. *Orientation in School Health.* New York: Harper & Brothers, 1941.

Nash, Jay B., Moench, Francis J., and Saurborn, Jeannette B. *Physical Education: Organiza-tion and Administration.* New York: A. S. Barnes and Company, 1951, Chapters IV, X, XIV.

National Committee on School Health Policies of the National Conference for Cooperation in Health Education. *Suggested School Health Policies.* New York: Health Education Council, 1946.

National Education Association. The Department of Elementary School Principals. *Health in the Elementary Schools.* Washington: The Association, 1950.

National Tuberculosis Association. *A Health Program for Colleges.* A Report of the Third National Conference on Health in Colleges. New York: The Association, 1948.

Oberteuffer, Delbert. *School Health Education.* New York: Harper & Brothers, 1954.

Turner, C. E. *School Health and Health Education.* St. Louis: The C. V. Mosby Com-pany, 1952.

Voltmer, Edward F., and Esslinger, Arthur, A. *The Organization and Administration of Physi-cal Education.* New York: Appleton-Century-Crofts, Inc., 1949, Chapters III, VII, XVI.

Williams, Jesse F., and Abernathy, Ruth. *Health Education in Schools.* New York: Ronald Press, 1949.

Williams, Jesse Feiring and Brownell, Clifford Lee. *The Administration of Health Education and Physical Education.* Philadelphia: W. B. Saunders Company, 1951, Chapters I, XX.

Chapter VIII

LEGAL LIABILITY

The growth of school health and physical education programs in this country has brought with it many problems in the field of administration. One of these problems is legal liability. This is especially pertinent to these specialized areas because of the danger of accidents while engaging in the various activities that comprise the programs. Furthermore, the nature of these areas involves the use of special apparatus, excursions and trips, living in camps, utilizing first-aid practices, and other items which have implications for liability.

According to Bouvier's *Law Dictionary*, liability is "the responsibility, the state of one who is bound in law and justice to do something which may be enforced by action." Another definition is that "Liability is the condition of affairs which gives rise to an obligation to do a particular thing to be enforced by court action."[1]

Leaders in the fields of health and physical education should know how far they can go with various aspects of their programs and what precautions are necessary, in order not to be held legally liable in the event of an accident. The fact that approximately 50 per cent of accidents in which school pupils are involved occur in buildings; more than 40 per cent occur on playgrounds; and 10 per cent in going to and from school, shows the implications for these specialized fields.[2]

The administration, which in the final analysis is responsible for the program, should clearly understand the implications of their work in this respect. Fear of personal liability can thwart an otherwise good educational program.

When an accident resulting in personal injury occurs on school property, the question often arises as to whether damages can be recovered. The National Commission on Safety Education has this to say, "All school employees run the risk of suit by injured pupils on the basis of alleged negligence which causes bodily injury to pupils. Such injuries occur on playgrounds, in athletics, in science laboratories, or in shop classes. . . ."[3]

The legal rights of the individuals involved in such cases is worthy of study. Although the law varies from state to state, it is possible to discuss liability in a general way that has implications for all sections of the country.

I. LIABILITY AND PLAY

Some years ago the courts recognized the hazards involved in the play activities that are a part of the educational program. An injury occurred to a boy while

---

[1]National Education Research Division for the National Commission on Safety Education. *Who Is Liable for Pupil Injuries?* Washington 6, D. C.: National Education Association, October, 1950, p. 4.

[2]*Ibid.*, p. 5.

[3]*Ibid.*, p. 4.

he was playing tag. The court recognized the possibility and risk of some injury in physical education programs and would not award damages. However, it pointed out that care must be taken by both the participant and the authorities in charge. It further implied that the benefits derived from participating in physical education activities, such as tag, offset the occasional injury that might occur.

Many accidents occur on playgrounds and athletic fields. Stanford University.

The cited decision was handed down at a time when the attitude of the law was that a government agency, which would include the school, could not be held liable for the acts of its employees unless they so consented. Since that time a changing attitude in the courts has been in evidence. As more accidents occurred, the courts frequently decided in favor of the injured party, when negligence could be shown. The immunity derived from the old common law rule that a government agency cannot be sued without its consent is slowly changing in the eyes of the courts so that both federal government and the state may be sued. Those elements of a school curriculum which are compulsory, such as physical education, prompt courts to decide on the basis of what is in the best interests of the public. Safety, instead of being merely a moral responsibility, has become a legal responsibility. Those who uphold the doctrine that a government agency should be immune from liability, maintain that payments for injury to constituents is a misapplication of public funds. On the other hand, the liberal thinkers feel it is wrong for the cost of injuries to fall on one or a few persons, but instead, should be shared by all. To further their case these liberals cite the Constitutional provision that compensation must be given for the taking or damaging of private property. They argue that it is inconsistent that the Government cannot take or damage private property without just compensation on the one hand, yet on the other can injure or destroy the life of a person without liability for compensation. The liberal view is being used more and more by the courts.

II. TORT

A "tort" is a legal wrong resulting in direct or indirect injury to another individual or to property. A tortious act is a wrongful act and damages can be collected through court action. "Tort" can be committed through an act of "omission" or "commission." An act of "omission" results when the accident occurs during failure to perform a legal duty, such as when a teacher fails to obey a fire alarm after she has been informed of the procedure to be followed. An act of "commission" results when the accident occurs while an unlawful act is being performed, such as assault on a student.

The National Education Association points out that "A tort may arise out of the following acts: (a) an act which without lawful justification or excuse is intended by a person to cause harm and does cause the harm complained of; (b) an act in itself contrary to law or an omission of specific legal duty, which causes harm not intended by the person so acting or omitting; (c) an act or omission causing harm which the person so acting or omitting did not intend to cause, but which might and should, with due diligence, have been foreseen and prevented."[4] The teacher, leader, or other individual not only has a "legal responsibility" as described by law, but also is responsible for preventing injury. This means that in addition to complying with certain legal regulations such as proper facilities, there must be compliance with the principle that children should be taught without injury to them, that prudent care, such as a parent would give, must be exercised.

It is important to understand the legal meaning of the word "accident," in relation to the topic under discussion. According to *Black's Law Dictionary*, accident is defined as follows: "An accident is an unforeseen event occurring without the will or design of the person whose mere act causes it. In its proper use the term excludes negligence. It is an event which occurs without fault, carelessness, or want of proper circumspection for the person affected, or which could not have been avoided by the use of that kind and degree of care necessary to the exigency and in the circumstance in which he was placed." The case of *Lee v. Board of Education of City of New York* in 1941, for example, showed that prudent care was not exercised and the defendant was liable for negligence. A boy was hit by

---

[4]*Ibid.*, p. 5.

a car while playing football in the street as a part of the physical education program. The street had not been completely closed off to traffic. The Board of Education and the teacher were found negligent.

III. NEGLIGENCE

Questions of liability and negligence occupy a very prominent position in connection with the actions of teachers and leaders in school health and physical education programs.

The law in America pertaining to negligence is based upon common law, judicial rulings that have previously been made, or legal procedure that has been established. This type of law differs from that which has been written into the statutes by lawmaking bodies and is called statutory law.

Negligence implies that someone has not fulfilled his legal duty or has failed to do something which according to common-sense reasoning should have been done. Negligence can be avoided if there is common knowledge of basic legal principles and proper vigilance. One of the first things that must be determined in event of accident is whether there has been negligence.

Rosenfield defines negligence as follows: "Negligence consists in the failure to act as a reasonably prudent and careful person would under the circumstances involved."[5] The National Education Association's report elaborates further that "Negligence is any conduct which falls below the standard established by law for the protection of others against unreasonable risk of harm. In general, such conduct may be of two types: (a) an act which a reasonable man would have realized involved an unreasonable risk of injury to others, and (b) failure to do an act which is necessary for the protection or assistance of another and which one is under a duty to do.

"The law prohibits careless action; whatever is done must be done well and with reasonable caution. Failure to employ care not to harm others is a misfeasance. For example, an Oregon school bus driver who parked the bus across a driveway when he knew the pupils were coasting down the hill was held liable for injuries sustained by a pupil who coasted into the bus. (*Fahlstrom v. Denk,* 1933)."[6]

Negligence may be claimed when the plaintiff has suffered injury either to himself or to his property, when the defendant has not performed his legal duty and has been negligent, and when the plaintiff has Constitutional rights and is not guilty of contributory negligence. The teacher or leader for children in such cases is regarded as *in loco parentis,* i.e., acting in the place of the parent in relation to the child.

Since negligence implies failure to act as a reasonably prudent and careful person, necessary precautions should be taken, danger should be anticipated and common sense should be used. For example, if a group of very young children are permitted by a teacher to go up a high slide alone and without supervision, this is not acting as a prudent person would act. If the teacher of health education, after

---

[5]Harry N. Rosenfield. *Liability for School Accidents.* New York: Harper & Brothers, 1940.
[6]National Commission on Safety Education *op. cit.* p. 6.

giving a demonstration, leaves a deadly drug on her desk and it later results in the death of a child, this is not acting as a careful person should act. In the case previously cited of *Lee v. Board of Education of City of New York,* when the physical education class was held in a street where cars were also allowed to pass, negligence existed.

In respect to negligence, considerable weight is given in the law to the foreseeability of danger. One authority points out that "if a danger is obvious and a reasonably prudent person could have foreseen it and could have avoided the resulting harm by care and caution, the person who did not foresee or failed to prevent a foreseeable injury is liable for a tort on account of negligence."[7] If a teacher fails to take the needed precautions and care, negligence is constituted. However, it must be established upon the basis of facts in the case. It cannot be based upon mere conjecture.

Teachers and leaders must realize that children will behave in certain ways, that certain juvenile acts will cause injuries unless properly supervised, that hazards must be anticipated, reported and eliminated. The question that will be raised by most courts of law is: "Should the teacher or leader have had prudence enough to foresee the possible dangers or occurrence of an act?"

Two court actions point up legal reasoning on negligence as interpreted in one state. In the case of *Lane v. City of Buffalo* in 1931 the board of education was found not liable. In this case a child fell from a piece of apparatus in the school yard. It was found that the apparatus was in good condition and that proper supervision was present. In the case of *Cambaeri v. Board of Albany,* the defendant was found liable. The City of Buffalo owned a park which was supervised by the park department. While skating on the lake in the park a boy playing "Crack the Whip" hit a 12-year-old boy who was also skating. Workers and a policeman had been assigned to supervise activity and had been instructed not to allow games which were rough or dangerous.

Although there are no absolute, factual standards for determining negligence, certain guides have been established which should be familiar to teachers and others engaged in the work under consideration in this book. Attorney Cymrot in discussing negligence at a conference in New York City suggested the following:

1. The teacher must be acting within the scope of his employment and in the discharge of his duties in order to obtain the benefits of the statute.
2. There must be a breach of a recognized duty owed to the child.
3. There must be a negligent breach of such duty.
4. The accident and resulting injuries must be the natural and foreseeable consequence of the teacher's negligence arising from a negligent breach of duty.
5. The child must be a participant in an activity under the control of the teacher, or put in another way, the accident must have occurred under circumstances where the teacher owes a duty of care to the pupil.
6. A child's contributory negligence however modified, will bar his recovery for damages.
7. The plaintiff must establish the negligence of the teacher and his own freedom from contributory negligence by a fair preponderance of evidence. The burden of proof on both issues is on the plaintiff.

---

[7]*Loc. cit.*

8. Generally speaking, the Board of Education alone is responsible for accidents caused by the faulty maintenance of plants (schools) and equipment.[8]

Some states have a "save harmless law" which requires that school districts assume the liability of the teacher, negligence proved or not. For example in New Jersey the law reads:

Chapter 311, P.L. 1938. Boards assume liability of teachers. It shall be the duty of each board of education in any school district to save harmless and protect all teachers and members of supervisory and administrative staff from financial loss arising out of any claim, demand, suit or judgment by reason of alleged negligence or other act resulting in accidental bodily injury to any person within or without the school building; provided, such teacher or member of the supervisory or administrative staff at the time of the accident or injury was acting in the discharge of his duties within the scope of his employment and/or under the direction of said board of education; and said board of education may arrange for and maintain appropriate insurance with any company created by or under the laws of this state, or in any insurance company authorized by law to transact business in this state, or such board may elect to act as self-insurers to maintain the aforesaid protection.

IV. DEFENSES AGAINST NEGLIGENCE

Despite the fact that an individual is negligent, to collect damages it must also be shown that the negligence resulted in or was closely connected with the injury. The legal term used in such a situation is whether or not the negligence was "the proximate cause" (legal cause) of the injury. Furthermore, even though it be determined that negligence is the "proximate cause" of the injury, there are still certain defenses upon which a defendant may base his case. These are as follows:

A. Act of God

An "act of God" is a situation that exists because of certain conditions which are beyond the control of human beings. For example, a flash of lightning, a gust of wind, a cloudburst, and other such factors may result in injury. However, this assumption applies only in cases where injury would not have occurred had prudent action been taken.

B. Assumption of Risk

This legal defense is especially pertinent to games, sports, and other phases of the program in health education and physical education. It is assumed that an individual takes a certain risk when engaging in various games and sports where bodies are coming in contact with each other and where balls and apparatus are used. Participation in such activity assumes a normal risk.

C. Contributory Negligence

Another legal defense is contributory negligence. A person who does not act as would a normal individual of similar age and nature, thereby contributes to the

---

[8]City Wide Conference with Principals' Representatives and Men and Women Chairmen of Health Education. *Proceedings.* City of New York: Board of Education, Bureau of Health Education, 110 Livingston Street, Brooklyn 1, New York, March, 1953.

injury. In such cases negligence on the part of the defendant might be ruled out. Individuals are subject to contributory negligence if they expose themselves unnecessarily to dangers. The main consideration that seems to turn the tide in such cases is the age of the individual and the nature of the activity in which he engaged.

The National Education Association's report makes this statement in regard to contributory negligence: "Contributory negligence is defined in law as conduct on the part of the injured person which falls below the standard to which he should conform for his own protection and which is legally contributing cause, cooperating with the negligence of the defendant in bringing about the plaintiff's harm. Reasonable self-protection is to be expected of all sane adults. With some few exceptions, contributory negligence bars recovery against the defendant whose negligent conduct would otherwise make him liable to the plaintiff for the harm sustained by him. Both parties being in fault, neither can recover from the other for resulting harm. When there is mutual wrong and negligence on both sides, the law will not attempt to apportion the wrong between them.

"Contributory negligence is usually a matter of defense, and the burden of proof is put upon the defendant to convince the jury of the plaintiff's fault and of its casual connection with the harm sustained. Minors are not held to the same degree of care as is demanded of adults."[9]

Contributory negligence has implications for a difference in the responsibility of elementary school teachers as contrasted with high school teachers. The elementary school teacher, because the children are immature, has to assume greater responsibility for the safety of the child. That is, accidents in which an elementary school child is injured are not held in the same light from the standpoint of negligence as those involving high school students who are more mature. The courts might say that a high school student was mature enough to avoid doing the thing causing him to be injured; whereas if the same thing occurred with an elementary school child, the courts could say the child was too immature and that the teacher should have prevented or protected the child from doing the act in which he got injured.

V. NUISANCE

Action can be instituted for "nuisance" when the circumstances surrounding the act are dangerous to life or health, result in offense to the senses, are in violation of the laws of decency, or cause an obstruction to the reasonable use of property.

An authentic source states in regard to a "nuisance," "There are some conditions which are naturally dangerous and the danger is a continuing one. An inherent danger of this sort is called at law a "nuisance"; the one responsible is liable for maintaining a nuisance. His liability may be predicated upon negligence in permitting the continuing danger to exist, but even without a showing of negligence the mere fact that a nuisance does exist is usually sufficient to justify a determination of liability. For example, a junk pile in the corner of the grounds

---

[9]National Commission on Safety Education, *op. cit.* p. 9.

of a country school was considered a nuisance for which the district was liable when a pupil stumbled over a piece of junk and fell while playing at recess. *(Popow v. Central School District No. 1, Towns of Hillsdale et al., New York, 1938).* Dangerous playground equipment available for use by pupils of all ages and degrees of skill has also been determined to be a nuisance. *(Bush v. City of Norwalk, Connecticut, 1937).*

"On the other hand, allegations that the district has maintained a nuisance have been denied in some cases; for example, when a small child fell into a natural ditch near the schoolyard not guarded by a fence, the ditch was held not to be a nuisance for which the district would be liable. *(Whitfield v. East Baton Rouge Parish School Board, Louisiana, 1949).* The court said this ditch did not constitute a nuisance; nor did the principle of *res ipsa loquitur* apply. Under this principle the thing which causes the injury is under the management of the defendant and the accident is such that in the ordinary course of events, it would not have happened if the defendant had used proper care."[10]

Mr. Cymrot, Attorney at Law, in addressing the Health Education division of the New York City Schools had the following to say about an "attractive nuisance." "Teachers need to be aware of decisions of the courts pertaining to 'attractive nuisance,' . . . an attractive contrivance which is maintained, alluring to children but inherently dangerous to them. This constitutes neglect. But it is not every contrivance or apparatus that a jury may treat as an 'attractive nuisance.' Before liability may be imposed, there must always be something in the evidence tending to show that the device was something of a new or uncommon nature with which children might be supposed to be unfamiliar or not know of its danger. Many courts have held, however, that for children above the age of 10 years the doctrine of 'attractive nuisance' does not hold. Older children are expected to exercise such prudence as those of their age may be expected to possess."[11]

The following cases point up some court rulings in respect to "nuisance."

In the case of *Texas v. Reinhardt* in 1913, it was ruled that ball games with their noises and conduct were not a "nuisance" in the particular case in question and an injunction should not be issued stopping such activity.

In the case of *Iacono v. Fitzpatrick* in Rhode Island in 1938, a boy 17 years old, while playing touch football on a playground received an injury which later resulted in his death. He was attempting to catch a pass and in so doing crashed into a piece of apparatus. The court held that the apparatus was in evidence and the deceased knew of its presence. It further stated the city had not created or maintained a nuisance.

In the case of *Schwarz v. City of Cincinnati, Ohio,* the city had permitted an organization to have fireworks in one of its public parks. Next day a 12-year-old boy was injured after lighting an unexploded bomb which he found. The court ruled that the permit granted the association was ". . . not authority to create a nuisance . . . not authority to leave an unexploded bomb in the park." The city, which was the defendant in the case, was not held liable.

---

[10]*Ibid.,* p. 6.

[11]*City Wide Conference with Principals' Representatives and Men and Women Chairmen of Health Education, op. cit.*

VI. GOVERNMENTAL VERSUS PROPRIETARY FUNCTIONS

The government in a legal sense is engaged in two types of activity: one, governmental in nature and the other, proprietary in nature.

The *governmental function* refers to those particular activities which are of a sovereign nature. This theory dates back to the time when kings ruled under the "divine right" theory, were absolute in their power, and "could do no wrong." As such the sovereign was granted immunity and could not be sued without his consent for failing to exercise governmental powers or for negligence. Furthermore, a subordinate agency of the sovereign could not be sued. The municipality, according to this interpretation, acts as an agent of the state in a governmental capacity. The logic behind this reasoning is that the municipality is helping the state to govern the people who live within its geographical limits.

Many activities are classified under the *governmental function* interpretation. Such functions as education, police protection and public health fall in this category.

In regard to public education, the courts hold that this is a governmental function and therefore, entitled to state's immunity from liability for its own negligence. However, as has previously been pointed out, the attitude of the courts has changed and has taken on a broader social outlook which allows in some cases for the reimbursement of the injured.

Proprietary function pertains to government functions which are similar to those of a business enterprise. Such functions are for the benefit of the constituents within the corporate limits of the governmental agency. An example of this would be the manufacture, distribution, and sale of some product to the public. A cafeteria conducted for profit in a school is a proprietary function. In functions that are proprietary in nature a governmental agency is held liable in the same manner as an individual or a private corporation would be held liable.

From the above discussion it can be seen that education, recreation, and health are governmental functions. While this distinction between governmental and proprietary functions precludes a recovery from the governmental agency if the function were governmental in nature, the federal government and some of the states by legislation have eliminated this distinction.

VII. FEES

Most public recreation activities, facilities, and the like are offered free of charge to the public. However, there are certain activities which, because of the expenses involved, necessitate a fee in order that such activities may continue. For example, golf courses are expensive and charges are usually made so that they may be maintained. This is sometimes true also of such facilities as camps, bathing beaches, and swimming pools.

The fees charged have a bearing upon whether recreation is a governmental or a proprietary function. The courts in most states have upheld recreation as a governmental function, because of its contribution to public health and welfare, and also because its devices are free to the public at large. When fees are charged, however, the whole picture takes on a different aspect.

The attitude of the courts has been that the amount of the fee and whether or not the activity was profit-making in nature, are considerations in determining whether recreation is a governmental or a proprietary function. Incidental fees which are used in the conduct of the enterprise do not usually change the nature of the enterprise. However, if the enterprise is run for profit, the function changes from governmental to proprietary in nature.

VIII. LIABILITY OF THE MUNICIPALITY

It has been previously pointed out that a municipality as a governmental agency performs both governmental and proprietary functions.

When the municipality is performing a governmental function it is acting in the interests of the state, receives no profit or advantage, and is not liable for negligence on the part of its employees or for failure to perform these functions. However, this would not hold if there were a specific statute imposing liability on negligence. When the municipality is performing a proprietary function, i.e., some function for profit or advantage of the agency or people who comprise it, rather than the public in general, it is liable for negligence of those who are carrying out the function.

This discussion readily shows the importance of conducting recreation as a governmental function.

IX. LIABILITY OF THE SCHOOL DISTRICT

As a general rule the school district is not held liable for acts of negligence on the part of its officers or employees, provided a state statute does not exist to the contrary. The reasoning behind this is that the school district or district school board in maintaining public schools acts as an agent of the state. It performs a purely public or governmental duty imposed upon it by law for the benefit of the public and for the performance of which it receives no profit or advantage.

Some state laws, however, provide that the state may be sued in cases of negligence in the performance of certain duties such as providing for a safe environment and competent leadership. Furthermore, the school district's immunity in many cases does not cover such acts as those which bring damage or injury through trespass of another's premises, or where a nuisance exists on a school district's property, resulting in damage to other property.

X. LIABILITY OF SCHOOL, PARK, AND RECREATION BOARD MEMBERS

Generally speaking members are not personally liable for any duties, in their corporate capacity as a board member, which they perform negligently. Furthermore, they cannot be held personally liable for acts of employees of the district or organization over which they have jurisdiction on the theory of *respondeat superior* (let the master pay for the servant). Board members act in a corporate capacity and do not act for themselves. For example, in the State of Oregon the general rule as to the personal liability of members of district school boards is stated in 56C.J., page 348, section 223, as follows:

> School officers, or members of the board of education, or directors, trustees, or the like, of a school district or other local school organization are not personally liable for the negligence of persons rightfully employed by them in behalf of the district, and not under the direct personal supervision or control of such officer or member in doing the negligent act, since such employee is a servant of the district and not of the officer or board members, and the doctrine of *respondeat superior* accordingly has no application; and members of a district board are not personally liable for the negligence or other wrong of the board as such. A school officer or member of a district board is, however, personally liable for his own negligence or other tort, or that of an agent or employee of the district when acting directly under his supervision or by his direction.

However, a board member can be held liable for a *ministerial* act even though he cannot be held for the exercise of discretion as a member of the board. If the board acts in bad faith and with unworthy motives, and this can be shown, it can also be held liable.

XI. LIABILITY OF TEACHERS AND LEADERS

The individual is responsible for negligence of his own acts. With the exception of certain specific immunity, the teacher or leader in programs of health, physical education, and recreation is responsible for what he or she does. The Supreme Court of the United States has reaffirmed this principle and all should recognize the important implications it has. Immunity of the governmental agency such as a state, school district or board, does not release the teacher or leader of liability for his or her own negligent acts.

Teachers and leaders are expected to conduct their various activities in a careful and prudent manner. If this is not done, they are exposing themselves to law suits for their own negligence. As respects administrators, the National Education Association's report has the following to say: "The fact that administrators (speaking mainly of principals and superintendents) are rarely made defendants in pupil-injury cases seems unjust to the teachers who are found negligent because of inadequate supervision, and unjust also to the school boards who are required to defend themselves in such suits. When the injury is caused by defective equipment, it is the building principal who should have actual or constructive notice of the defect; when the injury is caused by inadequate playground supervision, the inadequacy of the supervision frequently exists because of arrangements made by the building principal. For example, a teacher in charge of one playground was required to stay in the building to teach a make-up class; another teacher was required to supervise large grounds on which 150 pupils were playing; another teacher neglected the playground to answer the telephone. All of these inadequacies in playground supervision were morally chargeable to administrators; in none of these instances did the court action direct a charge of responsibility to the administrator. Whether the administrator in such cases would have been held liable, if charged with negligence, is problematical. The issue has not been decided, since the administrator's legal responsibility for pupil injuries has never been discussed by the courts to an extent that would make possible the elucidation of general principles; the administrator's moral responsibilities must be conceded."[12]

XII. ACCIDENT-PRONE SETTINGS

Since many accidents occur on the playgrounds, during recess periods, in physical education classes, and at sports events, some very pertinent remarks are included here, which have been stated in the National Education Association's report.

A. Playground and Recess Games

". . . the unorganized games during recess and noon intermissions are more likely to result in pupil injuries than the organized games of physical education classes.   Playground injuries may be pure accidents, such as when a pupil ran against the flagpole while playing *(Hough v. Orleans Elementary School District of Humboldt County, California, 1943),* or when a pupil was hit by a ball *(Graff v. Board of Education of New York City, New York, 1940),* or by a stone batted by another pupil *(Wilber v. City of Binghamton, New York, 1946).*   The courts have said in connection with this type of injury that every act of every pupil cannot be anticipated.   However, the school district should make rules and regulations for pupils' conduct on playgrounds so as to minimize dangers.   For example, it was held to be negligence to permit pupils to ride bicycles on the playground while other pupils were playing.   *(Buzzard v. East Lake School District of Lake County, California, 1939).*

"Playgrounds should be supervised during unorganized play and such supervision should be adequate.   One teacher cannot supervise a large playground with over a hundred pupils playing *(Charonnat v. San Francisco Unified School District, California, 1943),* and when the supervision is either lacking or inadequate districts which are not immune are liable for negligence in not providing adequate supervision *(Forgnone v. Salvadore Union Elementary School District, California, 1940).* Pupils are known to engage in fights and may be expected to be injured in fights; it is the responsibility of the school authorities to attempt to prevent such injuries. The misconduct of the other pupils could be an intervening cause to break the chain of causation if the supervision is adequate; but when the supervision is not adequate, misconduct of other pupils is not an intervening superseding cause of the injury.

"If a pupil wanders away from the group during playground games and is injured by a dangerous condition into which he places himself, the teacher in charge of the playground may be liable for negligence in pupil supervision *(Miller v. Board of Education, Union Free School District, New York, 1943),* although the district would not be liable in common-law states because of its immunity *(Whitfield v. East Baton Rouge Parish School Board, Louisiana, 1949).*

"Supervision of unorganized play at recess or noon intermissions should be by competent personnel.   A school janitor is not qualified to supervise play.   *(Garber v. Central School District No. 1 of Town of Sharon, New York, 1937).*

---

[12]National Commission on Safety Education, *op. cit.* p. 14.

"All injuries sustained by pupils on playground equipment are excluded in the Washington statute imposing liability for certain other kinds of accidents. Injuries may occur because playground equipment is in a defective condition. The New York courts have not been consistent in their rulings on this point. In one New York case the district was not liable for injury caused by a defect in a slide because there was no evidence that the defect had existed a sufficient length of time for the school authorities to have knowledge of it *(Handy v. Hadley-Luzerne Union Free School District No. 1, New York, 1938)*, but another district in New York was held liable for a defect in a slide *(Howell v. Union Free School District No. 1, New York, 1937)*.

"Nor have the New York courts been consistent in fixing liability when the injury was sustained on playground equipment which was not defective but was dangerous for the individual pupil who played on it. One pupil who fell off a monkey bar was unable to collect damages because the court held specific supervision of each game and each piece of playground equipment would be an unreasonable requirement. This pupil merely met with an accident which was not the fault of the playground supervisor *(Miller v. Board of Education of Union Free School District No. 1, Town of Oyster Bay, New York, 1936)*. However, another district was declared liable for injuries sustained by a pupil who fell from a ramp during recess, the court holding that liability rested upon the maintenance of a dangerous piece of playground equipment. This ramp had been constructed for the use of older boys and even they were to use it only under supervision; the injured pupil was a small child *(Sullivan v. City of Binghamton, New York, 1946)*.

"Where children of all ages share a playground extra precautions should be taken to prevent accidents, since some children are more adept in using equipment than others and some playground equipment is dangerous to the unskilled."

B. Physical Education and Sports Events

"Pupil injuries in this area occur when playground or gymnasium equipment is defective, when pupils attempt an exercise or sport for which they have not been sufficiently trained, when there is inadequate supervision of the exercise, when other pupils conduct themselves in a negligent manner, and even when the pupils are mere spectators at sports events.

"It has been held that physical education teachers, or the school district in States where the district is subject to liability, are responsible for injuries caused by defective equipment. For example, there was liability for the injury to a pupil who was injured in a tumbling race when the mat, not firmly fixed, slipped on the slippery floor *(Cambareri v. Board of Education of Albany, New York, 1940)*.

"Defects in equipment should be known to the physical education instructor. There may be what is called actual or constructive notice of the defect. Actual knowledge is understandable; constructive notice means that the defect has existed for a sufficient time so that the instructor should have known of its existence, whether he did or not. Teachers of physical education should make periodic examination of all equipment at rather frequent intervals; otherwise they may be charged with negligence in not having corrected defects in equipment which have existed for a sufficient time that ignorance of the defect is a presumption of negligence.

"Physical education teachers may be liable also for injuries which occur to pupils who attempt to do an exercise which is beyond their skills. A running-jump somersault is one such instance *(Govel v. Board of Education of Albany, New York, 1944);* boxing is another *(LaValley v. Stanford, New York, 1947);* and a headstanding exercise is another *(Gardner v. State of New York, New York, 1939).* All of these exercises were found to be inherently dangerous by the courts, and the evidence showed that previous instruction had been inadequate and the pupils had not been warned of the dangers. However, where the previous instruction and the supervision during the exercise are both adequate, there is no liability so long as it cannot be proved that the teacher is generally incompetent *(Kolar v. Union Free School District No. 9, Town of Lenox, New York, 1939).* These cases suggest that teachers should not permit pupils to attempt exercises for which they have not been fully prepared by warnings of the dangers and preliminary exercises to develop the required skills.

"As in other types of pupil injuries, the physical education teacher is not liable if the injury occurred without his negligence. If caused by the negligence of another pupil, the teacher will likely be relieved of liability if the other pupil's misconduct was not foreseeable. Pure accidents occur in sports also and if there is no negligence there is no liability *(Mauer v. Board of Education of New York City, New York, 1945).*

"Sports events to which nonparticipating pupils and even the public are invited raise other problems of liability for the district or the physical education teacher in charge. If the locality is in a common-law State where the district is immune, the charge of an admission fee does not nullify the district's immunity or make the activity a proprietary function as an exception to the immunity rule *(Watson v. School District of Bay City, Michigan, 1949).* If the accident occurs in a State where the district is liable for at least certain kinds of injuries, such as California, the invitation to attend a sports event includes an invitation to use the nearby grounds and equipment, imposing liability for injury from hidden glass or other dangers *(Brown v. City of Oakland, California, 1942).* If a spectator is accidently hit by a ball, however, there is no liability; even when a pupil was injured by being hit by a bottle at a game there was no liability because the misconduct of the other spectator was not foreseeable *(Weldy v. Oakland High School District of Alameda County, California, 1937)."*[13]

XIII. SAFETY

It is important to take every precaution possible to prevent accidents by providing for the safety of students and other individuals who participate in programs of health education, physical education, and recreation. If such precautions are taken, the likelihood of law suit will diminish and the question of negligence will

---

[13]National Commission on Safety Education, *op. cit.,* pp. 18-20.

be eliminated. A few of the precautions that the leader or teacher should make provision for are as follows:

1. Instructor should be properly trained and qualified to perform specialized work.

2. Instructor should be present at all organized activities in the program.

3. Classes should be organized properly according to size, activity, physical condition, and other factors which have a bearing on safety and health of the individual.

Every precaution should be taken to prevent accidents. Students learn to handle a canoe in water safety course, University of Florida, Gainesville.

4. Health examinations should be given to all pupils.

5. A planned, written program for proper disposition of students who are injured or become sick should be followed.

6. Regular inspections should be made of such items as equipment, apparatus, ropes, chains, placing extra pressure upon them and taking other precautions to

make sure they are safe. They should also be checked for deterioration, looseness, fraying, splinters, etc.

7. Overcrowding athletic and other events should be avoided, building codes and fire regulations should be adhered to, and adequate lighting for all facilities should be provided.

8. Protective equipment such as mats should be utilized wherever possible. Any hazards such as projections or obstacles which are in area where activity is taking place should be eliminated. Floors should not be slippery. Shower rooms should have surfaces which are conducive to secure footing.

9. Sneakers should be worn on gymnasium floors and adequate space provided for each activity.

10. Activities should be adapted to the age and maturity of the participants, proper and competent supervision should be provided, and spotters should be utilized in apparatus and other similar activities.

11. The buildings and other facilities used should be inspected regularly for safety hazards such as loose tiles, broken fences, cracked glass, and uneven pavement. Defects should be reported immediately to responsible person and necessary precautions taken.

12. In planning play and other instructional areas the following precautions should be taken:

    a. There should be sufficient space for all games.

    b. Games which utilize balls and other equipment which can cause damage should be conducted in areas where there is minimum danger of injuring someone.

    c. Quiet games and activities which require working at benches, such as arts and crafts, should be in places which are well protected.

13. Truesdale lists certain questionable practices that teachers, coaches, nurses and trainers sometimes engage in:

1. Supply "pills" for headaches or as laxatives or for menstrual discomfort.
2. Examine and diagnose by the stethoscope.
3. Prescribe anti-cold pills or capsules.
4. Strap joint injuries under supposition of sprain, without expert assessment for possible fracture.
5. Permit return to play of a player with a head injury.
6. Play injured players not medically certified.
7. Permit return of students without medical certification to class, or particularly to activity, after illness.
8. Prescribe gargles or swabs for sore throats.
9. Use cutting tools (knives or razor blades) on callouses, corns, blisters, ingrown nails, etc.
10. Administer local anaesthesia to permit play after injury.
11. Employ physical forces such as heat or electric current to produce tissue change and decongestion and repair without medical order, or by unqualified persons.
12. Possibly further damage unconscious players by dashing water in the face, by slapping the face or by unwarranted use of aromatic spirits of ammonia to "bring them to."[14]

---

[14]John C. Truesdale, "So You're A Good Samaritan!", *The Journal of the American Association for Health, Physical Education, and Recreation,* 25; 25, February, 1954.

STANDARD STUDENT ACCIDENT REPORT FORM
Part A. Information on ALL Accidents

1. Name: _____ Home Address: _____
2. School: _____ Sex· M ☐; F ☐. Age· _____ Grade or classification: _____
3. Time accident occurred· Hour _____ A.M.; _____ P.M. Date: _____
4. Place of Accident   School Building ☐   School Grounds ☐   To or from School ☐   Home ☐   Elsewhere ☐

5. NATURE OF INJURY

Abrasion	_____	Fracture	_____
Amputation	_____	Laceration	_____
Asphyxiation	_____	Poisoning	_____
Bite	_____	Puncture	_____
Bruise	_____	Scalds	_____
Burn	_____	Scratches	_____
Concussion	_____	Shock (el.)	_____
Cut	_____	Sprain	_____
Dislocation	_____		

Other (specify) _____

DESCRIPTION OF THE ACCIDENT

How did accident happen? What was student doing? Where was student? List specifically unsafe acts and unsafe conditions existing. Specify any tool, machine or equipment involved. _____
_____
_____

PART OF BODY INJURED

Abdomen	_____	Foot	_____
Ankle	_____	Hand	_____
Arm	_____	Head	_____
Back	_____	Knee	_____
Chest	_____	Leg	_____
Ear	_____	Mouth	_____
Elbow	_____	Nose	_____
Eye	_____	Scalp	_____
Face	_____	Tooth	_____
Finger	_____	Wrist	_____

Other (specify) _____

6. Degree of Injury: Death ☐ Permanent Impairment ☐ Temporary Disability ☐ Nondisabling ☐
7. Total number of days lost from school: _____ (To be filled in when student returns to school)

Part B. Additional Information on School Jurisdiction Accidents

8. Teacher in charge when accident occurred (Enter name) :_____
Present at scene of accident: No: _____ Yes: _____

9. IMMEDIATE ACTION TAKEN

First-aid treatment · _____ By (Name):_____
Sent to school nurse _____ By (Name):_____
Sent home _____ By (Name):_____
Sent to physician _____ By (Name):_____
Physician's Name:_____
Sent to hospital _____ By (Name):_____
Name of hospital:_____

10. Was a parent or other individual notified? No:__ Yes:__ When:_____ How: _____
Name of individual notified: _____
By whom? (Enter name) : _____
11. Witnesses: 1. Name: _____ Address: _____
2. Name: _____ Address: _____

12. LOCATION

Specify Activity		Specify Activity		Remarks
Athletic field	_____	Locker	_____	What recommendations do you have for pre-
Auditorium	_____	Pool	_____	venting other accidents of this type? _____
Cafeteria	_____	Sch. grounds	_____	
Classroom	_____	shop	_____	
Corridor	_____	Showers	_____	
Dressing room	_____	Stairs	_____	
Gymnasium	_____	Toilets and		
Home Econ.	_____	washrooms	_____	
Laboratories	_____	Other (specify)	_____	

Signed: Principal: _____ Teacher: _____

(National Safety Council—Form School 1)   Printed in U.S.A. Rep. 200M—25302

Standard student accident report form recommended by National Safety Council

Truesdale also points out that "it is the duty of adults engaged in education not only to know of and be skillful in the proper techniques for protecting persons against injury, or protecting injured persons against aggravation, but also to know the limits beyond which the untrained or the partially trained person may not go."

14. In the event of accident the following or a similar procedure should be followed:

a. The nearest teacher or leader should proceed to the scene of the accident immediately, notifying the person in charge and nurse, if available, by messenger. Also, a doctor should be called at once if one is necessary.

b. A hurried examination of the injured person will give some idea as to the nature and extent of the injury and the emergency of the situation.

c. If the teacher or leader is well versed in first aid, assistance should be given (a qualified first aid certificate will usually absolve the teacher of negligence). Every teacher or leader who works in these specialized areas should and is expected to know first aid procedures. In any event everything should be done to make the injured person comfortable and reassure the injured until the services of a physician can be secured.

d. If the injury is serious an ambulance should be called.

e. After the injured person has been provided for, the person in charge should fill out the accident forms and take the statements of witnesses and file for future reference. Reports of accidents should be prepared promptly and sent to proper persons. They should be accurate as to detail and complete as to information. Among other things they should contain information about:

Name and address of injured person
Activity engaged in
Date, hour, and place
Person in charge
Witnesses
Cause and extent of injury
Medical attention given
Circumstances surrounding incident.

f. There should be a complete follow-up of accident, analysis of situation, and an eradication of any hazards that exist.

Mr. Herman Rosenthal, Assistant to the Law Secretary, City of New York, in addressing a health education conference in New York City pointed up the following remarks in respect to reporting accidents. "Reports should be complete, full and in detail. He advised that where a case does go into litigation, there is a delay in the court calendar of 2-3 years before the case is tried. A complete and detailed report is always better than a teacher's or a child's memory. He pointed out that the completion of accident reports was the function and duty of the teacher and in no case should a child be expected to prepare the report. Reports in the handwriting of children, he said, should be limited only to the statements and signatures of the injured and of the witnesses to the accident. He emphasized that should an injured child at the time of the accident be unable to prepare a written statement or affix his signature to a report, the teacher should prepare the necessary statement and signature and indicate the reasons for so doing. He further focused

GROVER CLEVELAND HIGH SCHOOL
HIMROD & GRANDVIEW AVE.
Ridgewood, New York

STATEMENT BY WITNESS
(Write in Ink)

Witness..Address...

Age.....................................Rank.............................Class.................................

Name of one injured............................Injured's Official Class.............Age of Injured................

Date of accident.................................Time.........................Day of week...................

A. Circumstances of Accident

1. Locate the position from which you witnessed the accident, using such phrases as, in front of, as I entered, standing on the, in back of, etc..
....
....

2. Locate the position where the accident occurred, using such phrases as, on the landing, exit 8 up, on the horizontal bar, etc...
....
....

3. Tell what you saw..
....
....
....

B. Additional remarks, if any...
....

C. Signature of Witness...

Statement by witness to accident. (Grover Cleveland High School, Ridgewood, New York.)

attention on the fact that teachers should not attempt to color or distort facts in order to protect the school, or the child, because such a practice does more harm than good.   An extremely important point he said was the need to report where the teacher was at the time of the accident, the extent of the supervision and the teacher control of the activity at the time of the accident.   Also, he said that with few exceptions reports should be submitted within 24 hours of the time of the accident.   He explained that in some cases this might not be possible, but in such cases no report need be delayed more than 48 hours."[15]

XIV. SUPERVISION

Children are entrusted by parents to recreation, health, and physical education programs and it is expected that adequate supervision will be provided so as to reduce to a minimum the possibility of accidents.

Questions of liability in regard to supervision pertain to two points, (1) The extent of the supervision, and (2) The quality of the supervision.

Regarding the first point, the question would be raised as to whether adequate supervision was provided.   This is a difficult question to answer because it would vary from situation to situation.   However, the answers to these questions: "Would additional supervision have eliminated the accident?" and "Is it reasonable to expect that additional supervision should have been provided?" will help to determine this.

In regard to the quality of the supervision, it is expected that competent personnel will handle specialized programs in health, physical education, and recreation.   If the supervisors of such activities do not possess proper training in such work, the question of negligence can be raised.

XV. WAIVERS AND CONSENT SLIPS

Waivers and consent slips are not synonymous.   A waiver is an agreement whereby one party waives a particular right.   On the other hand, a consent slip is an authorization, usually signed by the parent, permitting a child to take part in some activity.

In respect to a "waiver," a parent cannot waive the rights of a child who is under 21 years of age.   When a parent signs such a slip, he is merely waiving his or her right to sue for damages.   A parent can sue in two ways, from the standpoint of his rights as the parent and from the standpoint of the child's own rights which he has as an individual, irrespective of the parent.   A parent cannot waive the right of the child to sue as an individual.

"Consent slips" offer protection from the standpoint of showing that the child has the parent's permission to engage in an activity.

XVI. ATHLETIC PROTECTION FUNDS*

Athletic protection funds are increasingly being used in various states.   Such plans and funds usually have as characteristics: they are a non-profit venture, they

---

[15]*City Wide Conference with Principals' Representatives and Men and Women Chairmen of Health Education, op. cit.*
*For further discussion of insurance plans see Chapter XVIII.

are not compulsory, a specific fee is charged each person registered with the plan, and there is provision for recovery for specific injuries. Generally, the money is not paid out of tax funds but instead is paid either by the participants themselves or by the school or other agency.

In connection with such plans, it should be recognized that an individual, after receiving benefits, could in most states still bring action against the coach or other leader whose negligence contributed to the injury.

In respect to paying for liability and accident insurance out of public tax funds, the states vary as to their practices. For example, the state of Montana recently handed down a ruling through the Attorney General that school districts could not spend tax money for liability insurance or accident insurance to cover students in physical education or athletic activities.[16]

On the other hand the state legislature of Oregon permits school districts to carry liability insurance. This section is stated as follows in the revised code, O.R.S.:

> 332.180 Liability insurance; medical and hospital benefits insurance. Any district school board may enter into contracts of insurance for liability covering all activities engaged in by the district, for medical and hospital benefits for students engaging in athletic contests and for public liability and property damage covering motor vehicles operated by the district, and may pay the necessary premiums thereon. Failure to procure such insurance shall in no case be construed as negligence or lack of diligence on the part of the district school board or the members thereof.

Most athletic insurance plans in use in the schools today are entirely inadequate. Most plans indicate a certain amount of money as the maximum that can be collected. For example, a boy may lose the sight of an eye. According to the usual athletic protection fund, the loss of an eye will draw say, $1,000. This amount does not come even remotely close to paying for such a serious injury. In this case a hypothetical example could be taken by saying that the parents sue the athletic protection fund and the teacher for $30,000. In some states if the case is lost, the athletic fund will pay the $1,000 and the teacher the other $29,000. It can be seen that most of these insurance plans do not give complete and adequate coverage.

In many states teachers need additional protection against being sued for accidental injury to students. Legislation is needed permitting school funds to be used as protection against student injuries. In this way a school would be legally permitted and would have to purchase liability insurance to cover all pupils.

QUESTIONS AND EXERCISES

1. Consult the legal files in your local governmental unit to determine any court cases on record which have implications for the fields of health education, physical education and/or recreation. Describe the circumstances surrounding each.

2. Arrange a mock trial in your class. Have a jury, prosecutor, defendant, witnesses, and other features which are characteristic of a regular court trial. Your instructor will state the case before the court.

---

[16]Letter received from R. Rex Dalley, Executive Secretary, Montana High School Association, August 15, 1953.

3. Why is it important that leaders in health, physical education, and recreation have knowledge in respect to legal liability?

4. Define and illustrate each of the following: (a) liability, (b) tort, (c) negligence, (d) *in loco parentis,* (e) plaintiff, (f) nuisance, (g) misfeasance, (h) *respondeat superior,* and (i) proximate cause.

5. What are the defenses against negligence? Illustrate each.

6. What is the difference between governmental and proprietary functions? Illustrate each.

7. How does the charging of fees affect liability?

8. What is the extent of liability of (a) municipality, (b) school district, (c) board member, and (d) coach?

9. What are some safety procedures that should be followed by every physical education teacher?

10. Prepare a form to be used for the reporting of accidents.

11. What are the advantages of waivers and consent slips?

SELECTED REFERENCES

American Association for Health, Physical Education, and Recreation, National Association of Secondary-School Principals, and National Commission on Safety Education. *The Physical Education Instructor and Safety.* Washington, D. C.: National Education Association, 1948.

City Wide Conference with Principals' Representatives and Men and Women Chairmen of Health Education. *Proceedings.* City of New York: Board of Education, Bureau of Health Education, 110 Livingston Street, Brooklyn 1, New York, March, 1953.

Doscher, Nathan and Walke, Nelson. "The Status of Liability for School Physical Education Accidents and Its Relationship to the Health Program," *The Research Quarterly,* AAHPER, 23: 280, October, 1952.

Dyer, D. B., and Lichtig, J. G. *Liability in Public Recreation.* Milwaukee: C. C. Nelson Publishing Company, 1949.

Guenther, D. "National Survey of Physical Education and Sports Insurance Plans," *Research Quarterly,* AAHPER, 21: 1-20, March, 1950.

Guenther, D. "Problems Involving Legal Liability in Schools," *Journal of the American Association for Health, Physical Education, and Recreation,* 20: 511, October, 1949.

Leibee, Howard C. *Liability for Accidents in Physical Education, Athletics, Recreation.* Ann Arbor, Michigan: Ann Arbor Publishers, 1952.

Mantell, Herman P. *The Liability of Teachers and Other School Officers in New York State and Proposed New Legislation to Further Their Protection.* Doctorate Thesis, New York University, 1942.

Nash, Jay B., Moench, Francis J., and Saurborn, Jeannette B. *Physical Education: Organization and Administration.* New York: A. S. Barnes and Company, 1951, Chapter XX.

Remmlein, Madeline Kinter. "Legal Aspects of School Camping," *Youth Leaders Digest,* January, 1953, p. 142.

Research Division for the National Commission on Safety Education. *Who Is Liable for Pupil Injuries?* Washington, D. C.: National Education Association, October, 1950.

Rosenfield, Harry N. *Liability for School Accidents.* New York: Harper & Brothers, 1940.

Stack, Herbert J., Siebrecht, Elmer B., and Elkow, J. Duke. *Education for Safe Living.* Second edition. New York: Prentice-Hall, Inc., 1949.

State Legal Provisions in California Relating to Health Education, Physical Education, and Recreation. Sacramento, California: California State Department of Education, 1952.

Stone, Eleanor B., and Deyton, John W. *Corrective Therapy for the Handicapped Child.* New York: Prentice-Hall, Inc., 1951.

Thorndike, Augustus. *Athletic Injuries, Prevention, Diagnosis and Treatment.* Third edition. Philadelphia: Lea & Febiger, 1950.

Truesdale, John C. "So You're A Good Samaritan!" *The Journal of the American Association for Health, Physical Education and Recreation,* 25: 25, February, 1954.

Williams, Jesse Feiring, and Brownell, Clifford Lee. *The Administration of Health Education and Physical Education.* Philadelphia: W. B. Saunders Company, 1951, Chapter 23.

Chapter IX

THE PROFESSIONAL PREPARATION PROGRAM

All individuals interested in the advancement of school health and physical education recognize the importance of good programs of teacher preparation. Many of the problems facing the professions today, such as public misunderstanding and substandard programs at the community level, could be solved if teacher preparing institutions were turning out "top quality" leadership. Only through outstanding leadership will these areas be able to achieve their true potentialities and become recognized and respected by the public at large. Teacher preparing institutions should select and train that type of leadership which will achieve these potentialities and gain this respect. At the present time they are not meeting this most important responsibility.

I. WHERE ARE WE HEADING IN PROFESSIONAL PREPARATION?

Health and physical education have come a long way since the turn of the century in the preparation of their leaders. These specialized areas, which were just starting to take on a professional look in the latter part of the nineteenth century, have developed many programs which today are striving to turn out the "top-notch" leadership so essential to their progress. More leaders are being trained and the quality of leadership is becoming increasingly superior. The public is becoming more interested in these chosen fields of endeavor. Educators are gradually recognizing that such programs are no longer appendages on the school program, but instead are integral and important parts of total education. There is increasing recognition of the importance of developing sound health attitudes and health habits in the rank and file of the population. These are only a few indications of the progress that has been made over the years.

In order to insure further progress, it is essential that professional preparing institutions examine their roles as trainers of future leaders. They must examine carefully the candidates they are accepting into their professional programs, the experiences they provide for their trainees, the professional standards they have set, and the extent to which they aid their graduates.

In looking at the professional fields of health and physical education today it is possible to point with pride to the rise in the numbers preparing to enter these areas of endeavor. Since the first class of teachers was graduated from the Normal Institute of Physical Education in Boston in 1861, the number of institutions engaged in such work has risen rapidly. In 1918, there were 20 institutions preparing teachers; in 1929, 139; in 1946, approximately 361, and today there are nearly 600.

Within these institutions there are approximately 40,000 students.   Although there has been a gradual decrease in the last few years, future prospects indicate an increased demand for qualified teachers in these fields and consequently more will want to train for these professions.   It has been estimated there are approximately 100,000 working in these specialized fields today and there will be 125,000 by 1960. The professions are taking on size.   Like Topsy, they have grown.

Freshman majors in health and physical education at Illinois State Normal University working in flag football under the direction of experienced faculty members.

These professions have had a phenomenal growth in size, but they should also be examined to see if they have taken on stature, quality, and professional status. Professions cannot survive solely on the basis of size.   If national empires may be used as an example, one can look at history and see that such renowned leaders as Napoleon and Hitler built vast empires which became large in size, but soon crumbled and faded into history.   They overstretched their supply lines and collapsed because of lack of strength, internal unity, and high standards.   The internal strength of the professions of health and physical education should also be examined.

What is the intellectual quality of the membership in these special fields?   All will agree that many members represent the highest type of quality.   There are leaders in these special fields who through their brilliant minds, scholastic ability, and high standards have established themselves, become respected and gained prestige. However, is this true of most of the membership? If one takes the report of the Educational Testing Service of Princeton, New Jersey, as a criterion, a question can be raised. The Princeton Testing Service prepares college entrance examinations and has a national reputation in this field. Recently this service was requested by the armed services to set up draft deferment tests for men college students who were of military age. More than 400,000 such tests were administered. The tests were constructed to determine which students had sufficient educational aptitude to warrant continued college training. In analyzing the results of these tests, it was found that students going into the field of education were the lowest on the list. Within the field of education, health and physical education were at the bottom. It was impossible to go any lower. This was the cellar. Taking into consideration the nature of such tests, weaknesses that existed, and the demarcation between the various professional groups in the listing, it still represents an indictment of the professions.

According to experts such tests reveal the best minds, and the best are not entering the fields of health and physical education. If the best leadership is to become associated with such work, if the public is to recognize and respect such endeavors, it would seem that these specialized fields should rank toward the top rather than the bottom of any such listing. Why shouldn't these professions attract the best minds as well as the best physical specimens, for example?

Perhaps the quality of the individuals who comprise these professions is a result of the selective policies followed by many of the professional preparing institutions. A national study conducted by Robert E. Miner of Columbus, Ohio, recently showed that only 60 per cent of the 316 major institutions surveyed practice selective admissions, and some of these could not be classified as having what could be called stringent requirements.

Professor John H. Jenny of Temple University also conducted a national survey recently. He surveyed 228 institutions of higher learning. The results showed that only 17.5 per cent of the schools included speech as a required consideration in selection and 12.2 per cent, voice and diction. However, when Professor Jenny surveyed members of the National Professional Preparation Conference at Jackson's Mill, 92.6 per cent of these individuals favored speech and 82.9 per cent favored voice and diction as part of the selective process. This is only one quality of good leadership, but it is an important one. All will agree that leaders in such specialized fields of endeavor should be able to express themselves clearly and effectively. Their work involves a great deal of talking with people and interpreting their field to the public in general. This is an important quality, yet what is being done to insure leadership with such qualifications?

Health and physical education should be recognized as a place for the privileged few rather than for the rank and file. It should be an honor to be tapped on the shoulder and allowed to be a member of the profession rather than to know one can get into the group without any effort or prerequisites.

All want to look with pride at their colleagues. The members of the profession should be composed of individuals who can stand on an equal footing with individuals from every walk of life, whether it be in business, medicine, law, or education, or whether it be plunging ten yards off tackle or giving a speech on world affairs. This is the way a profession gets ahead, achieves, gains public recognition and prestige. *Above all it must be very clearly kept in mind that outstanding leadership depends on the product with which the professions start. Training can accomplish only so much.*

One reason the physical education profession has some people in the field who are lacking in intelligence and ability is that some schools will accept athletes even though they are not capable, just to have them for intercollegiate football and other athletics. This is the reason some of the majors are accepted in physical education in the first place. As long as this practice is carried on, the intelligence level of entering students and the level of their education when they complete their work cannot be expected to be raised. This is not to say that many athletes do not have a high level of intelligence. Many do, but too often these students are enrolled irrespective of their intelligence, scholarship, and other qualifications. It is important to screen athletes as it is all students.

A second question that may be asked, is "How professional are health and physical education members?" Do they keep up with the latest in professional literature? Do they attend professional meetings regularly? Do they contribute to the welfare of their field of work? The facts speak for themselves. There are a few carrying the load for the many. There are approximately 100,000 members in these chosen fields but there are only 20,000 members in the American Association for Health, Physical Education, and Recreation. The district and state membership rolls tell a similar story. In New York State, for example, there are nearly 7,000 in the field but only 3,000 members. Could it be that the pattern for such behavior starts in professional preparing institutions where, according to Jenny's survey previously cited, it was found that only 32 per cent of the institutions surveyed had major clubs affiliated with the American Association for Health, Physical Education, and Recreation? If members of the profession are to be professionally minded, training institutions must orient their students in their responsibilities and obligations to their profession. What better time is there for becoming interested in and knowing about one's national association, than as a student?

A third question that may be asked is "How united are we in professional preparation?" Are the divisions of health, physical education, and recreation working closely together, realizing that together they are much stronger than they would be separately? Or can a struggle for power be detected in some quarters? Do the men's and women's professional preparing programs work closely together, sharing facilities in accordance with need, and also sharing staff and money? Or are there instances where the men's and women's divisions are separate entities, each striving to outdo the other? Do the persons in health and physical education work closely with the individuals in athletics, endeavoring to help them develop high standards of competition? Or are there cases where it is feared athletics should be off by itself so that it cannot contaminate health and physical education? Isn't it possible to include athletics in the group and try to raise standards there rather than allow professional standards to be lowered? One cannot improve a thing by condemning and having nothing to do with it.

These questions will have to be answered by each professional preparing institution. Regardless of the situation, the simple and age-old maxim, "United we stand; divided we fall," should be clearly understood with all its implications. If the public detects weaknesses and confusion within, respect and prestige crumble without.

Another question that could be asked is, "How well do the professional areas work with other areas in professional preparing schools?" How much do they cut across departmental lines? Is everything being done so that elementary school teachers have a thorough understanding of these specialized fields and also our trainees have a better understanding of their area? Are cooperative projects worked out with the science, art, and social studies departments? Has an attempt been made to discuss a program with the English department to further the aim of having physical education students read, speak, and write as well as other students? Has everything possible been done to cooperate with the science departments in connection with camp work? What has been done to link up health education with the home economics, science, and other areas? These and many other questions should be asked if the desire is present to move ahead in professional preparing institutions. Staff personnel in health and physical education is comparatively small. The help of all phases of education and of all educators is needed. Through cooperation and close working relationships students can be provided with rich experiences which will insure outstanding leadership in the future.

These are a few of the problems that must be solved by professional preparing institutions in the years to come. Some can be solved almost immediately. Others will take considerable time. However, when they are solved, leadership in the fields of health and physical education will be able to accomplish the great potentialities they have for enriching human lives everywhere.

In spite of the problems which face professional preparing institutions, they can still look with pride to the accomplishments that have been and are being made to insure good leadership. There are encouraging reports coming in from every section of the country. Teacher preparation conferences are continually being held to upgrade professional work. California, Illinois, New York, Oregon, and Pennsylvania are only a few of the states that are moving ahead. In New York State a professional preparation committee is studying the competencies needed by all teachers and leaders in the specialized fields of health, physical education, and recreation with an eye to substituting a list of competencies for the traditional state certification requirements of semester hours. The American Association for Health, Physical Education, and Recreation is working closely with the American Association of Colleges for Teacher Education. Evaluative criteria have been developed which institutions of higher learning may use to judge their programs. Detroit and other places report placement of many men in physical education at the elementary level. Elementary and physical education departments have worked out professional preparation programs at some institutions. Five years of professional preparation which includes a more general education, and extended period of student teaching, double certification, and other advantages is becoming more common. Camping is playing an increasingly important role in the educational program. In the state of Michigan alone it is now reported that over 100 school systems have camping as part of the regular education program. Professional preparing institutions are acquiring camps and training their students for this essential and worth-while work.

There are many other encouraging signs. The future is bright, and leaders in the fields of health and physical education in the years ahead are going to be better qualified and more dynamic in their leadership, and accomplish greater things than they have thus far. Leadership is needed that will help these professions to become great. Leadership is needed that will be able to interpret professional work so clearly to the public that no doubts will be left as to the values of these fields of work. The job can be done. Professional preparing institutions will play the key role in doing such a job.

II. QUALIFICATIONS FOR HEALTH EDUCATORS

The personality of the health educator is of particular concern. The individual must be well-adjusted and well-integrated emotionally, mentally, and physically, if he or she is to do a good job in developing these characteristics in others. Such a person must also be interested in human beings and possess skill and understanding in human relations so that health objectives may be realized.

It is very important for the health educator to have a mastery of certain scientific knowledge, specialized skills, and have proper attitudes. Such knowledge, skills, and attitudes will help the health educator to identify the health needs and interests of individuals with whom he comes in contact, provide a health program which will meet these needs and interests, and promote the profession so that human lives may be enriched. This means that many experiences should be included in the training of persons entering this specialized field. These experiences can be divided into general education, professional education, and specialized education.

General education experiences should develop knowledge and skill in the communicative arts, understanding in sociological principles, an appreciation of the history of various peoples with their social, racial, and cultural characteristics, and the fine and practical arts which afford a means of expression, a means of releasing the emotions, a medium for richer understanding of life, and a medium for promoting mental health. The science area is very important to the health educator and should include such sciences as anatomy and kinesiology, physiology, bacteriology, biology, zoology, chemistry, physics, child and adolescent psychology, human growth and development, general psychology, and mental hygiene.

In professional education it is important for the health educator to have a mastery of the philosophies, techniques, principles, and evaluative procedures which are characteristic of the most advanced and best thinking in education.

The specialized health education area should include personal and community health, nutrition, family and child health, first aid and safety, methods and materials, organization and administration of school health programs, public health, including the basic principles of environmental sanitation and communicable disease control, and health counseling.

The Joint Committee of the American Association for Health, Physical Education, and Recreation makes the following recommendations for administrators to observe when hiring school health personnel and for developing outstanding leadership in this specialized field.

   1. Hiring health teachers, for large and medium-sized secondary schools, who have graduated with an undergraduate major in health education.

2. Hiring health educators, for teaching or administrative positions in large or medium-sized secondary schools, or in school systems, who have completed a graduate program in health education in an accredited institution, with a master's or doctoral degree.

3. Hiring teachers of biology, general science, home economics, social science, and physical education who have had an acceptable teaching minor in health education, if these staff members are expected to do any health teaching.

4. Requiring, and rewarding, additional in-service preparation in health education of all staff members serving as health teachers in the secondary schools.

5. Requesting, through their professional organizations, that teacher-education institutions provide better preparation in health education for *all* prospective secondary-school teachers and administrators.

6. Recruiting high-school boys and girls who have the aptitude and wish to enroll in an undergraduate health education major in preparation for a career in school health education.

7. Providing leadership in the further development of modernized health curricula in our secondary schools so that superior health teachers will have an opportunity to make significant contributions to general education for citizenship and life.[1]

Every health educator may not possess all of these qualifications. However, there should be a striving toward a well-rounded background which includes as many of these qualifications as possible.

III. QUALIFICATIONS FOR PHYSICAL EDUCATORS

Some special qualifications of the physical educator are as follows:

The physical educator should be a graduate of an approved teacher training institution preparing teachers for physical education. The college or university should be selected with care.

Since physical education is based upon the foundational sciences of anatomy, physiology, biology, kinesiology, sociology, and psychology, the leader in this field should be well versed in these areas.

The general education of physical educators is under continuous scrutiny and criticism. Such things as speech, knowledge of world affairs, mastery of the arts, and other aspects of this area should be an important part of the physical educator. Since the nature of positions in this area requires frequent appearances in public, adequate knowledge and skill in this area is essential.

Physical education work is strenuous and therefore demands that members of the profession be in a state of buoyant, robust health in order that they may carry out their duties with efficiency and regularity. It should also be remembered that physical educators are supposed to build healthy bodies. Therefore, they should be a good testimonial for their preachments.

Many moral and spiritual values are developed through participation in games and other physical education activities. It is essential, therefore, that the teacher of physical education have a proper background and possess such values that he or she will stress fair play, good sportsmanship, and a sound standard of values. The nature of his or her leadership should be such that the highest standards of moral and spiritual values are developed.

[1]American Association for Health, Physical Education and Recreation. *Administrative Problems in Health Education, Physical Education and Recreation.* Washington, D. C.: The Association, 1953, p. 20.

The physical educator should have a sincere interest in the teaching of physical education. Unless the individual has a firm belief in the value of his work and a desire to help extend the benefits of such an endeavor to others, he will not be an asset to the profession. A sincere interest in the teaching of physical education means that one enjoys teaching individuals, participating in the gamut of activities incorporated in such programs, helping others to realize the happiness and thrilling experiences of participation that he himself enjoys, and helping to develop citizenship traits conducive to democratic living. One must have a sincere love of the out-of-doors and of all the activities that make up the physical education program either indoors or out in the open. This means that anyone interested in physical education should enjoy sports and other activities. If there isn't a liking for these activities the individual is in the wrong profession.

The physical educator should possess an acceptable standard of motor ability. Physical skills are basic to the physical education profession. If the physical educator is to teach various games and activities to others, it is necessary that he or she have skill in many of them.

The physical educator must enjoy working with people, as he is continually required to associate with human beings in an informal atmosphere when teaching physical education activities. The values of such a program will be greatly increased if the physical educator teaches in a manner conducive to happiness, cooperation, and a spirit of friendship.

Mr. Emil Nyman, Principal of Lafayette School in Salt Lake City, Utah, lists the following items in respect to what he, as an administrator, expects of his physical education teachers. They are worthy of study.

1. Intelligent enough to talk about sex problems objectively.
2. Tactful enough to referee disputes fairly.
3. Altruistic enough to want to do some social service.
4. Trained enough in psychology to counsel young people.
5. Professional enough to serve his fellow workers in their improvement.
6. Kind enough to win young folks to his leadership.
7. Big enough to distinguish trifles from giants.
8. Doctor enough to heal the heartbreaks and soul injuries common to a big school.
9. Cultured enough to be a model in taste and language.
10. Creative enough to be able to put art into physical education activities and to appreciate originality in others.
11. Vision enough to tolerate the antics of young folk and to make the most of them.
12. Big enough to overflow into the lives of other teachers in the school to keep them balanced and encouraged.
13. Funny enough to be the clown of the organization if no one else turns up.
14. Wholesome enough to set the mental health climate of the school.
15. Religious enough to be secure, clean, optimistic, and courageous.
16. Skillful enough to provide practices in wholesome, constructive group living.
17. Moral enough to be a part in the development of conscience.
18. Adaptable enough to make a physical education health program in spite of weather, interferences, and lack of equipment.
19. Young enough to catch new ideas.

The American Association makes the following general recommendations for administrators interested in hiring physical education personnel:

1. Select physical education teachers from among the graduates of institutions which offer outstanding professional physical education programs.

2. Select physical education teachers who display a real enthusiasm for teaching as a life profession.

3. Select physical education teachers who have demonstrated outstanding ability in some field in addition to athletic coaching.

4. Select physical education teachers who are strongly recommended by qualified professional persons in addition to college athletic coaches.

5. Select physical education teachers who possess qualities with which young people can identify themselves.[2]

IV. THE IMPORTANCE OF BEING PROFESSIONAL

Another important problem of leadership with which health and physical educators must be especially concerned is that of being professional. Unless individuals in these special fields are "professional" there will be no constructive leadership.

The public respects and listens with interest whenever the American Medical Association makes a pronouncement; people everywhere are conscious of the strength of the American Bar Association; and individuals know that there is meaning and strength in the National Education Association. These organizations have gained prestige, become strong, and played a vital part in the growth of their respective professions because within their ranks are many members who are "professional."

Professions grow only as they receive the support of their members. Such support is given in many ways. Having a conviction that what one is doing renders a valuable service to mankind; being a member of national, state, and local professional organizations; promoting, attending, and participating in conventions, workshops, and meetings of professional organizations; reading professional literature; being cognizant of and promoting high educational standards; living the type of life that exemplifies the best for which the profession stands—these are a few of the responsibilities of one who wishes to bear the label of "professional" in its purest form. Individuals who believe in their profession and want to see it prosper will follow this professional pattern. Others who are indifferent, uninterested, and are seeking only personal gain will follow another road.

A survey of the fields of health and physical education indicates the prevalence of many professional responsibilities. Such an imposing list shows the fields to be wide in scope and important in nature. The responsibility to belong to a professional organization may be used as an example of the importance of being professional. Professional organizations exist for definite purposes, and these purposes have a bearing on the work, welfare, and public appraisal of professional workers. If all health and physical educators belonged to and worked for their professional

---

[2]*Administrative Problems in Health Education, Physical Education and Recreation,* pp. 53-54.

organizations, the concerted effort of such a large professional group would result in greater benefits and more prestige for the professions.

Health and physical educators should perform their professional responsibilities with zeal and interest. They should realize that professional ethics, strong and qualified leadership, high educational standards, and other factors conducive to increasing worth-while services to mankind hinge upon the extent to which each member of a professional group assumes his or her part in promoting the welfare of the group.

Health and physical educators have a responsibility to the community in which they work and to the public in general. They are the leaders to whom people look for direction and development of ideas in respect to their specialized endeavors. The public directly or indirectly is paying for such services. They have a right to expect a return on their investment. This is not possible unless a person is "professional." Furthermore, the professions of health and physical education have few equals for satisfactions derived from sincere professional efforts. BE PROFESSIONAL.

There are many other problems which are pertinent to any teacher preparation program in health and physical education. Space permits a discussion of only three of the most important, namely, the need for a cultural background, emphasis on competencies rather than courses, and the need for accrediting teacher preparing institutions.

V. THE NEED FOR A CULTURAL BACKGROUND

This country is experiencing an age of specialization, and the prospective teacher must have training in all phases of his or her particular field. However, there is still a genuine need for a broad background of knowledge in all areas of learning. In order that an individual may assume duties and responsibilities as a good teacher and also as a good citizen, he should be able to understand, think, and talk intelligently about not only the profession, but also the complexities of life as a whole.

The need for a broad cultural background seems to be especially applicable to teachers of health and physical education. Such specialists hold strategic positions. The nature of their work, close personal contact with students, place of leadership in the community, and the necessity for the coordination of their fields with other phases of the school and community programs, have implications which in many ways do not exist for the general classroom or academic teacher or leader in other areas.

Teachers of health and physical education possess many commendable qualities which make them stand out in the field of education. However, many members can be found occupying positions throughout the country who do not have a broad cultural background. These individuals use crude and careless language expressions, promote health and physical education as ends in themselves, fail to plan and organize their work in the light of sound educational principles, and are unable to converse or write in an intelligent manner. These judgments have received support in various studies that have been conducted over the years. W. E. Peik and G. B. Fitzgerald reported on a survey many years ago conducted by the

United States Office of Education in twenty-one universities and six colleges. This report pointed out that majors in the special fields were at the bottom of the teaching fields studied in respect to their cultural backgrounds. The study previously reported by Educational Testing Service of Princeton, New Jersey, shows that the situation has not changed.

Teacher training institutions must recognize the need for a general education that exists among leaders in these special fields and make the necessary provisions in their training programs. If such a job cannot be done in four years, perhaps a five-year program may be the solution. This extended training period would not only make it possible to obtain greater training in the general cultural area, but also would eliminate many of the undesirable features of the present "four plus one" concept, where the student shops around and takes his master's degree, many times in an area totally unrelated to his needs. The five-year program also provides students with the opportunity to pursue a second field of interest which could also result in broader cultural training.

Teacher training institutions should be concerned with establishing in each prospective teacher and leader a broad educational base. This broad base should include such things as English, history, psychology, economics, sociology, human growth and development, and the art of communication. It is also felt that there should be an intermingling of general and specialized elements of the curriculum throughout the training period. This special and general education should be woven into the fabric of the entire training period and should not be confined within certain limited compartments.

A broad background in all areas of knowledge is needed by leaders in these specialized fields. The curriculum should be flexible enough to insure that deficiencies in such important academic subjects as English, social studies, and science be made up whenever necessary to insure adequate preparation for the profession. If cultural training is part of the training of all leaders it will gain them the respect of the students, faculty, and the community. The individual who has secured his position primarily because he was an outstanding athlete on some college team, despite the fact that he may have language difficulties and lack breadth of knowledge, must become a thing of the past. Future training should guarantee health and physical education leaders who are enlightened and productive of good results. This is an age of specialization where the individual must be an expert in some particular vocation and also in the performance of his duties as an intelligent citizen.

VI. GREATER STRESS ON COMPETENCIES

There is a need for a greater stress on competencies in professional preparing institutions. The Jackson's Mill Professional Preparation Conference and other meetings and reports stress this trend. Professional preparation programs should be judged in light of the competencies they develop in their trainees rather than in the number of courses they offer in their curricula. It is important to offer a wide range of experiences but at the same time it is important to develop certain competencies in the form of skills, knowledges, and attitudes. This will ensure an adequate job being performed by the student when he or she gets a position out in the field.

Students have been known to take courses in swimming, for example, and yet complete the course without knowing or learning how to swim. On the other hand if each student were required to swim a certain distance and demonstrate other competencies, it would insure a much better trained individual. Furthermore, other practices which result in so-called "snap" courses from which the student fails to get any new information or skills, would disappear. In addition, the practice of making the physical education or health curriculum a haven for athletes who many times never attend the classes would also disappear.

There should be greater stress on competencies. A senior major in health and physical education at Illinois State Normal University demonstrates proficiency in archery, one of the many individual sports that she is preparing to teach in elementary or high schools in her state.

Questions have arisen as to how such a procedure should be accomplished. It would seem that first, a list of competencies should be established which all teachers and leaders, regardless of specialization, should possess. The Jackson's Mill Report and the results of similar conferences could be utilized as a guide for this compilation. Second, a list of competencies which are needed by specialized teachers of health and physical education could be compiled. Then a third step would be to develop measurement procedures and techniques which would be used as a means of evaluating these competencies. Such techniques should be as objective as possible so that it can be determined scientifically and accurately when competencies have been developed.

In order to aid professional preparing institutions in the development of such a plan, professional associations should work out guiding principles which would be of value in organizing training experiences for the development of these competencies. Everything possible should be done to help the institutions of higher learning do the best job possible. Only in this way will the best leadership be developed.

Illinois State Normal University students develop competencies for working with the handicapped by studying and working as camp counselors at a summer camp at Lake Bloomington.

Another move that would motivate professional preparing institutions to adopt a "competency" curriculum rather than a "course" curriculum would be to have states list their certification requirements in terms of competencies rather than the present semester- or quarter-hour requirements. If all candidates for positions in health and physical education were required to demonstrate proficiency in skills, knowledges, and attitudes, rather than present a transcript of courses taken, it would not be long before colleges and universities would have all the students in their schools participating in programs which would insure the meeting of such requirements. Furthermore, the quality of the leadership would be much higher than exists at the present time.

The fact that some states are moving in the direction of the "competency" idea is illustrated by the fact that recently the California State Department of Education published a progress report of the California Committee on the Revision of the Physical Education Credential Requirement. This report showed that a study of the functions and competencies of the modern physical education teacher was conducted. It then listed areas of study and learning experiences related to the development of competencies necessary to instruct in physical education, to organize and manage physical education programs, and in respect to school and community relationships. Roy E. Simpson, in a foreword to this report, aptly stated the purposes behind such a move when he said in part, ". . . The purpose of such revision is to keep the standards so developed that school personnel are qualified to provide the leadership and instruction necessary to keep the program of education geared to social progress. . . . The process of revising standards that are established for teacher certification should be furthered through continuous research. School administrators and teachers should be active participants in developing the research that is needed for this purpose. . . ."[3]

Another move in this direction is indicated by the action of the College Physical Education Association. The Committee on Curriculum Research of this Association developed a set of standards which could be used by professional preparing institutions as a basis for self-evaluation. This report listed certain competencies essential to good teaching in physical education.

There is increased recognition that better leadership must be provided in the fields of health and physical education. It is also realized that to insure such leadership preparing institutions must place more emphasis on preparing those individuals who demonstrate that they possess the competencies essential to performing high quality work.

VII. ACCREDITING PROFESSIONAL PREPARING INSTITUTIONS

There is an increasing need to develop a functional accrediting system whereby only those institutions who meet adequate standards will be allowed to train leaders in health and physical education. As has been pointed out earlier in this chapter, the number of such institutions has risen rapidly in recent years. In 1946, there were only 361 whereas today there are approximately 600. Many of these institutions are trying to present a training program which meets the highest standards of the profession. However, there are some programs that are totally inadequate in regard to staff, facilities, curricula, quality of students, and other essential items. Therefore, it is necessary to establish some accrediting system to ensure that only those institutions which meet high standards will be allowed to perform such important work.

The American Association for Health, Physical Education, and Recreation has been very much interested in this problem and has been working closely with the

---

[3] *A Proposed Program for the Preparation of Teachers of Physical Education.* A Progress Report of the California Committee on the revision of the physical education credential requirement. Sacremento: Bulletin of the California State Department of Education. Vol. XXII, No. 3, January, 1953.

National Association of Colleges for Teacher Education in an attempt to work out an accrediting procedure. Evaluation schedules have been developed in the areas of health and physical education. These may be procured from the national office and used by professional preparing institutions to evaluate their programs. Such important items are considered as admission requirements for students, preparation of faculty, teaching load of faculty, curriculum-instructional patterns, laboratory expenses, library facilities, student personnel services, field work experiences, facilities, and equipment. It is possible for each institution to evaluate itself in light of these criteria.

Leadership is an essential for the professions of health and physical education. An Illinois State Normal University senior gives a demonstration lesson on badminton to a group of high school girls. Observing in the background is the supervising staff member.

The National Continuing Committee for the Improvement of Professional Preparation in Health Education, Physical Education, and Recreation has also been working on this problem. Various states have shown an interest in accreditation. Many of them have committees on accreditation and are developing rating scales, schedules, and criteria for use in evaluation of professional preparing programs.

Accrediting procedures can assure the maintenance of high standards in regard to program, faculty, facilities, and other phases of the professional preparing program. Such procedures, however, will never be effective unless a strong system is developed with "teeth" in it, so that stringent policies can be required.

QUESTIONS AND EXERCISES

1. Draw up a list of competencies which you feel are essential for all teachers.

2. Draw up a list of competencies which you feel are essential for teachers of health and/or physical education.

3. Evaluate the professional preparation program through which you are passing, according to the standards established by the American Association for Health, Physical Education, and Recreation.

4. To what extent does selection of students for professional preparing programs have a bearing on the leadership produced for the professions?

5. What do you feel should be the requirements for admittance to teacher training?

6. Why should a student belong to his or her professional association?

7. Why is there a need for a general education background?

8. What standards would you establish for accrediting professional preparing institutions in order to ensure proper training for all teachers?

9. According to your own thinking, write an essay of 250 words on the subject, "Where Are We Heading in Professional Preparation"?

SELECTED REFERENCES

American Association for Health, Physical Education, and Recreation. *Evaluation Schedules for Major Programs in Health Education, Physical Education, and Recreation.* Prepared for the American Association of Colleges of Teacher Education accreditation plan, 1952.

A Proposed Program for the Preparation of Teachers of Physical Education. A Progress Report of the California Committee on the revision of the physical education credential requirement. Sacramento: Bulletin of the California State Department of Education, XXII, January, 1953.

A Report of the National Conference on Graduate Study in Health Education, Physical Education and Recreation. Held at Pere Marquette State Park, Illinois, January, 1950. Chicago: The Athletic Institute, 209 South State Street.

Berridge, Harold L. "Standards for Institutional Accrediting," *Journal of the American Association for Health, Physical Education, and Recreation,* 21:65, February, 1950.

Brownell, Clifford Lee. *Principles of Health Education Applied.* New York: McGraw-Hill Book Company, Inc., 1949, Chapter 12.

Bucher, Charles A. *Foundations of Physical Education.* Saint Louis: The C. V. Mosby Company, 1952, Chapters XV-XVIII.

Butler, George D. *Introduction to Community Recreation.* New York: McGraw-Hill Book Company, Inc., 1949, Chapters VIII-X.

Conference on the Undergraduate Professional Preparation of Students Majoring in Health Education. Washington, D. C.: Office of Education, 1949.

Hjelte, George. *The Administration of Public Recreation.* New York: The Macmillan Company, 1948, Chapter XXI.

Joint Committee on Health Problems in Education of the National Education Association and American Medical Association. *Health Education.* Charles C. Wilson, Editor. Washington, D. C.: National Education Association, 1948, Chapter XIV.

Nash, Jay B., Moench, Francis J., and Saurborn, Jeannette B. *Physical Education: Organization and Administration.* New York: A. S. Barnes and Company, 1951, Chapter XIX.

Nordly, Carl. "A State Evaluates Teacher Education," *Journal of the American Association for Health, Physical Education, and Recreation,* 24: 27, April, 1953.

Nordly, Carl. "Unifying the Profession," *Journal of the American Association for Health, Physical Education, and Recreation,* 21: 14, October, 1950.

Snyder, Raymond, and Scott, Harry. *Professional Preparation in Health, Physical Education, and Recreation.* New York: McGraw-Hill Book Company, Inc., 1953.

Stafford, Frank S., and Kilander, H. F. *Teacher Education for the Improvement of School Health Programs.* Office of Education, Bulletin 1948, No. 16. Washington, D. C.: U.S. Government Printing Office, 1948.

The National Conference on Undergraduate Professional Preparation in Physical Education, Health Education, and Recreation. Held at Jackson's Mill, Weston, West Virginia, 1948. Chicago: The Athletic Institute, 209 South State Street.

The Oregon Association for Health, Physical Education and Recreation. *Teacher Education Standards in Physical Education.* Eugene, Oregon: School of Health and Physical Education, 1952.

Chapter X

MEASUREMENT AND EVALUATION

Measurement and evaluation programs are becoming more and more prominent in school health and physical education. It is being increasingly recognized that in order to show the benefits derived from this specialized work and in order to conduct it in the most efficient way possible, measurement and evaluation are essential considerations.

The term "measurement" is used here to refer to the use of techniques to determine the degree to which a trait, ability, or characteristic exists in an individual. The term "evaluation" refers to the conduct of the various components of the program for the achievement of individual traits, abilities, and characteristics.[1]

During the last twenty-five years many measurement and evaluation techniques have been developed in the fields of health and physical education. Some of these have been carefully constructed in a scientific manner, but many fall below acceptable standards. The administrator should focus his attention and that of his staff on the materials that give valid and reliable results. Furthermore, all interested persons should be encouraged to construct new techniques in areas where shortages exist.

There are measurement and evaluation techniques other than tests. Some of these are rating scales, check lists, photographic devices, controlled observation, and various measuring instruments.

The Joint Committee on Health Problems in Education of the National Education Association and the American Medical Association[2] states that the most common evaluation instruments or procedures that are used by health teachers are: (1) observations, (2) surveys, (3) questionnaires and check lists, (4) interviews, (5) diaries and other autobiographical records kept by students, (6) health records, (7) records of other health conditions or improvements, (8) samples of students' work, (9) case studies, and (10) health tests.

I. PURPOSES OF MEASUREMENT AND EVALUATION

Many purposes exist to support the utilization of measurement and evaluation techniques in the administration of school health and physical education programs. A few of these will be discussed.

[1]Leonard A. Larson, and Rachael D. Yocom. *Measurement and Evaluation in Physical, Health and Recreation Education.* Saint Louis: The C. V. Mosby Company, 1951.

[2]Joint Committee on Health Problems in Education of the National Education Association and American Medical Association. *Health Education.* Charles C. Wilson, Editor. Washington, D. C.: National Education Association, 1948, p. 339.

Measurement and evaluation help to determine the progress being made and the degree to which objectives are being met. They aid in discovering the needs of the participants. They identify strengths and weaknesses of students and teachers, aid in curriculum planning, and show where emphasis should be placed. They also give direction, and help to supply information for guidance purposes.

Grout[3] in pointing up the need for measurement and evaluation in health education specifically refers to their value in determining the place where emphasis should be placed in the teaching of health and the procedures which are effective and ineffective. She also points out their use in aiding pupils to determine their own progress in respect to health practices, as a basis for giving grades, and as a means of interpreting the program to administrators and the public in general.

The information provided by measurement and evaluation techniques can also be utilized in other ways. In the area of measurement, findings can be used for such purposes as grouping individuals according to similar mental, physical, and other traits, which will insure better instruction. They yield information which can be used as an indication of an individual's achievement in various skills and activities. They provide information which can be used to predict future performance and development. They afford data on attitudes that determine whether or not the participant has proper motivation and focus attention on future action that should be taken in the program.[4]

The types of information that evaluation techniques yield will help in determining the needs pertinent to the way a program is conducted. This includes information on such administrative factors as policies, finance, records, leadership, facilities, time, research needs, equipment, and participation.[5] These are of special significance to the administration.

II. FRAMEWORK FOR MEASUREMENT PROCEDURES

To give the reader a clearer knowledge of some of the types of information that can be measured concerning some of the objectives of health and physical education, a partial framework is listed below. It is presented for the purpose of giving an indication of the vast scope of measurement and how it can influence these specialized programs. Objectives and terms used in framework are defined for purposes of clarification.

A. Objectives
1. *Organic development objective* refers to the activity phase of the program which builds physical power in an individual through the development of the various organic systems of the body.
2. *Skill development objective* deals with that phase of the program which develops coordinations, rhythms, and poise, through which some particular act may be performed with proficiency.
3. *Mental development objective* deals with that phase of the program which develops a comprehensive knowledge of principles, historical background, rules, techniques, values, and strategies.

[3]Ruth E. Grout. *Health Teaching in Schools.* Philadelphia: W. B. Saunders Company, 1953, p. 259.
[4]Larson and Yocom. *op. cit.* p. 28.
[5]*Loc. cit.*

4. *Human relations development objective* refers to that phase of the program which aids an individual in making personal and group adjustments and in developing desirable standards of conduct essential to good citizenship.

B. Definitions

1. *Classification information* refers to those elements which can be used as a basis for segregating individuals into homogeneous groups for which they are reasonably well suited mentally, physically, emotionally, and socially.
2. *Achievement information* refers to those elements which can be measured to determine the scope and magnitude of an individual's achievement in organic development, skills, knowledge, and adaptability.
3. *Diagnostic information* refers to those elements which can be used to determine the causal factors of development and performance.
4. *Prognostic information* refers to those elements which can be used as valid forecasters of development and performance.
5. *Basic element* is an aspect of organic, neuromuscular, or mental growth which is a foundation for, and makes possible the development of, a skill.
6. *Fundamental skill* refers to a basic skill which is common to, and essential for participation in, most forms of activity.
7. *Activity skill* refers to a skill which is pertinent to successful participation in a particular activity.

C. Types of Information Concerning the Objectives

1. *Organic Development Objective*

a. Classification information
    (1) age, weight, height
    (2) strength
    (3) posture
    (4) sensory capacity
    (5) physical fitness
    (6) anthropometric measurements
    (7) mental capacity
    (8) power
    (9) energy
    (10) cardiac efficiency
        etc.

b. Achievement information
    (1) strength
    (2) endurance
    (3) speed
    (4) sensory capacity
    (5) physical fitness
    (6) power
    (7) energy
    (8) posture
    (9) cardiac efficiency
    (10) nutrition
        etc.

c. Diagnostic information
    (1) age, weight, height
    (2) strength
    (3) endurance
    (4) nutrition
    (5) speed
    (6) sensory capacity
    (7) physical fitness
    (8) power
    (9) energy
    (10) cardiac efficiency
    (11) posture
        etc.

d. Prognostic information
    (1) age, weight, height
    (2) posture
    (3) speed
    (4) endurance
    (5) sensory capacity
    (6) physical fitness
    (7) power
    (8) energy
    (9) cardiac efficiency
        etc.

2. *Skill Development Objective*

    a. Classification information

        (1) Basic elements (concerned mainly with physical activity—would need development for other types)

            (a) age, weight, height
            (b) endurance
            (c) strength
            (d) native motor ability
            (e) motor educability
            (f) reaction time
            (g) motor interest
            (h) sensory capacity
                etc.

        (2) Fundamental skills (mainly concerned with physical activity—other aspects would need to be developed)

            (a) running
            (b) throwing
            (c) kicking
            (d) jumping
            (e) dodging
            (f) leaping
            (g) vaulting
            (h) climbing
            (i) skipping

            (j) accuracy
            (k) objective body control
            (l) agility
            (m) timing
            (n) balance
            (o) spring
            (p) hand-eye, foot-eye, arm-eye coordinations
                etc.

        (3) Activity skills (would need to be broken down into the various components affecting the development of each skill)

    b. Achievement information

        (1) Basic elements (similar to Basic elements under Classification information)

        (2) Fundamental skills (similar to Fundamental skills under Classification information)

        (3) Activity skills (would need to be broken down into the various components affecting the development of each skill)

    c. Diagnostic information

        (1) Basic elements

            (a) nutrition
            (b) health habits such as sleep, rest, and mental state
            (c) cardiac efficiency
            (d) sensory capacity
            (e) motor interest
            (f) reaction time
            (g) motor educability
            (h) native motor ability
            (i) strength
            (j) endurance
            (k) age, weight, height
                etc.

        (2) Fundamental skills (similar to Fundamental skills under Classification information)

        (3) Activity skills (would need to be broken down into the various components affecting the development of each skill)

d. Prognostic information
  (1) Basic elements (similar to the Basic elements under Diagnostic in-formation)
  (2) Fundamental skills (similar to Fundamental skills under Classification information)
  (3) Activity skills (would need to be broken down into the various components affecting the development of each skill)

3. *Mental Development Objective*

a. Classification information
  (1) mental capacity
  (2) health education, physical education and recreation background
  (3) academic background
  (4) moral background
  (5) home environment
      etc.

b. Achievement information—such knowledge, attitudes, and practices as:
  (1) rules of games
  (2) first aid procedures
  (3) general health, health habits, proper living, health knowledge
      (a) personal
      (b) community
      (c) mental
      (d) social
      (e) emotional
  (4) rules of safety
  (5) proper forms in games, athletic events, swimming, dancing, and other physical activities
  (6) etiquette in certain game situations
  (7) team play
  (8) strategy in games and events
  (9) regulations governing meets, tournaments, and other athletic events
  (10) duties of officials
  (11) physical activities
  (12) values of health and physical education
  (13) techniques
  (14) historical background of games, activities, etc.
  (15) principles of hygiene and sanitation
  (16) effect of exercise on body
  (17) best kind of exercise to take under certain circumstances
      etc

c. Diagnostic information
  (1) mental capacity
  (2) health and physical education background
  (3) academic background
  (4) interest
  (5) home environment
  (6) physical fitness
  (7) achievement records
  (8) health records
      etc.

d. Prognostic information
  (1) mental capacity
  (2) interest
  (3) physical fitness
  (4) achievement records
  (5) health records
       etc.

4. *Human Relations Development Objective*
  a. Classification information
  (1) character
  (2) personality
  (3) mental health
  (4) social attitudes
  (5) conduct
  (6) habits
  (7) citizenship
  (8) emotions
  (9) drives
  (10) appreciations
  (11) interests
  (12) capacity for leadership
  (13) ability to transfer training
  (14) group living
  (15) sportsmanship
  (16) service to community
       etc.

  b. Achievement information
  (1) character and personality
    (a) honesty
    (b) loyalty
    (c) fair play
    (d) good sportsmanship
    (e) courage
    (f) unselfishness
       etc.

  (2) leadership
    (a) initiative
    (b) cooperation
    (c) quickness of decision
    (d) fairness and judgment
    (e) vision and imagination
    (f) executive ability
    (g) ability to get along
        with others
    (h) personal magnetism
       etc.

  (3) transfer of training
    (a) from game situations to other situations in life
    (b) motor transfer—capacity to solve motor situations and to make
        a new coordinated movement accurately
       etc.

  (4) habits and practices
    (a) health (eating, sleeping, bathing, etc.)
    (b) exercise and recreation
       etc.

  (5) attitudes and appreciations
    (a) value of health
    (b) value of physical recreation
    (c) good sportsmanship
    (d) team play
    (e) value of acquiring certain skills
    (f) appreciation of recreation and exercise
    (g) appreciation of health and practicing health habits
    (h) attitude toward cheating
    (i) attitude toward winning

(j) attitude toward intra- versus inter-school competition
(k) appreciation of playing with the "dub"
(l) appreciation of training for competition
(m) appreciation of ways of spending leisure time
(n) appreciation of awards and rewards
    etc.

(6) social attitudes
    (a) toward individuals of different race, color, and creed
    (b) toward good citizenship
        etc.

(7) emotions

(8) service to community
    etc.

c. Diagnostic information

(1) health and physical edu-
    cation background
(2) mental capacity
(3) character
(4) family background
(5) companions
(6) personality

(7) emotional control
(8) drives
(9) interests
(10) group living
(11) sportsmanship
(12) physical fitness
     etc.

d. Prognostic information

(1) sportsmanship
(2) character
(3) personality
(4) mental capacity
(5) group living
(6) leadership
(7) emotional control
(8) habits

(9) attitudes and appreciations
(10) physical fitness
(11) interests
(12) personal ambitions
(13) home environment
(14) parental influence
     etc.

III. FRAMEWORK FOR EVALUATION PROCEDURES

A partial framework of evaluation procedures is listed below to give the reader a clearer knowledge of some of the types of information that can be evaluated.

A. Administration
   1. publicity
   2. finance
   3. policies
   4. organization
   5. records
   6. community relationship
      etc.

B. Leadership
   1. qualifications
   2. training
   3. remuneration
   4. number
   5. performance of duty
      etc.

    C. Facilities
       1. buildings
       2. land
       3. library
          etc.

    D. Equipment
       1. indoor
       2. outdoor
          etc.

    E. Activities
       1. area
       2. equipment
       3. personnel
       4. time
          etc.

    F. Participation
       1. minimum time
       2. desirable time
       3. utilization of facilities
          etc.

IV. GENERAL ADMINISTRATIVE GUIDES IN MEASUREMENT AND EVALUATION

Some general guides for the administration of a measurement and evaluation program are listed below:

1. Experts in the area of measurement claim that it is possible to measure or evaluate anything that exists in amount. This applies equally well to the various features of the program of activities; the individuals who participate in the program; the facilities, equipment, supplies that are utilized; the leadership that is provided, and any other functions which influence the program. Teachers and administrators should recognize the potentialities this premise has for determining the type of job they are doing.

2. Administrators should recognize the importance of measurement and evaluation to growth. Only so far as it is known how objectives are being met will optimum growth ensue. Furthermore, the effectiveness of certain methods of teaching and materials of instructions should be determined if the best program is to be provided.

3. The administrator should recognize the need for a clear statement of objectives together with a planned program of procedures to realize stated objectives, before selecting techniques for the measurement and evaluation program.

4. The administrator should use measurement and evaluation techniques as a means to an end and not as ends in themselves. They are necessary to develop better programs of school health and physical education so that human lives will be thereby enriched. If they are not utilized in such a manner, they cannot be justified.

5. Measurement and evaluation should be compatible and coordinated with the philosophy that is guiding the program. Measurement and evaluation help one to work in the right direction, as indicated by philosophy.

6. Measurement and evaluation techniques must meet acceptable criteria. In order that findings may be accurate, scientifically constructed techniques should be used in preference to those which are empirically constructed.

7. The administrator must see that the measurement and evaluation phases of the total program are planned, equipment and trained leadership provided, and time allotted so that they can be properly carried out. These phases of the program should be conducted with as much economy of time as possible. This will be realized only as techniques are administered efficiently.

8. Results gained from administering measurement and evaluation techniques must be utilized. There must be a "follow through" to insure that findings are used to help the individual and program. Furthermore, in interpreting results the "whole" individual plus his environment should be taken into consideration to make the findings most meaningful.

9. Measurement and evaluation should be continuous. Just as the program continues from day to day, week to week, and year to year, so must measurement and evaluation. There is a need for continual appraisal in order to insure that weaknesses are overcome, progress is made, and objectives are attained.

V. CRITERIA FOR TEST CONSTRUCTION AND SELECTION

Criteria refer to those particular standards which may be used to evaluate measurement and evaluation materials in the field of education. Such criteria as validity, reliability, objectivity, norms, and administrative economy provide the scientific basis for the selection and construction of tests. Administrators should be particularly concerned that the tests they utilize meet these criteria. If they do, properly interpreted results should aid considerably in developing adequate school health and physical education programs.

A definition of each criterion for test construction and selection and questions that could be asked by the administrator to determine whether or not the tests he desires to use meet the criteria listed, are stated below:

The Criteria for Test Construction[6]
A. Validity
   A technique has validity if it measures accurately what it claims to measure.
   1. Does it cover the area for which it is designed?
   2. Is it applicable to proper ages and grades?
   3. Is criterion with which material was correlated acceptable?
   4. Is the size of the correlation coefficient acceptable?
   5. Does technique give information concerning objectives?
   6. Is the sampling adequate, representative, and random?
   7. Is evidence cited as to whether it is a classification, achievement, diagnostic, or prognostic technique?
   8. Has technique been tried in recommended area of application?

[6]Leonard A. Larson. *Lecture Notes.* Course No. 280.62 in Advanced Methods and Materials in Physical Education, Health, and Recreation. New York University, 1946-47.

B. Reliability

The consistency of measurement and evaluation on the same individual or group under the same conditions and by the same examiner.

1. Is the size of the coefficient correlation acceptable?
2. What are the means of the two tests?
3. What are the conditions under which reliability has been determined?
4. Is the method used for the determination of reliability valid? (Test-retest, split-halves, parallel forms)
5. Is the sample adequate, representative, and random?
6. Has the reliability of the technique been determined by using the same group or individuals for which technique is recommended?

C. Objectivity

The degree to which a technique may be administered to the same individuals or group by a different examiner and obtain the same results.

1. Is there a manual of instructions which is simple and complete?
2. Is the method used for determination of objectivity valid? (Test-retest, parallel forms, etc.)
3. Is the sample adequate, representative, and random?
4. Has the objectivity of the technique been determined by using the same group for which technique is recommended?
5. Are the means cited?
6. What is the difference in the mean scores?
7. Are the conditions satisfactory under which objectivity has been determined?
8. Are the procedures easily understood by examiner and by the subject?
9. Are alternate forms of tests provided in instances where they are necessary?

D. Norms

Levels of group performance or a statistical average which is most frequent for a group.

1. What is the basis for construction of the norm? (age, grade, ability)
2. Is the sample adequate, representative, and random?
3. Are norms local or national?
4. Are norms tentative, arbitrary, or experimental?
5. Are all significant, extraneous factors eliminated?
6. Is the statistical refinement sufficient?
7. Is the appropriate statistical tool used?

E. Administrative Economy

Procedures that deal with the conduct of the program.

1. How much time is required to administer the technique?
2. What is the approximate cost of the equipment used in the administration of the technique?
3. Is the technique easy to administer?
4. How much training is necessary for the examiners?
5. Are objectives of test compatible with objectives of the program?
6. Is the measurement or evaluational technique designed for school or research purposes?
7. How many examiners are needed?
8. Is the technique within the scope of a health or physical educator's training?

VI. THE NEED FOR A STANDARDIZATION OF MEASUREMENT AND EVALUATION MATERIALS

There are at least three reasons why the need is great for a standardization of measurement and evaluation materials for the fields of health and physical education.

In the first place, many of the techniques being used today have been developed by individuals who have failed to use or interpret correctly scientific methods of construction. As a result, there are materials being used in our schools which have either failed to be scientifically evaluated or else have fallen below acceptable standards. In light of these conditions, it is necessary to ensure that only materials which meet acceptable criteria will be used. Standardization would make such a practice possible.

In the second place, it is impossible to make comparisons between individuals of different localities, due to the different techniques being used in each section. When a student transfers from one geographic locality to another, the instructor is at a loss to analyze his status, because of the lack of standards for all sections of the country. As a result, the instructor must start from the beginning in determining an individual's physical condition, traits, or characteristics. Standardization would make it possible for records to be interpreted intelligently, regardless of who administers the technique or the locality in which it is administered.

In the third place, it is difficult to measure progress on a national basis without the use of standards. It is imperative that measurement and evaluation materials be standardized so that the professions can know whether they are meeting the objectives that have been set, can evaluate the various types of programs and instruction, and can know what they are achieving through these programs. Standardization would make it possible to better determine individual and program weaknesses, quality of instruction, and progress achieved. Furthermore, standardization would serve as a means of motivation and comparison.

VII. AVAILABLE SCIENTIFIC MEASUREMENT AND EVALUATION MATERIALS

A few years ago the American Association for Health, Physical Education and Recreation through its president Dr. William L. Hughes, requested the National Research Council of the same organization to conduct a project which would result in a standardized measurement and evaluation program for health, physical education, and recreation. The Research Council in turn limited the project to an evaluation of tests in these specialized fields. The results of this project are of special importance to the field of administration. The project gives analytical reviews of selected tests that meet the criteria which were established by the Research Council as a basis for selecting and evaluating the tests. This report[7] should be a source book for every administrator in the field. As stated by the Steering Committee responsible for this publication, "Much discussion has been had in health, physical education, and recreation pertaining to the respective values of

[7]National Research Council, AAHPER. *Measurement and Evaluation Materials in Health, Physical Education and Recreation.* Washington, D. C.: AAHPER, 1950.

the various tests in these fields. In this report, only an impartial survey of the various tests has been made. There has been no attempt to indicate the best test or tests in each area, or to otherwise arrange the tests according to merit. It is left entirely to the administrator and teacher to select those which will best serve his purpose. The information given, however, may be used as a guide to achieve this end."[8]

As listed in the Table of Contents to this published project, selected tests that meet the criteria established cover the following areas:

1. *Circulatory-Respiratory Tests*
   Cureton All-Out Treadmill Test
   Henry Tests of Vasomotor Weakness
   MacCurdy-Larson Organic Efficiency Test
   Schneider Cardiovascular Test
   Turner Test of Circulatory Reaction to Prolonged Standing
   Tuttle Pulse-Ratio Test

2. *Anthropometric, Posture, Body Mechanics Measurements*
   Cureton-Holmes Tests for Functional Fitness of the Feet
   Cureton-Gunby Conformateur Test of Antero-Posterior Posture
   Cureton-Wickens Center of Gravity Test
   Cureton Technique for Scaling Postural Photographs and Silhouettes
   Cureton-Nordstrom Skeletal Build Index
   Cureton-Grover Fat Test
   Cureton Tissue Symmetry Test

3. *Muscular Strength, Power and Endurance Tests*
   Anderson Strength Index for High School Girls
   Carpenter Strength Test for Women
   Cureton Muscular Endurance Tests
   Larson Dynamic Strength Test for Men
   MacCurdy Test of Physical Capacity
   McCloy Athletic Strength Index
   Rogers Physical Capacity Test and Physical Fitness Index
   Wendler Strength Index

4. *Flexibility Tests*
   Cureton Flexibility Tests
   Leighton Flexometer Tests

5. *Motor Fitness Tests*
   Bookwalter Motor Fitness Tests
   Cureton-Illinois Motor Fitness Tests
   O'Connor-Cureton Motor Fitness Tests for High School Girls

6. *General Motor Skills Tests*
   Brace Test of Motor Ability
   Carpenter Test of Motor Educability for Primary Grade Children
   Cozens Test of General Athletic Ability
   Humiston Test of Motor Ability for Women
   Larson Test of Motor Ability for Men
   Johnson Test of Motor Educability
   Iowa Revision of the Brace Motor Ability Test

[8]*Ibid.*, p. vii.

Metheny Revision of the Johnson Test
Powell-Howe Motor Ability Tests for High School Girls
Scott Test of Motor Ability for Women

7. *Sports Skills Tests*
  Borleske Touch Football Test for Men
  Cureton Swimming Tests
  Cureton Swimming Endurance Tests
  Dyer Backboard Test of Tennis Ability
  Johnson Basketball Test for Men
  Lehsten Basketball Test for Men
  Rodgers-Heath Soccer Skills Tests for Elementary Schools
  Russell-Lange Volleyball Test for Girls
  Schmithals-French Field Hockey Tests for Women
  Young-Moser Basketball Test for Women

8. *Knowledge and Understanding Tests*
  Brewer-Schrammel Health Knowledge and Attitudes Test
  French Tests for Professional Courses in Knowledge and Sports
  Gates-Strang Health Knowledge Tests
  Hewitt Comprehensive Tennis Knowledge Tests
  Johns Health Practice Inventory
  Kilander Health Knowledge Test
  Phillips Badminton Knowledge Tests
  Scott Badminton Knowledge Test
  Scott Swimming Knowledge Test
  Scott Tennis Knowledge Test
  Shaw-Troyer Health Education Tests

9. *Attitudes and Appreciations Tests*
  Byrd Health Attitude Scale
  Franzen, Derryberry and McCall Health Awareness Test

10. *Social Adaptations Tests*
  (None)

Although these are the tests recommended as meeting acceptable scientific standards, it should also be remembered that there are other techniques which can be utilized in health, physical education, and recreation programs. These include such techniques as the following: observations, photographs, surveys, records and reports, interviews and conferences, check lists and questionnaires, medical examinations, ratings of health practices and habits, and rating scales for leadership, facilities, and other aspects of programs.

VIII. MINIMUM AND DESIRABLE STANDARDS

Larson and Yocom[9] have developed a list of minimum and desirable standards for a measurement and evaluation program in health, physical educational, and recreation based on the premise that these specialized fields as pertains to measurement, contribute to the attainment of objectives of organic development, skill or motor development, knowledge or mental development, and adjustment or human relations development. In the area of evaluation they are constructed on the

---

[9]Larson and Yocom, *op. cit.*, p. 450.

premise that independent considerations are necessary in each of the areas of health, physical education, and recreation for the various factors considered. These standards are reproduced in the accompanying table.

MEASUREMENT OF PROGRAM OUTCOMES (PRODUCT)	MINIMUM STANDARDS	DESIRABLE STANDARDS
ORGANIC	1. Medical examinations or a cardiovascular test 2. Physical (motor) fitness test	1. Medical examination (including a cardiovascular test) 2. Muscular strength 3. Body build 4. Growth, nutrition, development 5. Posture and body mechanics
SKILLS	1. General motor ability	1. Tests for each sport
KNOWLEDGE	1. Teacher-made tests	1. Standardized tests and teacher-made tests
ADJUSTMENT	1. Controlled Observation	1. Standardized tests

EVALUATION OF THE PROCESS OF EDUCATIONAL ACTIVITY	MINIMUM STANDARDS	DESIRABLE STANDARDS
PHYSICAL EDUCATION, HEALTH EDUCATION, RECREATION	1. Administration 2. Leadership 3. Facilities-equipment 4. Program activities 5. Time-participation 6. Records 7. Research (Construction of standards to meet the conditions pertaining to each component from standard textbook sources)	1. Administration 2. Leadership 3. Facilities-equipment 4. Program activities 5. Time-participation 6. Records 7. Research

QUESTIONS AND EXERCISES

1. Define the terms "measurement" and "evaluation." Why are they important to the successful administration of any program of health, physical education, or recreation?

2. List as many measurement and evaluation techniques as possible that are utilized in the schools. Take three of these and describe their use in detail.

3. What is the relationship of measurement and evaluation to objectives?

4. Why is it important to have classification, achievement, diagnostic, and prognostic information about each individual participating in the program of health, physical education and/or recreation?

5. What are some general guides in respect to the measurement and evaluation program that should be known by every administrator and teacher?

6. List and describe the various criteria that are essential to the construction and selection of scientific tests.

7. How would the standardization of measurement and evaluation materials contribute to better programs of health, physical education, and recreation?

8. What are the minimum and desirable standards for a measurement and evaluation program?

9. What part can self-evaluating check lists play in the development of better schools and programs of health, physical education, and recreation?

10. Develop what you consider to be a satisfactory and practical measurement and evaluation program for a health, physical education and/or recreation program.

SELECTED REFERENCES

Bovard, John F., Cozens, Frederick W., and Hagman, E. Patricia. *Tests and Measurements in Physical Education.* Philadelphia: W. B. Saunders Company, 1949.
Brace, D. K. *Measuring Motor Ability.* New York: A. S. Barnes & Company, 1927.

Clarke, H. Harrison. *The Application of Measurement to Health and Physical Education.* New York: Prentice-Hall, Inc., 1950.

Cozens, F. W. *Achievement Scales in Physical Education for College Men.* Philadelphia: Lea and Febiger, 1936.

Cozens, F. W., Cubberly, Hazel J., and Neilson, N. P. *Achievement Scales in Physical Education Activities for Secondary School Girls and College Women.* New York: A. S. Barnes & Company, 1937.

Fisher, R. A. *Statistical Methods for Research Workers.* New York: Hafner Publishing Company, Inc., 1948.

Garrett, Henry E. *Statistics in Psychology and Education.* New York: Longmans, Green and Company, 1947.

Glassow, R. B., and Broer, Marion R. *Measuring Achievement in Physical Education.* Philadelphia: W. B. Saunders Company, 1938.

Grout, Ruth E. *Health Teaching in Schools.* Philadelphia: W. B. Saunders Company, 1953, Chapter 10.

Joint Committee on Health Problems in Education of the National Education Association and the American Medical Association. *Health Education.* Charles C. Wilson, Editor. Washington, D. C.: National Education Association, 1948, Chapter XVIII.

Joint Committee on Health Problems in Education of the National Education Association and the American Medical Association. *School Health Services.* Charles C. Wilson, Editor. Washington, D. C.: National Education Association, 1953.

Lamkin, Nina B. *Health Education in Rural Schools and Communities.* New York. A. S. Barnes and Company, 1946, Chapter XIV.

Larson, Leonard A., and Yocom, Rachael Dunaven. *Measurement and Evaluation in Physical, Health, and Recreation Education.* St. Louis: The C. V. Mosby Company, 1951.

Lindquist, E. F. *A First Course in Statistics.* New York: Houghton Mifflin Company, 1942.

Lindquist, E. F. *Statistical Analysis in Educational Research.* New York: Houghton Mifflin Company, 1940.

McCloy, Charles Harold, and Young, Norma Dorothy. *Tests and Measurements in Health and Physical Education.* New York: F. S. Crofts & Co., 1954.

National Research Council. American Association for Health, Physical Education and Recreation. *Measurement and Evaluation Materials in Health, Physical Education, and Recreation.* Washington, D. C.: AAHPER, 1950.

National Research Council. American Association for Health, Physical Education and Recreation. *Research Methods Applied to Health, Physical Education, and Recreation.* Washington, D. C.: AAHPER, 1949.

Neilson, N. P., and Cozens, F. W. *Achievement Scales in Physical Education Activities.* New York: A. S. Barnes and Company, 1934.

Oberteuffer, Delbert. *School Health Education.* New York: Harper & Brothers, 1949, Chapters 9 and 19.

Ross, C. C., and Stanley, Julian C. *Measurement in Today's Schools.* New York: Prentice-Hall, Inc., 1954.

Scott, M. Gladys, and French, Esther. *Better Teaching Through Testing.* New York: A. S. Barnes and Company, 1945.

Strang, Ruth M., and Smiley, Dean F. *The Role of the Teacher in Health Education.* New York: The Macmillan Company, 1950, Chapter VII.

Chapter XI

PUBLIC RELATIONS

Before World War II the United States Coast Guard was not well known. The Army, Navy, and Marines overshadowed this part of the armed services. To acquaint the public with the work of the Coast Guard, build up morale of the men, encourage volunteers, and develop better appreciation of this branch of the service a large-scale publicity organization was set up. The Coast Guard became a very well-known branch of the service through the media of press releases, posters, leaflets, booklets, films, radio; the establishment of a Combat Correspondent Section; careful selection and indoctrination of correspondents; selective distribution of stories; release of such books as *Sinbad of the Coast Guard,* still pictures of Coast Guardsmen in action, motion pictures such as "To the Shores of Iwo Jima," stage shows such as "Tars and Spars" with Sid Caesar, pictures and information for home-town consumption, a planned historical program of the Coast Guard's accomplishments; and many other techniques and media. The results of this publicity are well known. The accomplishments of the Coast Guard became common knowledge. The effective system of coverage of home-town news was adopted by the other branches of the service. The Coast Guard was continually called upon to supply talent and illustrations of outstanding war accomplishments for bond rallies and victory drives. The recruitment program was an outstanding success. Pictures of Coast Guardsmen in action and tales of their feats became a topic of conversation in all corners of the world.

This story of the Coast Guard is public relations in action. The public understanding and appreciation which came about as a result of an organized program of public relations can be adapted to other organizations with effective results.

I. WHAT IS PUBLIC RELATIONS?

"Public relations" is a much defined term. Some of the common definitions for this term as given by experts in this specialized field are as follows: Philip Lesly speaks of it as comprising the activities and attitudes which are used to influence, judge, and control the opinion of any individual, group, or groups of persons, in the interest of some other individuals. Professor Harwood L. Childs defines it as a name for those activities and relations with others which are public and have significance socially. J. Handly Wright and Byron H. Christian refer to it as a program that has the characteristics of careful planning and proper conduct, which in turn will result in public understanding and confidence. Edward L. Bernays lists three items in his definition, first, information which is for public consumption, second, an attempt to modify the attitudes and actions of the public through persuasion, and third, the objective of attempting to integrate the attitudes and actions of the public and of the organization or people who are conducting the public relations program. Benjamin Fine defines it as follows: "Public relations is more than a narrow set of rules—it is a broad concept. It is the entire body of relationships that go to make up our impressions of an individual, an organization, or an idea. In building good public relations, we must be aware of all the forces, drives, emotions and conflicting and contradicting factors that are part of our social life and civilization."[1]

These selected definitions of public relations help to clarify its importance for any organization, institution, or group of individuals trying to develop an enterprise, profession, or business. Public relations takes into consideration such important things as consumer's interests, human relationships, public understanding, and good will. In business it attempts to show the important place that specialized enterprises have in society and how they exist and operate in the public interest. In education it is concerned with public opinion, the needs of the school, and acquainting constituents with what is being done in the public interest. It also concerns itself with acquainting the public with the educational problems which must be considered in order to render a greater service.

The American Association of School Administrators points out the purposes of school public relations as including, "(a) to inform the public about the work of the schools, (b) to establish confidence in the schools, (c) to rally support for proper maintenance of the educational program (d) to develop awareness of the importance of education in a democracy, (e) to improve the partnership concept by uniting parents and teachers in meeting the educational needs of children, (f) to integrate the home, the school, and the community in improving educational opportunities for all children, (g) to evaluate the offerings of the schools in meeting the needs of the children in the community, and (h) to correct misunderstandings as to the aims and objectives of the schools."[2]

Public relations means that the opinion of the populace must be taken into consideration. Public opinion is very powerful and individuals, organizations, and institutions succeed or fail in terms of its influence. Therefore, in order to have good public relations the interests of human beings and what is good for people in general must be considered.

The practice of public relations is pertinent to all areas of human activity; religion, education, business, politics, military, government, labor, and other affairs in which individuals engage. A good public relations program is not hit-and-miss. It is planned with considerable care, and great amounts of time and effort are necessary to produce results. Furthermore, it is not something that solely the "top brass," management, executives, or administrative officers, should be interested in. In order for any organization to have a good program, all members must be public relations-conscious.

---

[1]Benjamin Fine. *Educational Publicity*. New York: Harper & Brothers, 1943, pp. 255-256.
[2]American Association of School Administrators. *Public Relations for America's Schools. Twenty-Eighth Yearbook*. Washington, D. C.: The Association, 1950, p. 14.

The extent to which interest has grown in the field of public relations is indicated by the number of individuals who are specializing in this area. *The Public Relations Directory and Yearbook* lists personnel who specialize in this work. A recent edition of this publication listed nearly five hundred persons in sixty-five cities in twenty-four states who were doing work in this area on an independent basis, approximately 4,000 who were directors of public relations with business firms, approximately 1,500 who were associated with trade and professional groups, and nearly 600 who were with social organizations. In a recent Manhattan telephone directory there were approximately 400 names listed under the heading of "Public Relations." In contrast, in 1935, there were only ten names.

One purpose of school public relations is "To inform the public about the work of the schools." Wisconsin State College, La Crosse, Wisconsin. (La Crosse Tribune Photo.)

The importance of public relations is being increasingly recognized for the part it can play in educational, business, or social advancement. All need public support and understanding in order to survive. Public relations helps in obtaining these essentials.

II. THE IMPORTANCE OF PUBLIC RELATIONS TO ADMINISTRATORS

Although every member of an organization must be public relations-conscious, administrators especially must be cognizant of a planned program. The reasons for this premise are many. The administrator acts in the capacity of a leader and as such the example he sets will be followed to a considerable degree by others in the organization. The administrator is the logical and responsible one to initiate and maintain a sound public relations program. He is continually coming in contact with agencies and influential persons outside his organization. He is looked to more frequently than others as the spokesman for the group.

This is a competitive society. Many similar organizations are competing for public opinion, prestige, members, clientele and consumers. Through public relations, competition is made more effective. As Justice Holmes has said, ". . . the ultimate good desired is better reached by free trade in ideas, the best test of truth is the power of the thought to get itself accepted in the competition of the market, and the truth is the only ground upon which their wishes safely can be carried out."

Whether one is a representative of a health agency, physical education department, educational institution, church, political party, or labor union, there is competition for support and public favor. In all of this competition, public relations plays a very important part. It can point out the contributions of a profession to society as well as correct misunderstanding, ignorance, and apathy.

To administrators, public relations can furnish the knowledge and techniques that will enable them to be more effective in their work. They must know how to reach the group with which they are working and the public in general. Public relations helps them to better understand the viewpoints of others and know how to suggest and influence courses of action which affect them.

III. PUBLIC RELATIONS MEDIA

There are many media which can be utilized in a public relations program. Some have more significance in certain localities than others. Some are more readily accessible than others. Health and physical education persons should survey their communities to determine media which can be utilized and will be most effective in their public relations program.

It should be pointed out, however, that the *program* and *staff* represent the best media for an effective public relations program. Through the activities and experiences that are provided and the leadership that is given, much good will may be built for any school, department, or profession. This should never be forgotten.

A. Newspapers

The newspaper is one of the most common and useful media for disseminating information. It reaches a large audience and can be very helpful in interpreting health and physical education to the public at large. According to the American Association of School Administrators,[3] certain questions should be asked to determine what makes a good news story. Some of these questions are: Is the news of interest to the public? Are the facts correct? Is it direct in style, written in third person, in a layman's vocabulary, and well organized? Does it include news on individuals who are closely related to the schools? Does the article have a plan of action and does it play a significant part in interpreting the school program?

---

[3]*Ibid.*, pp. 283-285.

When a story is submitted to a newspaper there are certain standard rules that apply in the preparation of copy:

1. Prepare all copy in typewritten form as neatly as possible, double spaced, and on one side of the paper only.

2. The name, address and telephone number of your organization should be on page one, in the upper left-hand corner. Also at the top of page one, but below the address, should be the headline and release date for the story.

3. Paragraphs should be short, and if the story necessitates more than one page, write the word "More" at the end of each page. At the top of each additional page, list the name of the story in the upper left-hand corner. The symbol # # # should be placed at the end of the article to indicate the end.

B. Pictures and Graphic Materials

Pictures represent a very effective medium for public relations. Two words should be kept in mind by the persons who take and select the pictures for publication. These words are "action" and "people." Pictures that reflect "action" are much more interesting and appealing than "still' pictures. Furthermore, pictures that have people in them are much more effective than ones that do not possess this essential ingredient. It should also be recognized that usually a few people are better than many persons. Finally, such considerations as good background, accuracy in details, clearness, and educational significance should not be forgotten.

Educational problems such as budgets, statistical information in regard to growth of school population, information about participation in various school activities, and many other items can be made more interesting, intelligible, and appealing if presented through charts, graphs, and diagrams which are colorful and artistic.

C. Magazines

It has been estimated that there are in the neighborhood of 10,000 periodicals being published today. These include popular magazines, professional journals, trade publications, and others.

Such national magazines as *Look, Life, Woman's Home Companion, McCalls, Reader's Digest* and *The Saturday Evening Post* are excellent for publicity purposes. It is, however, very difficult to get stories in such publications because of their rigid requirements and the fact that they like to cover the stories with their own staff. Many times it is better to suggest ideas to them rather than to submit a manuscript. There are other methods that may be used. One can attempt to interest the editors in some particular work being done and have them send a staff writer to cover the story. It might be possible to get a free-lance writer interested in the organization and have him develop a story. Someone on the department staff who possesses writing skill can be assigned to write a piece for magazine consumption and then submit it to various periodicals for consideration.

D. Public Speaking

Public speaking can be a very effective medium for public relations. Through public addresses to civic and social groups in the community, public affairs, gatherings, professional meetings, and to any organization or group which desires to know more about the work that is being performed, a good opportunity is afforded for interpreting one's profession to the public. However, it is very important to do a commendable job or the result can be poor rather than good public relations.

In order to make a good speech, one should observe many fundamentals. A few that may be listed are mastery of the subject, sincere interest and enthusiasm, being more interested in putting thoughts across to the public than in putting the speaker across, being direct, straightforward, and well prepared, giving a brief presentation, and using clear and distinct enunciation. The American Association of School Administrators[4] suggests various steps in the preparation of an effective speech. These are as follows:

1. Know place and purposes of speech.
2. Select and properly phrase the topic.
3. Prepare an outline for preliminary thought.
4. Collect material bearing on speech from every available source.
5. Prepare outline more in detail for delivery.
6. Practice giving speech.
7. Make another outline for use in actually giving speech.
8. Deliver speech.
9. Evaluate speech.

If the organization is of sufficient size, a speakers' bureau may be an asset. This may be utilized if there are several qualified speakers within an organization. Various civic, school, church, and other leaders within a community can be informed of the services that the organization has to offer along this line. Then, when the requests come in, speakers can be assigned on the basis of qualifications and availability. The entire department or organization should set up facilities and make information and material available for the preparation of such speeches. If desired by the members of the organization, in-service training courses could even be worked out in conjunction with the English department or some experienced person, in developing this particular phase of the public relations program.

E. Discussion Groups

Discussion groups, forums, and similar meetings are frequently held in various communities. At such gatherings, representatives from the community, which usually include educators, industrialists, businessmen, physicians, lawyers, clergymen, union leaders, and others, discuss topics of general interest. This is an excellent setting to clarify issues, clear up misunderstandings, enlighten civic leaders on particular fields of endeavor, and discuss the pros and cons of community projects. Health and physical education persons should play a larger role in such meetings than has been the case in the past. Much good could be done for these specialized fields through this medium.

F. Radio and Television

Radio and television are powerful media of communication because of their universal appeal. These public relations media are well worth money spent for the

---

[4]*Ibid.*, p. 281.

purpose, if this is the only way they are available. First, however, the possibilities of obtaining free time should be thoroughly examined. The idea of public service will influence some radio and television station managers to grant free time to an organization. This may be in the nature of an item included in a newscast program, a spot announcement, or a public service program which utilizes a quarter, half, or even a full hour.

There are some radio and television stations that are reserved for educational purposes. This possibility should be examined carefully. Many schools have stations of their own which may be utilized.

Sometimes one must take advantage of these media on short notice; therefore, it is important for an organization to be prepared with written plans which can be put into operation immediately. This might make the difference between being accepted or rejected for such an assignment. The organization must also be prepared to assume the work involved in rehearsals, preparation of scenery, or other items that are essential in presenting such a program.

Radio and television offer one of the best means of reaching the greatest number of people at one time. As such, organizations concerned with specialized work of health and physical education should continually utilize their imaginations to translate the story of their professions into material which can be utilized effectively by these media.

G. Films

Films can present dramatically and informatively such stories as an organization's services to the public and highlights in the training of its leaders. They constitute a most effective media for presenting a story in a short period of time. A series of visual impressions will remain long in the minds of the audience.

Since such a great majority of the American people enjoy movies today, it is important to consider them in any public relations program. Movies are not only a form of entertainment but also an effective medium of information and education. Films stimulate attention, create interest, and provide a way of getting across information not inherent in printed matter.

Movies, slides, slidefilm, and other phases of these visual aids have been utilized by a number of departments of health and physical education to present their programs to the public and to interest individuals in their work. Voluntary associations, professional associations, and official agencies in these fields have also used them to advantage.

H. Posters, Exhibits, Brochures, Demonstrations, Miscellaneous Media

Posters, exhibits, and brochures should be recognized as playing an important part in any public relations program concerned with health and physical education. Brochures which are well illustrated, brief, and attractive can visually and informatively depict activities, facilities, projects, and services that a department or organization has as part of its total program.

Drawings, paintings, charts, graphs, pictures, and other aids, when placed upon posters and given proper distribution, will illustrate activities, show progress, and present information visually. These media will attract and interest public thinking.

Exhibits, when properly prepared, interestingly presented, and properly located, such as in a store window or some other prominent spot, can do much to demonstrate work that is being done by an organization.

Demonstrations which present the total program of an organization or profession in an entertaining and informative manner have a place in any public relations program.

Demonstrations as part of a public relations program. Gamma Phi Gym Circus. (Illinois State Normal University.)

Other miscellaneous media, such as correspondence in the forms of letters and messages to parents, student publications, and reports offer opportunities to develop good relations and favorable understanding in respect to schools and the work they are doing. Every opportunity must be utilized in order to build good public relations.

IV. GET THE FACTS

In order for any public relations to be successful, accurate facts must be presented. To establish what facts are to be given to the public, the particular public at which the program is directed must be known. Contrary to general belief there is no *one* public. There are an infinite number of publics varying according to interests, problems, and other factors which make individuals different.

A public is a group of people who are drawn together by common interests, who are located in a specific geographic area, or who are characterized by some other common feature. There are approximately 160 million people in the United States composing hundreds of different publics. There are over 9 million farmers, 16 million organized laborers, 45 million unorganized workers, 36 million students, 2 million professional people and 14 million veterans. Classes of publics may be national, regional, and local in scope. They can be classified according to race or nationality, age, religion, occupation, politics, sex, income, profession, economic level, or business, fraternal, and educational backgrounds. As one can readily see, there are many publics. Each organization or group that has a special interest is a public. The public relations-minded person must always think in terms of the publics with which he desires to promote understanding and how they can best be reached.

In order to have a meaningful and purposeful public relations program, it is essential to obtain some facts about these various publics. It is necessary to know their understanding of the professions, their needs and interests, their health practices and hobbies, and other essential information.

Public opinion decides whether a profession is important or not, whether it meets an essential need, whether it is making a contribution to enriched living. It determines the success or failure of a department, school, institution, or profession. Public opinion is dynamic and continually changing. Public opinion results from the interaction of people. Public opinion is king in this game of life and it behooves any group of individuals or organization that wants to survive to know as much about it as possible.

To get information on what the public thinks, why it thinks as it does, and how it reaches its conclusions, various techniques may be used. Surveys, questionnaires, opinion polls, interviews, expert opinion, discussions, and other techniques have proved valuable. Anyone interested in public relations should be acquainted with these various techniques.

Public opinion is formed to a great degree as a result of influences in early life, such as the effect of parents, home, and environment; on the basis of people's own experiences in everyday living, what they see, hear, and experience in other ways; and finally by media of communication such as newspapers, radio, and television. It is important not only to be aware of these facts, but also to remember that one is dealing with many different publics, each requiring a special source of research and study in order to know the most effective way to plan, organize, and administer the public relations program.

V. QUALIFICATIONS FOR THE PUBLIC RELATIONS PERSON

There are many qualifications that may be listed for a person who desires to specialize in the area of public relations. Such qualifications as writing and speaking ability, knowledge of and interest in human beings, showmanship, stamina, business sense, knowledge of mass communication media, judgment, ability to convince, skill in emotional appeal, analytical mind, sense of logic, ability to think accurately, broad cultural background, discretion, character, and integrity are a few that are important. It would be very difficult, however, to find a person who would possess all these qualifications. A few of the most important qualifications are discussed in more detail.

It is important that any person engaged in public relations work possess character and integrity. These are qualifications of primary importance. The public relations person must always keep the public's interest and welfare in mind. Temptations to exploit the public for selfish motives must not prevail. Truthfulness and the presentation of reliable and accurate information are prime requisites in such a responsibility. Discretion is another important qualification. It must be remembered that the relationship of a public relations person to the client is confidential.

Another qualification is an interest in human beings and a fervent desire to help them live a better life. The public relations program is a means to an end and not an end in itself. Through public relations, people and society in general will be aided. The idea of service must be more prominent than the idea of monetary return. The truly great public relations person is one who works for organizations, groups of people, professions, or causes, and for the good that will be rendered to society.

A broad general education is an important consideration for any individual desiring public relations work. Such knowledge will result in a better understanding of society and the foundations upon which it rests. Sociology, psychology, communications, economics, and political science are of special importance in this work. Also important is knowledge of the scientific method in research.

Some knowledge of special skills and techniques is also desirable. If a person does not have specific skill in painting, sketching, writing, and similar skills essential in public relations, it is important at least to know what to emphasize, have creative ideas that can be put into print, understand the procedures behind newspaper reporting, and know the fundamentals of press, radio and other essential media. Such knowledge will make it possible to hire someone else to perform the actual skill. However, the ideas and creative ability should be in the possession of the public relations person.

VI. SOME PRINCIPLES OF PUBLIC RELATIONS

A few of the principles that should be observed in developing a public relations program are listed.

1. Public relations should be considered internally before they are developed externally. The support of everyone within the organization, from the top administrator down to the last worker should be procured. Furthermore, such items as purpose of program, person or persons responsible, funds available, media to be utilized, and tools to carry on the program should be first considerations.

2. A public relations program should be outlined and put in writing, and every member of the organization should become familiar with it. The better it is known and understood, the better chance it has of succeeding.

3. The persons directly in charge of the public relations program must have complete knowledge of the professional services that are being rendered; the attitudes of those who are members of the profession and of the organization represented; and the nature, background, and reactions of the consumers and of all the "publics" that are directly or indirectly related to the job being performed.

4. After all the information has been gathered, a program should be developed which meets the needs as shown by the research that has been done.

5. There should be adequate funds available to do the job. Furthermore, the person or persons in charge of the public relations program should be given freedom in spending this money in whatever ways they feel will be most helpful and productive for the organization.

6. The formation of a public relations staff will be determined by the needs of the organization, the amount of money available, the attitude of the administration and the size of the organization. If additional staff is available, special talents should be sought so as to provide effectively for a well-rounded program.

7. Individuals assigned public relations work should modestly stay in the background instead of seeking the limelight, keep abreast of the things that affect the program, develop a wide acquaintance, and make contacts that will be helpful.

8. In developing a public relations program, such items as the following should be checked: Is there a handbook or a newsletter to keep members of the organization informed? Is there a system for dispensing information to local radio and press outlets? Is there a booklet, flyer, or printed matter which tells the story of the organization? Do members of the organization participate regularly in community affairs? Is there provision for a speakers' bureau where civic clubs and other organizations may procure speakers on various topics? Does the organization hold open house for parents and interested persons? Does the organization have a film or other visual material which can be shown to interested groups and which explains and interprets the work?

9. A good public relations program will utilize all available resources and machinery to disseminate information to the public in order to ensure adequate coverage.

VII. PUBLIC RELATIONS AND EDUCATION

Education is recognized as an essential in present-day society. In order that knowledge and experience may be transmitted from generation to generation, education is necessary. This is the essential that gives continuity to any culture.

A major obstacle today to education is in the area of public relations. Unless the public understands the work being performed by the schools, educators cannot expect their support. Today a great segment of the American public does not understand and appreciate the work that is being performed in the schools.

The need for a broad public relations program is evidenced by many facts in American life. Approximately six out of every ten persons in the United States never take work beyond the eighth grade. The American people spend more for tobacco each year than they do for education and twice as much for liquor. Schools are overflowing and there is a need for 10 billion dollars for new buildings alone.   It has been estimated that by April, 1960, the number of pupils attending elementary school will increase 42 per cent and high school, 20 per cent.   Schools must absorb more than 1,000,000 pupils a year, yet the necessary provisions have not been made.   There is need for greater financial support, increased teachers' salaries, more buildings, and better teacher training.   The necessary improvements cannot be obtained without public understanding and public support.

Edward L. Bernays in his book entitled *Public Relations* lists the results of several polls which point up the misunderstanding of the public in respect to education.

The American Institute of Public Opinion took a poll recently on the question: "What do you think is the most important problem today?" There was not one reply which said "Education."   The National Opinion Research Center in the same year conducted a survey and asked the question: "When you think of the problems facing the United States, which one comes to your mind first?" Of the persons that were interviewed only 6 per cent indicated general social problems, which included education, health, and welfare.

Another poll asked the question: "Would you like to attend classes and take special courses for adults in some school or college?"   "No" or "I don't know" were the answers of 59 per cent of the persons interviewed and only 41 per cent gave the answer "Yes."

The National Education Association conducted a survey which included the factor of teachers' salaries.   Of the persons surveyed, 33 per cent felt that teachers' salaries are satisfactory, 2 per cent thought they were high and 20 per cent did not have sufficient information on which to base an opinion.

A Gallup poll showed that 87 per cent of the people are satisfied with the schools their children attend.

Elmer Roper conducted a poll which showed that 71.6 per cent of the people in this country are either very satisfied or fairly well satisfied with the public school system.   Less than one-half of the people indicated that teachers were underpaid and yet the poll showed that teachers received the highest percentage when the public was asked to "rank the order of importance to the community of public school teachers, clergymen, public officials, merchants, and lawyers."

Other surveys have shown the same results.   The public in general is not informed in respect to education.   What is true of education in general is even more true of health and physical education which are important phases of the educational program.   This has important implications for a well-organized and long-term public relations program.

Bernays in addressing the American Association of School Administrators recently listed some pertinent remarks which he felt were essential to public understanding and action on the part of the American people.

He pointed out that three forces are responsible for social change; namely, public opinion, voluntary groups, and the law which is dependent upon public opinion.   In the light of this principle, voluntary groups are needed to aid in informing the public about education.   These voluntary groups should consist of leading civic leaders as well as professional educators.   Lay and professional groups must coordinate their programs closely and gear their campaigns to everyone from kindergarten to college throughout the entire country. One of the most important considerations is that a unified front be presented to the public. All should agree on the issues and present them in the same light. If the various professional associations that are now organized and exist on national, district, state, and local levels and the various lay organizations could speak with one voice and with unison and similarity of purpose, much could be accomplished.

Bernays also recommended a central board of strategy to establish policy and goals and iron out problems so that a unified approach would be followed. Through such a board, research could be conducted to ascertain and reach a common agreement at the various levels as to what the needs of education are. It could also determine the reasons for the apathy, indifference, and misunderstanding on the part of the public. It could wage a unified battle against enemies of public education.

Another step in the over-all public relations program would be a clear-cut operational program. Such a program would provide for a continuous campaign, personnel, money, utilization of mass communication media, close cooperation between school and parents and between the school and community in general, and a more active role for teachers in community activities.

The American Association of School Administrators[5] lists various principles which it considers essential to school public relations. They are:

a. School public relations must be honest in intent and execution.
b. School public relations must be intrinsic (school program should be recognized as worth while in itself).
c. School public relations must be continuous.
d. School public relations must be positive in approach.
e. School public relations should be comprehensive.
f. School public relations should be sensitive to its publics.
g. The ideas communicated must be simple.

Through such a public relations program, all the people would have a better understanding of education in this country.

VIII. PUBLIC RELATIONS IN SCHOOL HEALTH AND PHYSICAL EDUCATION PROGRAMS

Do professional people in health and physical education know what the man-on-the-street thinks about their professions? Have they asked the milkman, their neighbor, the lady behind the soda fountain such questions as, "Have you ever heard of these specialized fields?" "What do these terms mean to you?" "Do you think they make a contribution to enriched living?" Some individuals have done this and confess they are not proud or pleased with the answers received. They realize more and more the importance of good public relations in their fields. When they talk with the average layman about their professional fields they become increasingly aware of the fact that public misunderstanding exists. Physical education may be used as an example.

[5]*Ibid.*, pp. 16-33.

The public thinks of a physical educator as someone like Jack Dempsey, Gene Tunney, Hank Greenberg, Bernarr MacFadden, or Gayelord Hauser. During World War II when the Armed Forces were looking for individuals to head their physical fitness programs, they tapped the boxer, the ball player, or some other outstanding professional athlete on the shoulder and said, "You're the one we want. We've read about you and your great physical feats." They felt they were getting the most qualified physical educators to undertake the vital job of making the nation strong. The public thinks of physical education solely as the development of the "physical." Most individuals are not conscious of the mental, social, and other objectives which may be even more important.

Health and physical education need an effective program of public relations to inform the public of the various facets of their work. Cheerleading clinic sponsored by Illinois State Normal University.

Some sportswriters are responsible for a great amount of this ignorance and unconcern in regard to physical education. They view sports, games, and other physical activities as media for showing the physical dominance of one individual, school, or league. Too often they are not interested in the so-called educational aspects and ridicule the physical educator. They have been misinformed. They stress what will attract—the sensational and the spectacular. They do not want to minimize "big time" athletics because they have public appeal. They make good copy and give the sportswriters money and prestige. Intramurals, sports and play days, on the other hand, do not have this glamour.

Recently when the cry for "de-emphasis" in college athletics reaches its peak, sportswriters suggested that in order to keep "big time" athletes from getting a "free ride" through college, they should not be allowed to major in physical education where they have such "snap" courses as dancing, handball, and arts and crafts.

There are many other instances where journalists have set themselves up as authorities in the area of physical education, and the ironical part of the whole thing is that next to the comics, the sports page is the most widely read section of the paper. What is written there is taken as literal truth by an estimated 90 per cent of the people.

As long as the public interprets physical education in the sportswriter's terms, the profession is lost. Although there are some sportswriters who understand professional goals and desire to work in this direction, many take an approach completely contrary to that of educators. They emphasize the pennant winner, the champ, the big-rival game. They're interested in what the public and spectator want—not what is best for the participant.

This same confusion exists in health. The public in general is swayed by the various pills, concoctions, and cures that are advertized over the television and radio and appear in newspapers and periodicals. Educators do not appreciate health education as a specialized area. Many cannot see the value of a concentrated course. This area is often combined with the program in physical education, and little stress is placed upon it in the educational offerings. Although great strides have been made in recent years, the public still views the field with indifference. A broad public relations program is essential to correct such misunderstanding.

The fields of health and physical education must concentrate on public relations to a greater extent than they are at the present time. A few recommendations are suggested as to various approaches that may be taken.

The professions must be organized and administered so that they have more interest and appeal to children and adults alike. Certainly the first consideration is that a varied program be offered which is adapted to the various groups in the school and community and which meets the needs and interests of these individuals. If a good program is not offered, the public cannot be expected to cooperate and give their support. The various programs in health and physical education should be closely coordinated so that public needs and interests are provided for. Bernays advocated a Central Board of Strategy for education as a whole. It would also seem wise for the professional areas of health and physical education to have a central board of strategy at the national level concerned with public relations. They could then present a unified front to the public on all issues.

A touch of glamour would help to interest the public more in these specialized fields of endeavor. Why does a woman who has an important date put on her long, dangling earrings, high-heeled shoes, and exotic perfume? She wants to appeal, to attract and impress the man so that he will ask for a second date. Why do department stores and other business establishments devote large amounts of money, personnel, great effort and time to preparing store windows? They are trying to attract the attention of passers-by. They want them to stop and become so interested that they will enter the store to see the merchandise.

A certain amount of glamour, "window dressing" or "eye wash" is needed to attract the public to health and physical education. A little icing must be put on the cake so that this work will appeal to the public at large. After the public is brought inside, they will see the good work that is being done and will appreciate and understand the professions much better. First, however, it is important to attract and interest. To a great degree the public in general has not been attracted to such programs. Members of the profession and a few others know of the fine job that is being done. However, the public at large certainly does not.

In order to provide this "window dressing" why shouldn't politicians and key civic people be brought in to see the programs in action? In most cases they are anxious to be invited. Write up the occasion in the newspapers. Have pictures taken and printed on the front page. It's publicity for the politicians but it is also publicity for the professions. If the public sees an interest on the part of their leaders, they will follow.

Why not develop a greater child-parent relationship? Why not set aside one night a month, or a week, or as often as necessary, for a concentrated effort to invite the parents to see the programs in action and even to participate? Parents are interested in their children and would be most anxious to come if they were invited.

Furthermore, in health and physical education public relations programs, members must write and speak more in lay terms. At the present time a great portion of the American public does not understand what is said by educators. The college graduate, schoolteacher, and a few others understand, but the man behind the counter, the factory mechanic, and the laborer do not, and it should be remembered that they constitute the majority of individuals in this country.

The professions of health and physical education use such terms as "organic development" or "bone ossification" that have no meaning to the average layman. The only way the mass of the American public is to be reached is to get down to their level, their vocabulary and their thinking.

It is interesting to note that the books that have found the biggest American audience and have sold considerably more than two and one-half million copies each include such works as *Uncle Tom's Cabin, Ben-Hur, Gone With the Wind, How to Win Friends and Influence People, A Tree Grows in Brooklyn* and *See Here, Private Hargrove*. Each of these books has been written in simple language and none requires more than an eighth-grade reading skill. Some require only seventh-grade reading skill. Even the Bible states in Corinthians the importance of speaking in lay terms: "Except ye utter by the tongue words easy to be understood, how shall it be known what is spoken? For ye shall speak into the air."

Another point is that the professions should be getting more newspaper and other printed publicity. Local newspapers, area newspapers, and other publications should frequently contain articles written in lay terms for public consumption. Sometimes it appears that members of the profession spend too much time writing for professional journals and trying to educate members of the professions rather than trying to get more publicity in popular journals and trying to educate the lay public. An article in *Ladies' Home Journal* or *Woman's Home Companion, The Reader's Digest, Saturday Evening Post* or *Look* would be read by fifteen, twenty, or fifty million people.   This represents an excellent opportunity to reach the public.

The professions should also try to educate sportswriters, journalists, and other key persons in the publicity world.   Many take the wrong approach or do not print professional items because they are not familiar with the true facts.   They should be invited to professional conventions, meetings, schools, playgrounds, and recreational centers.   A positive attempt should be made to present professional educational philosophy and goals.

A "top notch" public relations program should be established in the American Association for Health, Physical Education, and Recreation and there should be greater concentration on such problems at national, district, and state conventions. Committees should be formed and panel and discussion groups organized to show every member of the profession how he or she can be a public relations expert. Lay groups should be organized on a voluntary basis.   Such groups can open many doors where professional groups are ineffective.   The professions of health and physical education are going to be strong only as they become aggressive and determined, and inform all the people of what they are trying to do.   Every professional person has a responsibility in his own community.   Furthermore, such agencies as the United States Office of Education, American Medical Association, official and voluntary agencies, and allied professional organizations can help. Radio and television should be utilized to a greater degree than they are at present. Educational TV stations are being established and time on radio is available.

The American Medical Association's radio broadcast some time ago entitled "Exercise and Athletics," carried over the National Broadcasting Company's hookup and narrated by Charles Laughton, was an excellent program.   It reached the public and impressed them favorably.   It certainly did a great deal of good for physical education.

The professions of health and physical education have a destiny.   Through a concerted effort it is possible to bring to the American public a better understanding of their work.   It can only be done, however, if each and every professional member concentrates on being a public relations person in his or her own community and attempts to inform others in lay terms of the goals they are trying to accomplish.   No opportunity should be allowed to pass to acquaint as many people as possible with these essential fields of endeavor.   The public should be shown the real worth of this work to which so many individuals have devoted their lives and energies.

QUESTIONS AND EXERCISES

1. Outline what you consider to be an effective public relations plan for a school program of health or physical education.

2. Prepare a news release on some event or phase of the department program.   Follow through with it for publication or broadcast.

3. Analyze the strengths and weaknesses of the present public relations program of the American Association for Health, Physical Education, and Recreation.   Send a letter to headquarters on your findings.

4. After careful firsthand study, list the main features of the public relations program of some successful business concern.   Show how some of the same techniques, media, and ideas may be applied to your professional field of endeavor.

5. What is meant by the fact that we are dealing in public relations with not just one, but many "publics"?

6. Why is a knowledge of public relations important to teachers and administrators alike?

7. Discuss the potentialities of five public relations media in promoting physical education, health education, and recreation.

8. Prepare a speech which is to be given before a lay audience on the importance of physical education and health education to community welfare. Give speech before class.

9. Prepare a bibliography of films which could be utilized effectively to interpret your profession to the public.

10. What qualifications would you need to become a full-time public relations person in your field?

11. List and discuss some principles that should be observed in public relations.

12. To what extent have the schools done a good public relations job?

SELECTED REFERENCES

American Association for Health, Physical Education, and Recreation. *Physical Education—An Interpretation.* Washington, D. C.: The Association.

American Association for Health, Physical Education, and Recreation and National School Public Relations Association. *Putting PR into HPER.* Washington, D. C.: The Association, 1201 Sixteenth Street, N.W., 1953.

American Association of School Administrators. *Public Relations for America's Schools. Twenty-Eighth Yearbook.* Washington, D. C.: The Association, 1952.

Bernays, Edward L. *Public Relations.* Norman, Oklahoma: University of Oklahoma Press, 1952.

Bucher, Charles A. "Sportswriters—Physical Educator's Nemesis," *The Physical Educator,* X: 51, May, 1953.

Doob, Leonard W. *Public Opinion and Propaganda.* New York: Henry Holt and Company, 1948.

Fine, Benjamin. *Educational Publicity.* New York: Harper & Brothers, 1943.

Flesch, Rudolf. *The Art of Readable Writing.* New York: Harper & Brothers, 1949.

Gunning, Robert. *The Technique of Clear Writing.* New York: McGraw-Hill Book Company, Inc., 1952.

Harlow, Rex F., and Black, Marvin M. *Practical Public Relations.* New York: Harper & Brothers, 1947.

Harral, Stewart. *Patterns of Publicity Copy.* Norman, Oklahoma: University of Oklahoma Press, 1950.

Harral, Stewart. *Tested Public Relations for Schools.* Norman, Oklahoma: University of Oklahoma Press, 1952.

Hull, J. Henrich. "Public Relations Can 'Make or Break,'" *Nation's Schools,* 40: 27, October, 1947.

Lesly, Philip (Editor). *Public Relations in Action.* New York: Ziff-Davis Publishing Company, 1947.

National Recreation Association. *The ABC's of Public Relations for Recreation.* New York: National Recreation Association, 1946.

National School Public Relations Association. *It Starts in the Classroom.* Washington, D. C.: National Education Association, 1951.

National School Public Relations Association. *Print It Right.* Washington, D. C.: National Education Association, 1953.

Parten, Mildred. *Surveys, Polls, and Samples.* New York: Harper & Brothers, 1950.

Plackard, Dwight Hillis, and Blackmon, Clifton. *Blueprint for Public Relations.* McGraw-Hill Book Company, Inc., 1947.

Postley, Maurice G., "How to Improve Your Public Relations," *American School Board Journal,* 116: 19, May, 1948.

Wilder, Ira, "Public Relations and the Modern School," *New York State Journal of Health, Physical Education and Recreation,* 3: 5, Spring, 1951.

Wright, J. Handly, and Christian, Byron H. *Public Relations in Management.* New York: McGraw-Hill Book Company, Inc., 1949.

Chapter XII

FACILITIES FOR A HEALTHFUL ENVIRONMENT

The physical and the nonphysical environments are very important to health and to education. It is important to have such essentials as ample space, adequate sanitary facilities, and provisions for various activities, as well as to have an environment which provides for a person's mental and emotional well-being.

The physical environment will be discussed in this chapter. The nonphysical environment will be discussed in Chapter XIII. The latter will include various factors such as administrative policies, the personality of the teacher and leader, human relationships, and individual differences, with the implications they have for establishing a healthful and educational environment in which groups can work profitably together.

In discussing the physical facilities for school health and physical education programs, it also seems important to bring in certain recommendations for recreation. In many localities both physical education and recreation utilize the same facilities. Planning for such facilities should be done on an all-community basis.

A detailed description with extensive layouts and dimensions of facilities will not be provided. Since many books and references, some of which are listed at the end of the chapter, deal with this information in detail, it does not seem wise to include it here. Furthermore, it seems important for the professional student to understand the over-all, general principles of facilities rather than minute details such as dimensions and diagrams. When the need arises for practical use of such information, references containing the specific details can be consulted and supplemented by talks with architects and others specialized in that particular field.

I. BASIC CONSIDERATIONS IN PLANNING

There are many considerations that should be taken into consideration when planning a healthful and educational environment for programs of health, physical education, and recreation. Some of the more important of these follow:

(1) All planning should be based on goals which recognize that the total physical and nonphysical environments must be safe, attractive, comfortable, clean, practical, and adapted to the needs of the individual.

(2) The planning should include a consideration of the total school health and physical education facilities and the recreational facilities of the community. The programs and facilities of these areas are essential to any community. Since they are closely allied, they should be planned coordinately and based on the needs of the community. Each should be part of the over-all community pattern.

Percent of Pupils Housed in Satisfactory, Fair, and Unsatisfactory School Plants — by State

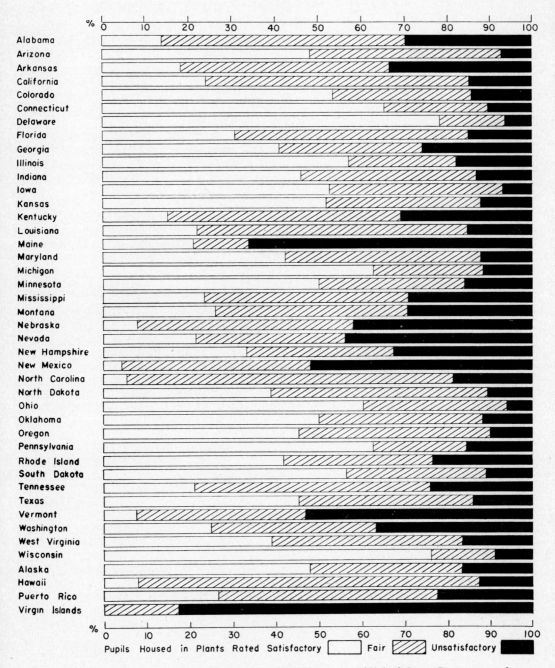

Pupils Housed in Plants Rated Satisfactory ☐ Fair ▨ Unsatisfactory ■

Report of the status phase of the school facilities survey. (United States Department of Health, Education, and Welfare, Office of Education, School Housing Section, December, 1953.)

Percent of Plants Rated Satisfactory, Fair, and Unsatisfactory – by State

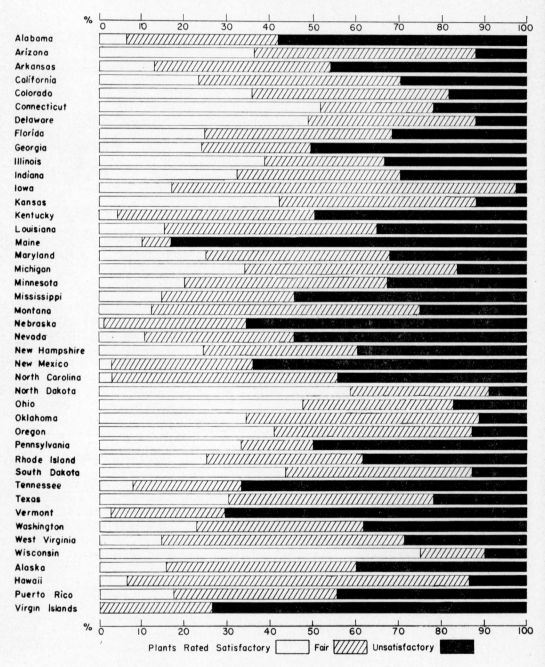

Per cent of plants rated satisfactory, fair, and unsatisfactory by state. (Report of the status phase of the school facilities survey. United States Department of Health, Education, and Welfare, Office of Education, School Housing Section, December, 1953.)

(3) Facilities in a school, recreational center, or public health building should be geared to health standards. They play an important part in protecting the health of individuals and in determining the educational outcomes.

(4) School buildings should be constructed with community recreation in mind. The arrangement of facilities is an important consideration since they will be used at various times of the day and night by the adult population interested in community recreation. Foresight in planning buildings and facilities will allow for such essential services.

Size of School Sites

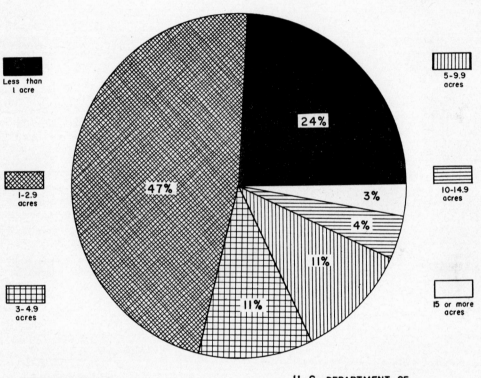

Less than 1 acre

1-2.9 acres

3-4.9 acres

5-9.9 acres

10-14.9 acres

15 or more acres

24%

3%

4%

11%

11%

47%

Data from 43 States
enrolling 20,156,045 pupils

U. S. DEPARTMENT OF
HEALTH, EDUCATION, AND WELFARE
OFFICE OF EDUCATION - School Housing Section

Size of school sites. (Report of the status phase of the school facilities survey. United States Department of Health, Education, and Welfare, Office of Education, School Housing Section, December 1953.)

(5) Facilities play a part in disease control. The extent to which schools provide for play areas, ample space, sanitary considerations, proper ventilation, heating and cleanliness, will to some extent determine how effectively disease is controlled.

(6) Administrators must make plans for facilities long before an architect is consulted. Technical information can be procured, in the form of standards and guides, from various sources such as state departments of education, professional

literature, building score-cards, and various manuals. Information may also be secured from such important groups as the American Association of School Administrators, National Council on Schoolhouse Construction, and American Institute of Architects.

(7) Standards should be utilized as guides and as a starting point. They will prove to be very helpful. However, it is important to keep in mind that standards cannot always be used entirely as developed. They usually have to be modified in light of local needs, conditions, and resources.

Percent of Pupils per Acre of Site

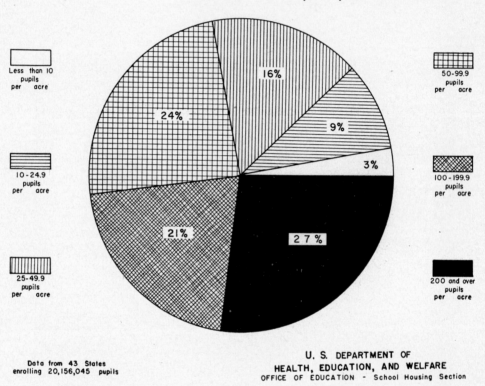

Data from 43 States
enrolling 20,156,045 pupils

U. S. DEPARTMENT OF
HEALTH, EDUCATION, AND WELFARE
OFFICE OF EDUCATION - School Housing Section

Percentage of pupils per acre of site. United States Department of Health, Education, and Welfare, Office of Education, School Housing Section, December, 1953.)

(8) Building and sanitary codes administered by the local and state departments of public health, and the technical advice and consultation services available through these sources should be known and utilized by administrators in the planning and constructing of facilities. Information concerned with acceptable building materials, specifications, minimum standards of sanitation, and other details may be procured from these informed sources.

(9) Health, physical education, and recreation personnel should play important roles in the planning and operation of facilities. The specialized knowledge that such individuals have is very important. Provisions should be made so that

their expert opinion will be utilized in the promotion of a healthful and proper environment. The recreation person, for example, should be consulted on the construction of a new school so that adequate provision is made for the recreation of individuals in the community at large.

(10) Facilities should be planned with an eye to the future. Too often schools and other facilities are constructed and outgrown within a very short time. Units should be sufficiently large to accommodate peak-load participation in the various activities. The peak-load estimates should be made with future growth in mind.

(11) Planning should provide for adequate allotment of space to the activity and program areas. They should receive priority in space allotment. The administrative offices and service units, although important, should not be planned and developed in a spacious and luxurious manner which goes beyond efficiency and necessity.

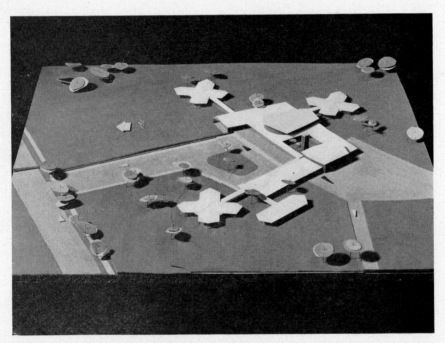

Planning should include consideration of the total school health and physical education facilities as well as the recreational facilities of the community. (Model of Heathcote School, Scarsdale, New York. Suter, Hedrich-Blessing, Chicago.)

(12) Geographical and climatic conditions should be taken into consideration in planning facilities. By doing this, the full potentialities for conducting activities out-of-doors, as well as indoors can be realized.

(13) Architects do not always pay as much attention as they should to the educational and health features, when planning buildings and facilities. Therefore, it is important that they be briefed on certain requirements that educators feel are essential in order that the health and welfare of children and adults may be provided for. Such a procedure is usually welcomed by the architect and will aid him in rendering a greater service to the community.

(14) Facilities should take into consideration all the necessary safety features so essential in programs of health, physical education, and recreation. Health service substations near the gymnasium and other play areas, proper surfacing of activity areas, adequate space, and proper lighting are a few of these considerations.

(15) It should be kept in mind that the construction of school health, physical education, and recreational facilities often tend to set a pattern which will influence parents, civic leaders, and others. This in turn will promote a healthful and safe environment for the entire community.

II. GENERAL TRENDS IN SCHOOL CONSTRUCTION

The designs of school buildings and other facilities concerned with school health and physical education programs and recreation today stress two factors: the educational needs of the children and others who pursue programs in such areas, and the need for economy at a time when construction costs are so high.

Trends in school construction stress the educational needs of children. Kester Avenue School, Los Angeles, California.

The trend is to do away with many of the so-called "frills" in order to achieve economy but at the same time not to compromise educational standards. School leaders advocate taking greater advantage of labor-, material-, and space-saving devices. For example, they suggest that the ceilings in regular classrooms be cut down from the traditional twelve feet to eight feet. They maintain that good lighting can be gained under most conditions with only eight-foot ceilings. Also, multipurpose halls can be constructed to double as exhibit and social areas, and gymnasiums can be used for physical education and community purposes, rather than merely for spectator entertainment.

It has further been pointed out that several practices are not economical in some of the construction going on today. An example of this is the application of Gothic and Colonial architecture, merely to enhance appearance. Buildings should be planned with emphasis on the functional, inside aspects, rather than on the outside ornamentation. Also, it is not economical to have a large auditorium constructed that will be only half-filled except on commencement day.

These features have received the support of the American Association of School Administrators. Bright plastic floor covering, improved lighting, and painted walls that are colorful are important. Classrooms should be large with movable furniture, work alcoves, and conference rooms. Large, well-planned play areas are important features in the selection of a school site, with 10 to 20 acres of land frequently being used for such sites. Both on the elementary and secondary levels, one-story buildings are becoming increasingly common. Single-story construction is safer, more economical, and decreases noise. Walls are being constructed with special attention to acoustical treatment to reduce noise. In many cases laminated-wood beams are being utilized instead of steel. Ceilings which slope are being increasingly utilized in order to improve light distribution and to reduce the space to be heated. Many rooms and facilities are being located to facilitate community use. Finally, there is evidence of the practicability of single-loaded corridors, which run along the outer walls of the building. In this way classrooms open onto the hall from only one side.

The important consideration in all construction is that educational need is not sacrificed for economy. However, when economy can be practiced without any disadvantages to the educational program, more and better functional facilities may be built with the money that is saved.

In addition to the few general building trends that have been mentioned, it is important to deal more specifically with those details important in the areas of health, physical education, and recreation.

III. GENERAL HEALTH FEATURES OF SCHOOL CONSTRUCTION

The general health features of the physical environment will be discussed here under the following headings: School Site, Building, Lighting, Heating and Ventilation, Furniture, School Plant Sanitation, and Acoustics.

A. The School Site

There are many things to consider in selecting a suitable site for a school. These considerations will differ depending on the community. Whether it is a rural or an urban community will have a bearing on the location of the site. In an urban community it is desirable to have the school situated near transportation facilities, but at the same time located away from industrial concerns, railroads, noise, heavy traffic, fumes, and smoke. Consideration should be given to the trends in population movements and future development of the area in which the buildings are planned. Adequate space for play and recreation should be provided. Some standards recommend five acres of land for elementary schools, ten to twelve acres for junior high schools, and twenty acres for senior high schools. The play area should consist of a minimum of one hundred square feet for every child.

Attention should be given to the esthetic features of a site because of its effect on the physical and emotional well-being of students and staff. The surroundings should be well landscaped, attractive, and free from disturbing noises or odors.

The American Association of School Administrators and the National Council on Schoolhouse Construction can supply detailed information on the selection of a school site.

Adequate space for play and recreation should be provided. Heathcote School, Scarsdale, New York.

B. The Building

Some trends in modern building construction have already been discussed and consideration of some of the special areas is still to come. Suffice it to say here that the trend is toward one-story construction, where that is possible, with stress on planning from a functional rather than an ornamentation point of view. The building should be constructed from the standpoint of use. As much natural lighting as possible should be utilized with sunshine an important consideration. The materials used should make the building attractive and safe. According to the National Safety Council a high percentage of children-accidents occur in school buildings. Every precaution should be taken to protect against accidents from fire, slippery floors, and other dangers. The walls should be painted with light colors and treated acoustically. Doors should open outward. Space for clothing should be provided.

These are only a few of the considerations in planning a school building. It is important that an architect plan such facilities with special regard to the educational needs of those who utilize it. Educators should formulate a plan and use it in discussions with the architect.

C. Lighting

Proper lighting is important to conserve vision, to prevent fatigue, and to improve morale. There should be proper lighting both as to quality and quantity.

As much natural lighting as possible should be provided in schools. Washington Irving Elementary School, Waverly, Iowa. (Picture furnished by Burnett and Logan, Chicago.)

In the past it has been recommended that natural light should come into the room from the left and that artificial light should be provided as needed. There is a trend now toward allowing natural light from more than one direction. Artificial light, moreover, should come from many sources rather than one, so as to prevent too much concentration of light in one place. Switches for artificial light should be located in many parts of the room.

Light intensity in most classrooms, according to expert opinion, varies from 15 to 50 foot-candles.* Most authorities suggest between 20 and 40 foot-candles

*A foot-candle is the unit by which light is measured in intensity at a given point.

for reading and close work.   In gymnasiums and swimming pools it is recommended that intensity range from 15 to 25 foot-candles four feet from the floor and at water level.   Glare is undesirable and should be eliminated.   Fluorescent lights should be properly installed and adjusted for best results.   Strong contrasts of color such as light walls and dark floors should be avoided.

Windows, according to most experts, should extend as far up toward the ceiling as possible and should consume space equal to about one-fourth to one-fifth of the floor area.

Window shades aid in controlling light.   They should be durable, of light color, and located in the middle of the window so that they may be adjusted either up or down.

A good source of information for acceptable standards on lighting is the Illuminating Engineering Society, 51 Madison Avenue, New York.

The school building should be constructed from the standpoint of use. Kester Avenue School, Los Angeles, California.

D. Heating and Ventilation

Efficiency in the classroom, gymnasium, special activities rooms, and other places is determined to some extent by thermal comfort.   Thermal comfort is determined in the main by heating and ventilation.

The purposes of heating and ventilation are many.   Some of the more common are: to remove excess heat, unpleasant odors, and in some cases gases, vapors, fumes, and dust from the room; to prevent rapid temperature fluctuations; to diffuse the heat within a room; and to supply heat to counteract loss from the human body through radiation and otherwise.

Heating standards vary according to the activities engaged in and the clothing worn by the participants. The following represents an approximate average of various suggested standards for temperatures.

Classrooms, offices, and cafeterias—68-72 degrees (30 inches above floor).

Kitchens, closed corridors, shops, and laboratories—65-68 degrees (60 inches above floor).

Gymnasiums and activity rooms—55-65 degrees (60 inches above floor).

Locker and shower rooms—70-78 degrees (60 inches above floor).

Swimming pools—80-85 degrees (60 inches above the deck).

As respects ventilation, the range of recommendations is from 8 to 21 cubic feet of fresh air per minute per occupant. Adequate ventilating systems are especially needed in dressing, shower, and locker rooms, toilet rooms, gymnasiums, and swimming pools. The recommended humidity ranges from 35 to 60 per cent. The type and amount of ventilation will vary with the specific needs of the particular area to be served. A good source for ventilating and heating information is the American Society of Heating and Ventilating Engineers, 51 Madison Avenue, New York.

E. Furniture

The furniture that pupils use most are desks and chairs. Seats and desks which are adjustable and movable are recommended by most educators. There are many different kinds of seats and desks which are available in both wood and metal. The desk should be of proper height and fit the pupil comfortably and properly. Desks should be arranged to provide the best light for the students.

F. School Plant Sanitation

Various items concerned with school plant sanitation should not be overlooked. Sanitation facilities should be well provided and well maintained. The water supply should be safe and adequate. If any question exists, the local or state health department should be consulted. In regard to water supply, one authority suggests that at least 25 gallons per pupil per day is needed for all purposes.

Drinking fountains of various heights should be recessed in corridor walls and should be of material which is easily cleaned. Approximately one drinking fountain should be provided for every 75 pupils. A stream of water should flow from the fountain in such a manner that it is not necessary for the mouth of the drinker to get too near the drain bowl.

Water closets, urinals, lavatories, and washroom equipment, such as soap dispensers, toilet paper holders, waste containers, mirrors, bookshelves, and hand-drying facilities should be provided as needed.

Waste disposal should be adequately cared for. There should be provision for cleanup and removal of stray paper and other materials that make the grounds and buildings a health and safety hazard and unsightly. Proper sewage disposal and prompt garbage disposal should also be provided.

G. Acoustics

Concentration is necessary in many kinds of school and recreational work. Noise distracts attention, causes nervous strain, and results in the loss of many of the activity's benefits. Therefore, noise should be eliminated as effectively as possible. This can be achieved by acoustical treatment of such important places as corridors, gymnasiums, swimming pools, shops, music rooms, and libraries.

Acoustical materials include plasters, fibers, boards, tiles, and various types of fabrics. Some areas should be given special attention. Floor covering which reduces noise can be used in corridors and acoustical material can be used in walls. In classrooms, special attention should be given to materials which absorb sound in the upper walls and to tight floor coverings. In cafeterias there should be sound-absorption materials on floors, tables, counter tops, ceilings, and walls. Furthermore, the kitchen with its noises should be separated from the dining room. The music room and shop areas should be isolated as much as possible in addition to having acoustically treated walls. Swimming pools and gymnasiums need special treatment to control the various noises that are associated with joyous and enthusiastic play participation. Ceiling and wall acoustical treatment will help control noises in the gymnasium, while the use of mineral acoustical material, which will not be affected by high humidity, will be found helpful in the swimming pool.

IV. INDOOR FACILITIES

Several special areas and facilities are needed by programs of health, physical education, and recreation. A few of the indoor areas which are important and prominent in the conduct of these specialized programs are briefly discussed in this section. They are as follows: (A) Administrative and Staff Offices, (B) Locker, Shower, and Drying Rooms, (C) Gymnasiums, (D) Special Activity Areas, (E) Health Service Suite, (F) Classrooms, (G) Cafeteria, (H) Swimming Pool, and (I) Auxiliary Rooms.

A. Administrative and Staff Offices

It is important, as far as it is practical and possible, for professional persons working in health, physical education, and recreation to have a section of a building set aside for administrative and staff offices. As a minimum there should be a large central office with a waiting room. The central office will provide a place where the secretarial and clerical work can be performed, space for keeping records and files and storage closets for office supplies. The waiting room can serve as a reception point, where students and visitors can wait until staff members are ready to see them.

Separate offices for the staff members should be provided, if possible. This allows for a place where conferences can be held in private and without interruption. This is a very important consideration for health counseling and for discussing scholastic, family, recreational, and other problems. If separate offices are not practical, a desk should be provided for each staff member. In this event, there should be a private room available to staff members for conferences.

Houck Physical Education Building.   Southeast Missouri State College, Cape Girardeau, Missouri.

Yost Field House.   Department of Physical Education and Athletics, University of Michigan.

Other facilities that make for a more efficient and enjoyable administrative and staff setup are staff dressing rooms, departmental library, conference room, and toilet and lavatory facilities.

B. Locker, Shower, and Drying Rooms

Health, physical education, and recreation activities require facilities for storage of clothes, showering, and drying. These are essential to good health and for a well-organized program. The reason such facilities are often not fully utilized is that poor planning makes them inadequate and uncomfortable.

Locker and shower rooms should not be located in the basement because direct outside windows are very desirable for such facilities. They should also be readily accessible to activity areas. Locker rooms should not be congested places that students want to get out of as soon as possible. Instead, they should provide ample room, both storage and dressing type lockers, stationary benches to sit upon, mirrors to aid in dressing, lighting fixtures that are recessed, and drinking fountains.

An average of fourteen square feet per individual at peak load, exclusive of the space utilized by the lockers, is required to provide proper space.

Storage lockers should be provided for each individual in the school or recreational program. An additional ten per cent should be installed for purposes of expanded enrollments or membership. These are lockers for the permanent use of each individual and can be utilized to hold essential clothing and other supplies. They can be smaller than the dressing lockers and some recommended sizes are: $7\frac{1}{2}'' \times 12'' \times 24''$; $6'' \times 12'' \times 36''$; $7\frac{1}{2}'' \times 12'' \times 18''$. The basket type lockers are not looked upon with favor by most experts because of the hygiene factor, the fact that an attendant is required for good administration of this system, and because of the necessity of carting the baskets from place to place.

Dressing lockers are utilized by participants only when actually engaging in activity. They are larger in size, usually $12'' \times 12'' \times 54''$ or $12'' \times 12'' \times 48''$ in elementary schools and $12'' \times 12'' \times 72''$ for secondary schools and colleges and for community recreation programs.

Shower rooms should be provided which have the gang type shower for boys and a combination of the gang and cubicle type showers for girls. The Jackson's Mill Facilities Conference[1] recommended that girls have a number of shower heads equal to 40 per cent of the enrollment at peak load and the boys, 30 per cent of the enrollment at peak load. Another recommendation is one shower head for four boys and one for three girls at peak load. These should be four feet apart. If showers are installed where a graded change of water temperature is provided and where the individual progresses through such a gradation, the number of shower heads can be reduced. The shower rooms should also be equipped with liquid soap dispensers, good ventilation and heating, floors constructed of nonslip material, and recessed plumbing. The ceiling should be dome-shaped so that it will more readily shed water.

The drying room adjacent to the shower room is an essential. This should be equipped with proper drainage, good ventilation, towel bar, and a ledge which can be used to place a foot upon while drying.

---

[1]National Facilities Conference. *A Guide for Planning Facilities for Athletics, Recreation, Physical and Health Education.* Chicago: The Athletic Institute, Inc., 1947.

C. Gymnasiums

The type and number of gymnasiums that should be part of a school or recreational plant will depend upon the number of individuals who will be participating, the variety of activities which will be conducted in this area, and the school level concerned.

General construction features to which most individuals will agree include smooth walls, hardwood floors (maple preferred—laid lengthwise) recessed lights, recessed radiators, adequate and well-screened windows, and storage space for the apparatus and other equipment that is utilized. It is also generally agreed that in schools it is best to have the gymnasium located in a separate wing of the building to isolate the noise and also as a convenient location for community groups which will be anxious to use such facilities.

Gymnasium in Washington Irving Elementary School, Waverly, Iowa. (Picture furnished by Burnett and Logan, Chicago.)

The American Association for Health, Physical Education, and Recreation has listed several important factors to keep in mind when planning the gymnasium:

1. Hard maple flooring which is resilient and nonslippery.
2. Smooth interior walls to a height of ten or twelve feet.
3. Upper walls need not be smooth.
4. The ceiling should reflect light and absorb sound, and there should be at least twenty-two to twenty-four feet from the floor to exposed beams.

5. Windows should be ten to twelve feet above floor and placed on long side of room.
6. Heating should be thermostatically controlled, radiators recessed with protecting grill or grate if placed at floor level.
7. Sub-flooring should be moisture- and termite-resistant and well ventilated.
8. Prior consideration must be given concerning the suspension of apparatus from the ceiling and the erection of wall-type apparatus.
9. Mechanical ventilation may be necessary.
10. Proper illumination meeting approved standards and selectively controlled for various activities must be designed.
11. Floor plates for standards and apparatus must be planned, as well as such items as backboards, electric clocks, and scoreboards, public address system, and provisions for press and radio.
12. Floor markings for various games should be placed after prime coat of seal has been applied and prior to application of the finishing coats.[2]

The number of teaching stations desired will play an important part in deciding the size and number of the gymnasiums. A teaching station is a place where a group meets with a teacher or leader for the conduct of certain activities. The degree to which a varied program is offered, the facilities that are available, and the number of staff members will determine the number of teaching stations that are utilized in any program.

In addition to an adequate number of teaching stations, it is also important to give attention to official size courts, adequate space for safe and enjoyable participation, and spectator space, if such is desired. When spectator space is provided, bleachers which can be telescoped and recessed in the walls are advisable as they do not take space away from activity participation.

Many gymnasiums have folding doors which divide them into halves and allow for activities to be conducted simultaneously on each side. This has proved satisfactory where separate gymnasiums could not be provided. The Jackson's Mill Facilities Conference recommended various base type gymnasiums. These included floor area for the elementary school gymnasium of 50' × 30', junior high school of 65' × 90', junior-senior high school of 65' × 102' and senior high school of 76' × 96' with ceiling heights of 20', 22', 22' and 22', respectively. These gymnasiums, with folding partitions, will provide basic units for programs.

Other considerations for gymnasiums should include provisions for basketball backboards, mountings for various apparatus that will be used, recessed drinking fountains, places for hanging mats, outlets for various electric appliances and cleaning devices, proper line markings for activities, bulletin boards, and other essentials to a well-rounded program.

D. Special Activity Areas

Although gymnasiums are large and take up considerable space, there should still be additional areas for activities essential to school programs of health and physical education, and recreation.

Wherever possible additional activity areas should be provided for remedial or adapted activities, apparatus, handball, squash, weight lifting, dancing, rhythms, fencing, dramatics and for various recreational activities such as arts and crafts,

[2]American Association for Health, Physical Education, and Recreation. *Administrative Problems in Health Education, Physical Education, and Recreation.* Washington, D. C.: the Association, 1953, p. 83.

lounging and resting, and bowling. The activities to be provided will depend on interests of participants and type of program. The recommended size of such auxiliary gymnasiums is 30′ × 50′ × 24′ or preferably 40′ × 60′ × 24′.

Another special room especially desirable in the elementary school is the "all-purpose" room which could be used for all types of activities, including games, music, dramatics, and social events.

In reference to special activity areas, it should also be pointed out that regulation classrooms can be converted into these special rooms. This may be feasible where the actual construction of such costly facilities may not be practical.

The remedial or adapted activities room should be equipped with such items as horizontal ladders, mirrors, mats, climbing ropes, stall bars and benches, pulley weights, dumbbells, Indian clubs, shoulder wheels, and such other equipment as is needed for the particular needs of the individuals participating.

E. Health Service Suite

To have a practical health service setup which can accommodate examination work, a suite is needed rather than just one room. Experts recommend at least four rooms which include examining, waiting, and rest rooms for both boys and girls. In addition there should be toilet facilities for each sex. Several exits from the examining room are recommended as a means of expediting the conduct of health services and eliminating confusion.

The health service suite may also become the school nurse's headquarters. In this case, there should be room for various items that are needed in her work, such as health records, desk, and files.

The color and furnishings of the waiting room should provide an attractive and cheerful atmosphere. A desk for clerical help can also be provided. There should be screens, if necessary, to give privacy to the examining and rest rooms which are part of the health suite and are attached to the waiting room.

The examining room should be large enough to accommodate all the necessary equipment, supplies, and measuring devices. Provisions for eye testing, weighing, first aid, examining procedures, parent interviews, and other essentials should be kept in mind.

The rest rooms should be large enough to hold necessary cots, tables, and other items. They should also be equipped with subdued lighting, walls and ceilings which keep noise to a minimum, and other conveniences which contribute to rest.

Plans for a health suite follow: these have been suggested by the American Medical Association.[3]

F. Classrooms

Classrooms which are utilized for health instruction should include the requirements discussed under seating, lighting, color of walls and ceilings, heating and ventilation, acoustics, and sanitation. All classrooms should be healthful, comfortable, and adaptable regardless of whether they are being used for health instruction or some other subject.

---

[3]W. W. Bauer. *Health Rooms for Schools*, American Medical Association, 1947, 3pp. (mimeo).

There is one feature, however, that should receive consideration if there is not a special room set aside for such a purpose. This is the use of audio-visual equipment. There are ample resources for audio-visual material which can be utilized

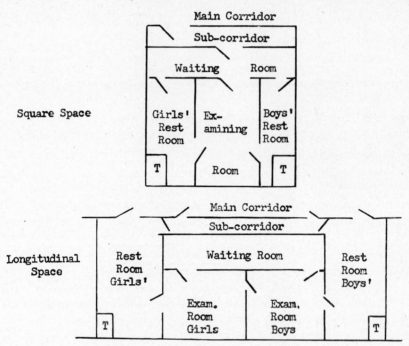

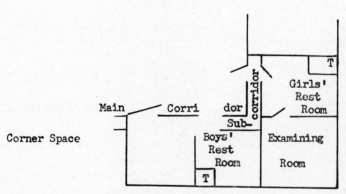

Plans for health suite. (Courtesy of Bureau of Health Education, American Medical Association.)

very effectively in any health instruction program. There should be available projection and sound equipment which includes an opaque projector, slide projector, filmstrip projector, motion picture projector, and turntables. There should also be outlets for electrical connections. Projection equipment should be installed in the rear of the room and audio equipment outlets in the front. There should be shades or other facilities for darkening the room. Finally, a screen should be available.

Another consideration in any health instruction room is a large display board which can be used to illustrate the material that is presented.

G. Cafeteria

The school lunch is a vital factor in the general health of any child and is an important part of his educational experiences. Furthermore, the cafeteria in any recreational or other building is an important consideration and concern of individuals engaged in health, physical education, and recreation work.

The cafeteria in a school should be located on the first floor and easily accessible from anywhere within the building as well as to a service driveway. The size depends upon the number of individuals to be served. In general, from 10 to 12 square feet per person is required at peak load for the dining-room area.

The kitchen area will depend in size upon the number of meals to be prepared. The kitchen should contain all the equipment and supplies essential to the preparation and serving of good meals. Such equipment as ranges, ovens, sinks, dishwashing machines, refrigerators, tables, service trucks, counters, and kitchen machines such as mixers, peelers, and slicers should be provided.

The dining-room part of the cafeteria should be equipped with the necessary tables and chairs, serving counter, refrigerated counters, silver, napkins, plates, trays, drinking fountain, and other essentials.

The physical appearance of the cafeteria should be attractive, with adequate lighting, light colors, and floors which are easy to clean. The cafeteria should be quiet and conducive to enjoyable and satisfactory eating conditions.

H. Swimming Pool

Present types of swimming pools have in the main two objectives, one to provide instructional and competitive programs and the other for recreation.

The swimming pool should be located on or above the ground level, with southern exposure, isolated from other units in the building, and easily accessible from the central dressing and locker rooms. The materials that have been found most adaptive to swimming pools are smooth, glazed, light-colored tile, or brick.

The standard indoor pool is seventy-five feet in length. The width should be a multiple of seven feet with a minimum of thirty-five feet. Depths vary from two feet six inches at the shallow end, to four feet six inches at the outer limits of the shallow area. The shallow or instructional area should comprise about two-thirds of the pool. The deeper areas taper to nine to twelve feet in depth. An added but important addition is a movable bulkhead which can be used to divide the pool into various instructional areas.

Most pools are constructed with overflow troughs at the water level which also afford excellent hand grips for practicing elementary skills. The deck space around the pool should be constructed of a nonslip material and provide ample space for land drills and demonstrations. The area above the water should be un-

Brundage Pool in Men's Physical Education Building, University of Connecticut.

Swimming Pool, Alabama College, Montevallo, Alabama.

obstructed. The ceiling should be at least 25 feet above the water if a three-meter diving board will be used. The walls and the ceiling of the pool should be acoustically treated.

The swimming pool should be constructed so as to receive as much natural light as possible, with the windows located on the sides rather than on the ends. Artificial lighting should be recessed in the ceilings. Good lighting is especially important in the areas where the diving boards are located. Underwater lighting is beautiful, but not an essential.

There should be an efficient system for adequately heating and circulating the water. The temperature of the water should range from 75 to 80 degrees.

If spectators are to be provided for, it is recommended that a gallery which is separate from the pool room proper be erected along the length of the pool.

An office adjacent to the pool where records and first-aid supplies can be kept is advisable. Such an office should be equipped with windows which overlook the entire length of the pool. Also, there should be lavatory and toilet facilities available.

The swimming pool is a costly operation. Therefore, it is essential that it be planned with the help of the best advice obtainable. The specialists who are well acquainted with such facilities and conduct swimming activities should be brought into conferences with the architect, a representative from the public health department, and experts in such essentials as lighting, heating, construction, and acoustics.

I. Auxiliary Rooms

The main types of auxiliary areas found in connection with school health and physical education and recreation facilities are supply, check-out, custodial, and laundry rooms.

Supply rooms should be easily accessible from the gymnasium and other activity areas. In these rooms will be stored balls, nets, standards, and other equipment needed for the conduct of the programs that are offered. The size of these rooms will vary according to the number of activities that are offered and the number of participants.

Check-out rooms should be provided on a seasonal basis. They will house the equipment and supplies that are used in various seasonal activities.

Custodial rooms provide a place for storing equipment and supplies which are utilized in the maintenance of these specialized facilities.

Laundries should be adequate in size to accommodate the laundering of such essential items as towels, uniforms, and swimming suits.

V. OUTDOOR FACILITIES

The outdoor facilities that will be discussed in this section are as follows: (A) School Play Areas, (B) Outdoor Swimming Pools, and (C) Camps.

A. School Play Areas

Many things must be taken into consideration when planning outdoor facilities for schools. The location, topography, soil drainage, water supply, size, shape, and natural features are a few important considerations before a site is selected. The outdoor facilities should be as near the gymnasium and locker rooms as possible and yet far enough from the classrooms so that the noise will not be a disturbing factor. In planning, it is best to avoid having streets or thoroughfares between the play areas and the school buildings proper. At the same time there should be parking facilities nearby to accommodate community use of the play areas.

The play areas should serve the needs and interests of the students for the entire school year and at the same time should provide a setting for activities during vacation periods. The needs and interests of the citizens of the community must also be taken into consideration, since the school play areas can be used for part of the community recreation program. This is especially important in some communities, where such facilities can be planned as education and recreation centers. Since the community uses the areas after the school day is over, the plan is feasible.

Outdoor gymnasium. University of Tampa, Florida.

The size of the playground area should be determined on the basis of activities offered in the program and the number of individuals who will be using the facilities at peak load. Possibilities for expansion should also be kept in mind.

There has been considerable discussion as to what constitutes proper surfacing under apparatus in school play areas. Although it is generally agreed that asphalt is appropriate for the general area, it has proved unsatisfactory under apparatus.

Lawrence E. Houston, Director of Physical Education for the Los Angeles City Schools directed an experimental program recently to determine the best type of surfacing. Out of forty different types and kinds that were offered by industry, nineteen were selected to be tried. Houston explains it in this way:

> It is interesting to note the evolution in materials tested. Their original installations were of existing materials such as sheet rubber and cork which, without experience or knowledge, were adapted to this new use. Uniformly they have proved unsatisfactory both as to durability and shock absorption and have been removed. Problems of cementing sections together, loosening and buckling caused by rain, weathering caused by sunlight, and abrasive deterioration of the surface have not been solved. Some substances absorbed very little shock, while others, although shock absorbing, produced a destructive rebound after impact.
>
> The installation of *Parafall* as a material for surfacing offered the most promise in satisfying the requirements of shock absorption, durability, and low upkeep. It is expensive, approximately $1.50 per square foot. But this high initial cost seems likely to be offset by its apparent long life.
>
> *Parafall* cushions a fall better than any other material tested, with no rebound; there are minimum signs of wear, weathering, and deterioration since its installation. Their experience seems to indicate that maintenance problems could be solved with a spray gun.[4]

Playground and recreation areas will be discussed under three headings, elementary, junior high, and senior high school.

1. Elementary School

The activities program in the elementary school suggests what facilities should be available. Children of the primary grades engage in big muscle activity involving adaptations of climbing, jumping, skipping, kicking, throwing, leaping, and catching. The children in the intermediate and upper elementary grades utilize not only these activities, but also such other ones as games of low organization, team games, and fundamental skills used in playing these games.

The playground area for an elementary school should be located near the building and should be easily accessible to the elementary classrooms. Although the amount of land will vary with the location of the school, it is recommended that the elementary school be on at least a ten-acre plot. The physical education and recreation areas would consist of the land not utilized for the buildings.

The kindergarten children should have a section of the playground for their exclusive use. This should be at least 5000 square feet in size and separated from the rest of the playground. It should consist of a surfaced area, a grass area, and a place for sand and digging. The sand area should be enclosed to prevent the sand from being scattered. It is also wise to have a shaded area where storytelling and similar activities may be conducted. Some essential equipment would include swings, slides, seesaws, climbing structures, tables, and seats.

The children above kindergarten in the elementary school should have play space which includes turf, apparatus, shaded, multiple-use paved, and recreation areas.

---

[4]Letter from Lawrence E. Houston, Director of Physical Education, Los Angeles Public Schools, to Board of Education, dated September 3, 1952.

The turf area provides space for many field and team games. Provisions for speed ball, soccer, field hockey, softball and field ball could be included.

The apparatus area should provide such equipment as climbing bars in the form of a Jungle Jim, horizontal bars, and Giant Strides. There should be ample space to provide for the safety of the participants.

The shaded area may provide space for such activities as marbles, hopscotch, or ring toss, and also storytelling.

The multiple-use paved area may be used for a variety of purposes and activities on a year-round basis by both school and community. It can house basketball, tennis, and handball courts, games of low organization, and other activities. This area should be paved with material that takes into consideration resiliency, safety, and durability. Rapid and efficient drainage is essential. Lines may be painted on the area for the various types of games. Schools should allow additional space adjacent to this area for possible future expansion.

Other recreation areas which have important implications for the community are a landscaped, park-like area, a place for quiet activities such as dramatics and informal gatherings, a wading pool, a place for older adults to congregate, and a place for children to have gardening opportunities.

2. The Junior High School

The junior high school play and recreation area, planned and developed for the children who attend the school and also for the adults in the community, should be located on a larger site than that for the elementary school. Some suggestions have been made that it consist of from ten to twenty-five or more acres. Local conditions will play a part in deciding the amount of area available.

Many of the facilities of the elementary school will be a part of the junior high school. In many cases, however, the various areas should be increased in size. There should be a place for small children, apparatus, quiet games, and wading pool as in the elementary schools. The multiple-use paved area and turf area for games should be increased in size.

The program for junior high school girls will stress a broad base in fundamentals for participation in such activities as archery, volleyball, tennis, and hockey.

The boys' program will include soccer, touch football, baseball, speed ball, softball, and golf. A track should also be included. Therefore, the necessary facilities should be provided for such activities, which will be part of the regular physical education class as well as the intramural program.

A landscaped park-like area should be provided for the various recreational activities that people in the community will like to engage in such as walking, picnicking, skating, and fly casting.

3. Senior High School

The senior high school physical education program is characterized to a more pronounced degree by a team game program in various activities. This emphasis, together with the fact that facilities are needed for the recreational use of the community, requires an even larger area than for the two previous educational levels. Estimates range from ten to forty acres for such a site.

Most of the areas that have been listed under the elementary and junior high schools should again be included at the senior high school. This means there would be facilities for young children such as apparatus, pool, and a place for quiet activities. Where there was an increase in size of many areas at the junior high over the elementary level, there should again be an increase in size at the high school level over the junior high.

There should be considerably more space for the various field games so that not only can physical education class instruction take place, but at the same time full-sized official fields will be available for such activities as softball, field hockey, soccer, speed ball, lacrosse, football, and baseball. This would be on an intramural as well as an interscholastic basis. Also, the community recreation program could make use of these facilities.

Football and track can be provided for in an area of approximately four acres, with the football field being placed within the track oval. A baseball field is questionable in such an area, because track and baseball are both spring sports. Baseball needs an area of about 350 feet by 350 feet. This allows for a minimum of 50 feet from home plate to the backstop and also allows for adequate space outside the first and third base lines.

B. Outdoor Swimming Pools

The outdoor swimming pool is a popular and important facility in many communities. To a great degree climatic conditions will determine the advisability of such a facility.

Outdoor pools are built in various shapes including oval, circular, T-shaped, and rectangular. Rectangular pools are most popular because of easier construction and because they lend themselves better to competitive swimming events.

The size of pools varies depending upon the number of persons they are to serve. One recommendation has been made that 12 square feet of water space per swimmer be allotted for swimming purposes. Or, if the deck is taken into consideration, 20 square feet of space for swimming and walking area per swimmer.

The deck for the outdoor pool should be larger than that for indoor pools. This larger space will serve to accommodate more people and also provide space for sun-bathing.

Shower facilities should be provided to insure that every swimmer takes a soapy shower in the nude before entering the water. A basket system for storing clothes has been found practical instead of the locker type of system that is used inside. In cases where the pool is located adjacent to the school it sometimes is practical to use the locker and shower facilities of the school. However, it is strongly advised that wherever possible separate shower and basket facilities be provided. Toilets should also be provided for the convenience of the swimmers.

Since swimming is popular at night as well as in the daytime, lights should be provided in order that a greater percentage of the population may participate in this healthful and enjoyable activity.

Diving boards generally are of wood or metal, but in recent years glass and plastic ones have proved popular. The standard heights of boards are one and three meters. The one-meter board should be over water nine to ten feet in depth and the three-meter board over water ten to twelve feet in depth. The board or any diving take-off area should have a nonskid covering. The boards should be securely fastened to the ground or foundation.

The rules and regulations concerning diving equipment should be clearly posted near the diving areas. Roping off and patrolling the area is a good safety precaution.

C. Camps*

Since camping is becoming an increasingly popular activity in both school and recreational programs, it should receive consideration.

Camps should be located within easy reach of the school and community. It should be a desirable location from the standpoint of scenic beauty, safety, accessibility, water and natural resources which are pertinent to the program that is offered. Activities usually offered include fishing, hiking, swimming, campcraft, boating, nature study and appropriate winter sports. The natural terrain and other resources can contribute much toward such a program.

There should be adequate housing, eating, sanitary, waterfront, and other facilities essential to camp life. These do not have to be as elaborate as those in the home or school, but instead can be very simple. Adequate facilities for protection against the elements are essential, however. Facilities should also meet acceptable standards of health and sanitation. In general, camp structures should be adapted to the climatic conditions of the particular area in which the camp is located. It is wise to consult public health authorities when selecting a camp site. Sometimes existing facilities can be converted to camp use. The camp site should be purchased outright or a long-term lease acquired.

QUESTIONS AND EXERCISES

1. Prepare a sketch of what you consider to be an ideal physical education plant. In your plans consider both outdoor and indoor facilities.
2. Plan a health suite which you consider to be ideal.
3. What are ten basic considerations in planning facilities?
4. Discuss the following statement: "The trend in schoolhouse construction is away from the so-called "frills."
5. Develop a list of standards for facilities in the following areas: (a) lighting, (b) heating and ventilation, (c) school plant sanitation, (d) furniture, (e) outdoor play areas, (f) locker, shower and drying rooms.
6. What are some of the essential factors to keep in mind when planning the gymnasium?
7. What should be provided in the school in the way of special activity areas?
8. What are some of the essential factors to keep in mind when planning the swimming pool?
9. What considerations should be made in school facilities for recreation?
10. Draw up a list of references for obtaining authoritative information on various aspects of facility construction and maintenance.

*See Chapter XX.

SELECTED REFERENCES

American Association of School Administrators. *American School Buildings,* Twenty-Seventh Yearbook. Washington: National Education Association, 1949.

American Association of School Administrators. *Health in Schools,* Twentieth Yearbook. Washington: National Education Association, 1951, Chapter V.

Butler, George D. *Introduction to Community Recreation.* New York: McGraw-Hill Book Company, Inc., 1949, Part III.

Butler, George D. *Standards for Municipal Recreation Areas.* New York: National Recreation Association, 1948.

Cincinnati Public Schools. *Manual for Architects.* Second Edition. Cincinnati: Board of Education, 1947.

Clarke, James Mitchell. *Public School Camping.* Stanford, California: Stanford University Press, 1951.

College Physical Education Association. *College Facilities for Physical Education, Health Education and Recreation.* College Physical Education Association, 1947.

Dimock, Hedley S. (Editor). *Administration of the Modern Camp.* New York: Association Press, 1950.

Essex, Don L. "School Plant and Equipment," *Review of Educational Research,* 18: 1-72, February, 1948.

"Facilities Survey Discloses One-fifth of Pupils in Unsafe Schools," *The Journal of School Health,* XXII; 253, November, 1952.

First Progress Report. *School Facilities Survey.* Washington, D. C.: School Housing Section, Office of Education, 1951-1952.

Florida State Department of Education. *School Plant Operation and Maintenance in Southern States.* Tallahassee: the Department, 1940.

Forsythe, Charles E., and Duncan, Ray O. *Administration of Physical Education.* New York: Prentice-Hall, Inc., 1951, Chapter 5.

Illuminating Engineering Society. *American Standard Practice for School Lighting.* New York: the Society, 1948.

Linn, Henry H., and others. *The School Custodian's Housekeeping Handbook.* New York: Bureau of Publications, Teachers College, Columbia University, 1948.

McCleary, Ralph D. *How to Choose a School Site.* Cambridge, Massachusetts: New England Development Council (13 Kirkland Street), 1947.

Meyer, Harold D., and Brightbill, Charles K. *Community Recreation.* Boston: D. C. Heath and Company, 1948, Section VIII.

Nash, Jay B., Moench, Francis J., and Saurborn, Jeannette B. *Physical Education: Organization and Administration.* New York: A. S. Barnes and Company, 1951, Chapters XI, XV.

National Council on Schoolhouse Construction, Plant Guide Committee. *Guide for Planning School Plants.* 1949 Edition. Nashville: The Council (secy.: W. D. McClurkin, George Peabody College for Teachers), 1949.

National Facilities Conference. *A Guide for Planning Facilities for Athletics, Recreation, Physical and Health Education.* Chicago: The Athletic Institute, Inc., 209 State Street, 1947.

Perkins, Lawrence B., and Cocking, Walter D. *Schools.* New York: Reinhold Publishing Corporation, 1949.

Report of the Status Phase. *School Facilities Survey.* Washington, D. C.: School Housing Section, Office of Education, 1953.

Second Progress Report. *School Facilities Survey.* Washington, D. C.: School Housing Section, Office of Education, 1952.

The State Education Department, The University of the State of New York. *Planning the Outdoor Physical Education Facilities for Central Schools.* Albany: New York State Education Department, 1947.

Voltmer, Edward F., and Esslinger, Arthur A. *The Organization and Administration of Physical Education.* New York: Appleton-Century-Crofts, Inc., 1949, Chapter VIII.

Wiley, Will E., and Wiley, John H. "New Developments in Elementary School Seating" *American School and University,* 1947-48. New York: American School Publishing Corporation (470 Fourth Avenue), 1947, pp. 184-187.

Williams, Jesse Feiring, and Brownell, Clifford Lee. *The Administration of Health Education and Physical Education.* Philadelphia: W. B. Saunders Company, 1951, Part III.

Chapter XIII

ADMINISTRATIVE PRACTICES FOR A
HEALTHFUL ENVIRONMENT

The World Health Organization defines health as follows: "Health is a state of complete physical, mental, and social well-being, and not merely the absence of disease or infirmity." In order to have a mentally healthful and educational environment, therefore, one should not be concerned merely with providing the proper physical facilities. It is necessary also to take into consideration the administrative practices that play such an important part in providing for the total health of the child. It has been estimated that one of every ten school children is emotionally disturbed. This fact shows the necessity for coming to grips with this problem in every way possible. Health and physical educators should be especially concerned with mental and emotional health because of their close relationship with physical health and illness. During the last ten years psychosomatics in education has increasingly been given more attention.

Mental health implies a state of mind which allows the individual to adjust in a satisfactory manner to whatever life has to offer. Good mental health cannot be thought of as a subject that is included in the school curriculum. Instead, it must permeate the total life of the educational institution. It means that programs are flexible and geared to individual needs, a permissive climate prevails, children are allowed considerable freedom, and students become self-reliant and responsible for their own actions. It means that the child is recognized and has a satisfying educational experience. The National Association for Mental Health points out that the well-adjusted person is the one who has the right attitudes and feelings toward himself, other people, and the demands that life places upon him. George Preston[1] has listed the qualities of mental health and says it consists of being able to live: (1) within the limits imposed by bodily equipment, (2) with other human beings, (3) happily, (4) productively, and (5) without being a nuisance.

School programs offer a wonderful laboratory for developing good human relations, democratic methods, responsibility, self-reliance, and other essentials to happy and purposeful living. The degree to which this laboratory is utilized for such purposes depends upon administrative officers, teachers, custodians, and other staff members. Such important considerations as the administrative policies established, teachers' personalities, program, human relations, and professional help that is given, will determine to what extent educational programs justify their existence in human betterment. Some of the important implications for a healthful and educational environment are discussed in more detail.

[1] G. H. Preston. *The Substance of Mental Health.* New York: Rinehart and Company, 1943, p. 112.

I. ADMINISTRATIVE PRACTICES

A few of the administrative practices that have a bearing upon the mental and emotional health of the students and participants are: organization of the school day, student achievement, play and recreation, homework, attendance, personnel policies, administrative emphasis, and discipline.

A. Organization of the School Day

The organization of the school day will have a bearing upon whether a healthful environment is provided for the child. The length of the school day must be in conformance with the age of the child. Classes should be scheduled in a manner that does not result in excessive fatigue. Subjects that require considerable concentration should be scheduled when the individual is more mentally efficient. Usually this is during the early part of the day. Boredom and tension will arise from scheduling similar classes close together, without any breaks. The program should be flexible to allow for variety, new developments, and the satisfying of children's interests. Adequate periods of rest and play should be provided, not only as a change from the more arduous routine of close concentration, but also as a necessity for utilizing the big muscles of the body. "Big-muscle" activity is essential during the growing years. The length of classes should be adequate for instructional purposes but not so excessively long that the law of diminishing returns sets in.

B. Student Achievement

Success is an experience that is essential to the development of self-confidence and an integrated person. One who experiences success will be better stimulated to do good work than one who consistently fails. The child who consistently fails is likely to have behavior disorders. In view of this, it is important that educational programs recognize their responsibility for developing each individual. Experiences should be provided which are adapted to the individual and are planned so that each person will have a series of successful experiences.

1. Individual Differences

It is important to recognize that individuals differ. They differ in respect to intellect, physique, skill, personality, and in many other ways. In a fifth-grade class, for example, although the average chronological age may be eleven years, the mental age could range from six to sixteen years. Similar differences abound in other characteristics.

It is very important for administrators, teachers, and leaders to recognize that these differences do exist and that programs must be planned accordingly. The same goals cannot be established for all. If goals are standardized, some individuals will become frustrated because it is impossible for them to achieve the standards, and others will become very bored, because there is no challenge. Goals should be established which are within the reach of everyone. Administrators and teachers sometimes become so engrossed in the idea of setting high standards that they forget to consider the individual.

2. Grades

Excessive emphasis should not be placed on marks. Too often the individual is interested more in the mark received than in the knowledge, attitudes, and self-improvement that are inherent in the activity. It seems that if marks must be given, as broad a category as possible should be used. These could be stated in such terms as "passed" or "did not pass" or "satisfactory" or "unsatisfactory." Whenever possible, descriptive statements of the student's progress should be given without any marks whatsoever. Parent-teacher conferences are probably the best way to evaluate a student's progress in the most effective manner. These procedures are being followed in some elementary schools with excellent results.

Marks, although supposedly an index of quality of work done, are poor guides for such purposes. Many tests that are given as a basis for marks do not measure what they are supposed to measure and have been found to be unreliable when rated by various persons. Furthermore, the human element always enters the picture.

Marks stimulate competition which is unhealthy in many of its aspects. Too often the underlying reason for such competition is to prove superiority over someone rather than to prove a mastery in a particular subject-matter field or skill. Under such circumstances harm frequently results to the mental health and personalities of students.

3. Tests and Examinations

It is generally agreed that some method is needed to check on the progress that has been made in the acquisition of knowledges, skills, or attitudes. Harmful effects of such tests and examinations result when they are used by teachers and leaders to instill fear in the individual. Frequently, individuals harm themselves physically, mentally, and emotionally when they become worked up over an approaching examination. They stay up all night cramming, can't sleep, are tense, and generally find it a very trying experience. Students should understand that examinations are a means by which greater help can be given to them. Such help is not possible unless information is gained as to what the person knows at certain points along the way.

4. Intelligence Ratings

Intelligence ratings can be of some value in the hands of a trained person. It is important to recognize, however, that such measuring devices are not definite, exact, and accurate in indicating the mental capacity of an individual. Furthermore, intelligence is only one factor which makes for success of an individual. In fact, it has been shown through Terman's study of gifted children, where all received high intelligence ratings, that intelligence does not necessarily insure the achievement of prominent position in life.

Furthermore, intelligence ratings are often in error. One test should never be used as the criterion. Instead, several tests should be given before definite conclusions are drawn. Even then, the work of Allison Davis and others at the University of Chicago has shown that intelligence tests, to a greater extent, measure a person's environment and the cultural experiences open to him, than his native intelligence.

C. Play and Recreation

The impression that achievement in so-called academic subjects is the only criterion necessary to insure successful living is erroneous. In addition, there should be achievement in the areas of human relations, personality development, physical development, acquisition of skills for leisure hours, and other areas even more vital to the success of the individual than so-called scholastic achievement.

Dr. William Menninger and other experts in the field of psychiatry point to the contributions of play and recreation to mental health. Furthermore, to achieve success in the competitive society of today, a person needs a sound body which possesses stamina and endurance and will support long hours of work. Also, the skills in physical activities, music, industrial arts, and allied areas that are learned during the early years of an individual's life will determine to a great degree his hobbies or leisure-time pursuits during adult years. For these and other reasons, it is important that physical education and other subjects falling into this category be recognized for the contribution they can make to the total growth of the individual. There are many persons in mental institutions today who were capable of working out the most difficult problems in calculus and were expert in their knowledge of geography and other subjects. Many of these individuals might have been spared their illness if they had recognized the importance of developing other skills which would have afforded a more balanced life.

D. Homework

Educators are increasingly recognizing that homework should be assigned only when it is in the best interest of the whole child. If it is given for the purpose of busy-work, to keep someone occupied during hours after dinner at night, or solely for enabling a person to surpass his classmates, it cannot be justified. Children as well as adults need time for play and recreation. They are entitled to time after school for such purposes. For young children in elementary school there should rarely be any homework because young bodies need great amounts of physical activity. Ample exercise is necessary for body organs and muscles that are developing and gaining strength for future years. In junior high school, the homework assigned should be very limited in nature. In high school it should not be given in such large amounts that it requires late hours of work. Instead, it should promote achievement and allow the student opportunity for independent work, and help to promote the development of the whole individual.

E. Attendance

In many states financial aid is based upon school attendance. In some cases this has resulted in harmful effects to the health of children. Administrators have been known to stress attendance to the point where students come to school with colds and other illnesses, when they should be home in bed. This not only endangers their own health, but at the same time it exposes many innocent children to harmful germs.

It is important to have regular attendance at school. However, if the student is ill and in need of rest or parental and medical care, it is much better that he stay home. In order not to abuse this privilege, administrators, teachers, and others should try to educate the parents as to what constitutes good reasons for absences from school.

Furthermore, if the student is well enough to attend school, then it would seem that he should attend all classes. Too often a student is dismissed from a physical education class because of some minor disorder. If the program is adapted to the needs of the individual, special consideration can be given to such cases. It is just as important that regular attendance prevail in physical education as in social studies, mathematics, or any other subject.

F. Personnel Policies

The administration's personnel policies in regard to teachers and other staff members will determine in some measure whether or not a healthful environment is created. A teacher who is required to punch a clock when she comes to work in the morning and leaves at night, is never greeted with a smile, never experiences an enjoyable conversation with the principal, is held responsible for many unnecessary details, is required to be at work regardless of how she feels, receives no administrative support when subject to community prejudices, and finds that the administrative policies that are established do not give her happiness, security, and confidence in doing her job cannot help but reflect such policies in her dealings with students and colleagues.

Administrators should try to establish the best possible working conditions for all members of a staff. Only if they feel happy and well adjusted in their jobs will a healthful environment exist.

G. Administrative Emphasis

The administrative emphasis should be on the children and those experiences which will help them to grow and develop into healthy and educated human beings. It should not be on subject-matter material, with rigid and inflexible programs designed to pump as much factual knowledge as possible into the heads of students. Administrative policies should be established which reflect human beings as the center of the program, allow for flexibility, encourage initiative on the part of the teacher, are adapted to the needs and interests of the participants, and provide in every way for a healthful physical and nonphysical environment.

H. Discipline

The school should be a place where individuals receive joy and satisfaction from their experiences. A spirit of cooperation should exist among the administration, staff, and members of the organization. The emphasis in student discipline should be on self-government. As much freedom as possible should be given. The individual who is surrounded on all sides by restrictions and is not trusted will rebel. As many educators have discovered, abrupt use of authority invites resistance. There should be a permissive attitude toward individual variations from acceptable behavior, coupled with a firm but kind insistence upon higher standards of conduct. Responsibility should go along with freedom. A climate of opinion should be established which allows as much freedom as possible without encroaching on the rights of others. A strong student government can be one of the best educational devices for self-discipline.

The school should be a place where individuals receive joy and satisfaction from their experiences. Washington Irving Elementary School, Waverly, Iowa. (Picture furnished by Burnett and Logan, Chicago.)

Regulations should not be accepted just because they are regulations. Rather, they should be accepted because they are essential to securing the rights of everyone so that all can enjoy and benefit from the programs that are offered.

If antisocial behavior develops, it is important to look into the reasons for such behavior and work to eliminate the causes, rather than to abruptly and harshly discipline some person. Unless this is done, such antisocial behavior will continue to show itself. Furthermore, in time it may become so obstreperous as to require isolation of the individual from society. If a constructive approach is taken, such measures may be avoided.

II. THE TEACHER

Good mental health in a school program is tied up very closely with the teacher. The manner in which the teacher and student interact with one another is very important. It is important for the teacher to think of youngsters as living, feeling, and developing human beings, who pursue different and varied courses on their ways to maturity. They are not inanimate objects or receptacles into which the instructor pours knowledge.

One of the main responsibilities of any teacher in health or physical education should be student counseling. Quite frequently specialists in these areas are the ones to whom the child goes in search of information. Anyone who is to perform such an important job as counseling should be well adjusted, understand himself, and get along well with others.

The teacher must be in good physical condition in order to do a good job. A teacher may come to a job in excellent physical condition, but if large classes are assigned, the salary is insufficient, and outside work is necessary, physical harm may result. Furthermore, if there is no provision for sick leave and as a result the teacher must be on the job even when sick or ill, her physical condition will suffer. When this happens, the students also suffer.

The teacher's personality has important implications for the mental and emotional health of those with whom he or she comes in contact. The teacher who is happy, wears a smile, is kind, considerate, and likes people in general will impart these qualities to the students. It is bound to "rub off" in the daily interaction that takes place. Conversely, the teacher or leader who is sarcastic, depressed, prejudiced, and intolerant will also impart these qualities to the children with whom he or she associates. The leader's personality is also reflected in the appearance of the classroom and the teaching methods employed.

Administrators should be cognizant of the factors that result in maladjusted personalities for members of their staffs. A few years ago the National Educational Association found that many faculty members were plagued by personal and working conditions which influenced their mental outlooks. Some of these were as follows: financial difficulties, economic problems, serious illness of relatives or friends, unsatisfactory progress of pupils, matters of personal health, being unmarried and without normal family relationships, disciplinary problems, an official rating by a superior, possible loss of position, work of a college course, being unhappily married, and religious problems. Many of these frustrating factors could have been eliminated.

All teachers should have satisfactory working conditions. They should receive an adequate salary to eliminate financial worries, be encouraged to develop out-of-school interests in the community, have hobbies in which they can engage after school hours and during vacation periods, and have adequate provisions for sick and sabbatical leaves and leaves of absence so that proper rest and adequate educational standards may be assured. Furthermore, there should be ample opportunities provided for affiliation with professional groups and the development of cultural and other interests conducive to better leadership qualifications. By providing for such essentials, teachers and leaders will be happier and have better mental and emotional health. In turn, this will be reflected in the total health of the children with whom they come in contact.

III. IMPLICATIONS OF THE PHYSICAL ENVIRONMENT

The physical environment has important educational implications for students and others. Appreciations of the esthetic values, of the beautiful and the ugly, of the attractive and the unattractive, of the clean and the unclean, of what is pleasing and what is displeasing are feelings developed through association with various aspects of the physical environment.

The administrator who sets up policies, the custodial staff that is in charge of maintenance, and the teacher who is responsible for the classroom or area play an important part in developing the right attitudes in the minds of those individuals whom they teach. Many children have become so enthusiastic and well-informed in school as to what constitutes an attractive place to live that they have carried the ideas into the home. Others have developed such an appreciation of beauty and the importance of cleanliness and sanitary procedures, they have injected this into the community, to the benefit of thousands of the inhabitants.

It has been said that one feels more radiant, happy, and cheerful when the sun is shining and the day is beautiful. This is also true when one is in attractive, clean, and healthful surroundings. Educational programs which provide for attractive and beautiful surroundings play an important part in developing attitudes which promote cleanliness, sanitary conditions, well-kept grounds, and respect for property.

A scientific study was recently conducted and reported in the press[2] which bears out the statement that even the behavior of students is better in an attractive environment. This study showed that bright colors and pleasing classroom designs have a very definite effect on the way children behave in school as well as on the marks they get. The study was conducted by a team of psychologists at Johns Hopkins University. The findings of the study which it took two years to conduct in three Baltimore elementary schools, with the cooperation of school officials and the Pittsburgh Plate Glass Company, were very interesting. These findings showed that color has great beneficial effects on behavior and scholastic performance. This was most noticeable among kindergarten children and more so among boys than among girls.

The study was conducted by selecting three schools in Baltimore that needed painting. Complete scholastic and attitude records were kept on the children before and after two of the schools were painted. Twenty thousand report cards representing 2,500 different pupils were tabulated. One of the schools was painted according to principles of proper coloring, another received a conventional paint treatment and the third was not painted, but was used as a scientific control.

The school that was painted according to the proper principles of color dynamics had corridor walls in yellow with doors and mopboards of palace gray. The rooms facing north were painted a pastel rose and the rooms facing south were

[2]*New York Times,* June 7, 1953.

painted in blues and greens.   Art classrooms were painted a neutral, light gray. The front walls in each room were painted a darker shade of the color used in that room.   Chalkboards were green.

The findings showed that in respect to the work, play, and language performance of kindergarten children, there was a 34 per cent improvement from the first to the second year in the school that had been painted scientifically.   However, there was only a 7 per cent improvement in the school painted with conventional color and 3 per cent in the unpainted school.

Performance traits studied in grades three through six included work habits, social habits, health and safety habits, language arts, arithmetic, social studies, science, art, and music.   In this group the scientifically painted school showed a 9 per cent improvement, the conventionally painted school a ½ per cent improvement, and the unpainted school a 3 per cent loss.

In a survey of children and faculty, both were enthusiastic about the colorful classrooms.   Fifty-eight per cent of the children stated that the "nice colors" had resulted in a difference in their attitude toward school.   One child had this to say, "My grades are much better.   The bright rooms make me feel happier and so I can do my work better."

The psychologists who worked on the study and who were impressed with the clearness of the results were Dr. Wendell R. Garner, Director, Dr. James Bond, Dr. Randolph Haynes, and Joseph Franklin.

IV. HUMAN RELATIONSHIPS

Human relationships are a most important consideration if one is to grow into a happy, successful, and well-adjusted individual.   Of all the traits that should be developed in health and physical education, human relationships rank toward the top of the list.   Through counseling, participation in group games and activities under good leadership, and other phases of the programs, the potentialities are great for developing good human relationships.

Each individual should be made to feel he belongs to the group and has something to contribute in its behalf.   There must never be an attempt to make a member of the group feel insignificant and unimportant.   More praise should be dispensed than criticism.   Every attempt should be made to help each person maintain his self-respect.   The atmosphere that pervades the classroom, gymnasium, or recreation center should be relaxed and friendly.   The emotional needs of every individual should be taken into consideration in the class or group activities that are held.

The teacher should have good relationships with his or her colleagues.   Any faculty or staff that is infested with cliques, jealousies and strife, communicates these attitudes to the students.   This is just as true here as in the case of quarreling parents who communicate their feelings to their children.   If one is to help others develop good human relationships, one must set an example which is worthy of emulation.

There must be good human relationships among the children themselves. They are dependent upon the feeling of the group toward them and whether or not they are accepted. It is important to have status among one's associates. The teacher can play an important part in helping to see that everyone gains recognition. This is especially important with such individuals as the dull child in the classroom, the awkward, uncoordinated youngster on the playfield, and the intellectually gifted student in a recreation setting.

The teacher should be careful not to accentuate any characteristic which makes a child markedly different from the rest of the group. This applies to the whole realm of deviations including scholastic, physical, mental, social, and economic.

Each individual should be made to feel that she belongs to the group and has something to contribute in its behalf. Alabama College, Montevallo, Alabama.

V. SCHOOL-COMMUNITY RELATIONSHIPS

The school is part of the community, and what goes on in such places as the home, church, social agency, or other places where individuals congregate will determine the total health of the child, just as much as what happens in the classroom. The school cannot do the job alone. Students attend school only five days a week and about 180 days a year. The rest of the time they are exposed to the influences of the larger community. What they encounter there will help to determine the degree to which they are emotionally and mentally well adjusted.

The parents play the most important role in the school-community relationship. Parents should be interested in their schools, participate actively in their parent-teacher associations, and know the aims and goals of the school. The parents, in the final analysis, determine what kind of job the school performs. If the schools are weak and not providing the experiences which make for well adjusted, secure, emotionally stable, and mentally alert children, the parents have only themselves to blame.

There are also many agencies and groups within the community which can work with the schools in having a favorable influence on the mental and emotional stability of youthful residents. Such organizations as youth clubs, churches, and recreational agencies play an important part. They can provide experiences which promote good social and mental development. The church, for example, can contribute in helping to satisfy the needs of individuals for emotional security. A person who has faith in a Supreme Being is secure in his thoughts in respect to the future and to his place in life. The community recreation program can provide settings where children and others find enjoyment and develop physical and social skills.

The school should work very closely with the community in the development of a better environment in which to live. Persons in health education have a major contribution to make in uniting their efforts with the health forces in the community. Specialists in physical education can contribute facilities, personnel, and leadership in developing a recreational program in the community which is closely coordinated with what is being done in school. Leaders in recreation have an important responsibility in developing a program which takes into consideration the school and other agency offerings. By sound planning, they can meet the needs and interests of the entire population.

VI. PROFESSIONAL SERVICES

The factors discussed thus far in respect to the nonphysical environment have been largely preventive in nature. They have attempted to show the importance of providing an environment where the individual has freedom, self-respect, and security and experiences satisfaction in his activities. However, despite emphasis upon preventive measures, there will always be some individuals who become behavior problems and will need professional help.

The teacher can play an important part by identifying those individuals who need help. She can also render guidance and such other aid as is possible in the school situation. The teacher can often do a great deal of good by studying the child thoroughly in respect to his school, home, and community environment. Through such study and by working closely with parents, many minor maladjustments can be eliminated. If further help is needed, she should refer the child to the proper professional persons.

In some schools there are counselors who have had preparation which goes beyond that of the ordinary teacher or leader. Their special knowledge of guidance and mental hygiene should be utilized in dealing with problem cases.

With the increasing emphasis being placed upon mental hygiene, many schools are utilizing the services of social workers, psychologists, and psychiatrists. The more serious cases should be referred to such professional people. They are trained in dealing with such problems and can render a great deal of personal help as well as promote a more healthful environment.

Recently, there has been a marked growth of child guidance clinics across the country. These are sponsored by various organizations interested in securing professional guidance for individuals with behavior problems. These clinics guide parents and community groups in good mental hygiene practices and needs, aid children who have various mental maladjustments, and seek support and understanding within the community to help promote better mental hygiene. They have trained people on their staffs who are competent to assist in preventing and solving problems which involve psychology.

QUESTIONS AND EXERCISES

1. Define what is meant by the "physical" and "nonphysical" environments. What are the implications of each for total health?

2. Prepare a research report on administrative practices for a healthful and educational environment as they relate to a school with which you are very familiar.

3. Prepare a list of administrative practices in health, physical education, or recreation which are nationally in evidence and should be eliminated in order to provide greater total health.

4. What part does each of the following play in mental health of school children: (a) organization of the school day, (b) achievement, (c) marks, (d) play and recreation, (e) homework, (f) attendance, and (g) discipline?

5. How does the mental and emotional health of a teacher affect the mental and emotional health of school children?

6. Consult case studies in some social agency and report on the teacher's role in these cases.

7. To what degree are the physical features of a school related to mental and emotional health?

8. Why is it so important to have good human relationships within the school?

9. How can the school and community coordinate their efforts to further better physical, mental, emotional, and social health for all residents?

10. What is the role of professional services in the school program?

SELECTED REFERENCES

American Association for Health, Physical Education, and Recreation. *Administrative Problems in Health Education, Physical Education, and Recreation.* Washington, D. C.: The Association, 1953, Chapters, 2, 4, 5, 6, 7.

American Association of School Administrators. *American School Buildings. Twenty-Seventh Yearbook.* Washington, D. C.: the Association, 1949.

American Association of School Administrators. *Health in Schools. Twentieth Yearbook.* Washington, D. C.: National Education Association, 1951, Chapter VI.

American Educational Research Association, "Growth and Development," *Review of Educational Research,* 20: 341-440, December, 1950.

Association for Supervision and Curriculum Development. *Fostering Mental Health in Our Schools. 1950 Yearbook.* Washington, D. C.: the Association, a department of the National Education Association, 1950.

Brownell, Clifford Lee. *Principles of Health Education Applied.* New York: McGraw-Hill Book Company, Inc., 1949, Chapters 5, 8.

Carroll, Herbert A. *Mental Hygiene.* New York: Prentice-Hall, Inc., 1951.

Fenton, Norman. *Mental Hygiene in School Practice.* Stanford University: Stanford University Press, 1943.

Grout, Ruth E. *Health Teaching in Schools.* Philadelphia: W. B. Saunders Company, 1953, Chapter 4.

Jacobs, Louis, "Mental Health in the School Health Program." *The Journal of School Health,* XXII: 288, December, 1952.

Jenkins, Gladys G., Shacter, Helen, and Bauer, William W. *These Are Your Children: How They Develop and How to Guide Them.* Chicago: Scott Foresman and Company, 1949.

Joint Committee on Health Problems in Education of the National Education Association and American Medical Association. *Health Education.* Charles C. Wilson, Editor. Washington, D. C.: National Education Association, 1948.

Joint Committee on Health Problems in Education of the National Education Association and American Medical Association. *Mental Hygiene in the Classroom.* Washington, D. C.: National Education Association, 1949.

Joint Committee on Health Problems in Education of the National Education Association and American Medical Association. *School Health Services.* Charles C. Wilson, Editor. Washington, D. C.: National Education Association, 1953.

Oberteuffer, Delbert. *School Health Education.* New York: Harper & Brothers, 1954, Chapter 12.

Office of Education, Federal Security Agency. *Life Adjustment Education for Every Youth.* Washington: United States Government Printing Office, 1951.

Olson, Willard C. *Child Development.* Boston: D. C. Heath and Company, 1949.

Chapter XIV

THE HEALTH EDUCATION PROGRAM

The school attempts to promote health in children and youth through a specialized program "that contributes to the understanding, maintenance, and improvement of the health of pupils and school personnel, including health services, health education, and healthful school living."[1]

The *healthful school living* phase of the school health program has been considered.* The *health services* phase of the total school program will be considered later.†

The *health education* phase of the total school program refers to "the process of providing learning experiences for the purpose of influencing knowledges, attitudes, and conduct relating to individual and group health."[2] This phase of the school health program will be discussed in this chapter.

I. HEALTH EDUCATION AND THE SCHOOLS

A recognition of the need for health education in the schools has developed through the years, as educators and the lay public have come to realize the importance of providing learning experiences which will result in healthful living for more people. Furthermore, they have come to see more clearly the relationship of knowledges, attitudes, and practices in respect to health.

The importance of health has been taught by educators since early times. Older generations tell about how they received instruction in physiology, learned how to trace the flow of blood through the body, and memorized long definitions of various anatomical and physiological aspects of the human body. This approach to health education, however, has changed over the years. Toward the end of the nineteenth century some new ideas were introduced into school curricula. This resulted from a feeling on the part of certain individuals that the evil effects of alcoholic beverages should be taught. They also felt there should be a greater emphasis on the hygienic aspects of living. As a result, these concepts became an important part of health teaching, especially in colleges. This emphasis continued until the early twentieth century. Then, the impact of World Wars I and II gave health education the impetus it needed to become firmly imbedded as an important part of the school program. The public became aroused, for example, by the

*See Chapters XII-XIII.
†See Chapter XV.
[1]"Report of the Committee on Terminology in School Health Education," *Journal of the American Association for Health, Physical Education and Recreation*, 22: 14, September, 1951.
[2]Report of the Committee on Terminology, *op. cit.*, p. 14.

number of defects discovered in young men through selective service examinations. There has been an increased emphasis on the school health program because of this public concern.   Results of this emphasis have included passing state laws, developing courses of study, publishing many textbooks dealing with health education, and providing for the training of special teachers in this area. Today, there is increased recognition that health education can play a very important role in helping to make individuals aware of their responsibility for not only their own health but also that of others.   Health is rapidly being regarded as "everybody's business."

II. HEALTH EDUCATION AND THE SCHOOL HEALTH PROGRAM

It has been pointed out that this chapter is primarily concerned with health education.   It is interested in those knowledges, attitudes, and practices essential to good health.   The teacher attempts to provide educational experiences and give

The school health program encourages and promotes healthful living.   (Courtesy of Indiana State Department of Health.)

a background of scientific knowledge upon which healthful living is based and thus help to develop favorable understanding and attitudes.   However, it must be recognized that health education is only one phase of the total school health program. School health services and healthful school living are also important.   The success of a school health program is dependent upon the successful functioning and coordination of all three.

Health education can play an important part in motivating children in the development of healthful habits and attitudes. Superstitions and fads can be proved unsound as a result of developing an attitude of appreciation for scientifically accurate knowledge. Such an attitude recognizes the importance of consulting qualified medical persons in regard to health matters, the dangers of self-diagnosis and self-medication, the need to distinguish between fact and fallacy, and the need to obtain health information from authoritative sources.

III. ADMINISTRATION OF HEALTH EDUCATION

The manner in which health education is administered will vary with the local situation. At the outset, however, it should be recognized that health education should be performed by individuals who are trained in the methodology of teaching. An individual who has studied educational psychology and other subjects which yield knowledges and techniques important to effective teaching is better prepared to do a good job of instruction in health, than is the individual who does not have such training. This does not exclude using representatives of the health department and voluntary health agencies as consultants and resource persons. They can be invaluable in drawing up courses of study and in the presentation of various phases of the health education program.

Local administration will again determine where health education should be located within the school structure. In many schools it is placed in such areas as physical education, science, and home economics. In other schools it is a separate area by itself. In the larger schools especially, it seems important to have a separate health education department with full-time personnel who have been trained in the area of health education. Such an administrative arrangement is conducive to good interrelationships between the school and public health agencies, to the development of a school health council, and to a well coordinated and well integrated school health program.

In smaller and medium-sized schools where inadequate budgets make it impossible to have full-time health educators, physical education personnel or others closely related and interested in the area of school health may be charged with this important responsibility. Under such conditions the following qualifications are needed.

(1) Good preparation in health education
(2) Interest in this field
(3) Sufficient time allotted to make instruction functional
(4) Adequate classroom facilities and instructional materials assigned.[3]

The physical education person many times is assigned such responsibilities as coaching, intramurals, and special events, in addition to physical education classes. If the responsibility for health education is given to such a teacher, in addition to these numerous other duties, some responsibility is going to suffer. In many cases, with pressure for winning teams, the class instruction program is neglected. School administrators should recognize that health education is a very important part of

---

[3]Edward B. Johns, "Three Current Administrative Problems in Health Education," *The Journal of School Health*, XX, 3, January, 1950.

the school offering. As such, it should not be placed just anywhere in the school structure and assigned to that person who happens to have a little training in this particular area, or whose interests and teaching load make it feasible. It should be given only to qualified persons and should receive ample time and facilities to make it effective.

Every school, regardless of size, should have someone on its staff assigned to coordinate the various aspects of the school health program. In larger schools this might be a full-time position. In smaller schools it could be the principal, physical education teacher, or some qualified staff member who has interest and responsibility in this area.

The *school health educator,* according to the Committee on Terminology, is "a person specially qualified to serve as a teacher, consultant, coordinator, or supervisor of health education in an individual school or a school system." *Health coordination,* according to this same committee, is "the process of developing relationships within the school health program and between school and community health programs which contribute to harmonious action in the solution of problems relating to pupil health." [4]

A health coordinator can render valuable service in seeing that a well-rounded health program exists. Health instruction can be more carefully planned. In addition to the direct health teaching, there can also be provision for the correlation and integration of health instruction with many subject-matter areas. Resource materials can be provided for classroom and other teachers involved in health teaching. School and community relationships can be developed. The total school health program can be guided to function as an integrated whole. Every school administrator should recognize the importance of the position and designate a person qualified for such a responsibility.

The administration of the health education program should also include a school health council or committee. The *school health council,* according to the committee on terminology, is "a representative group of persons organized for the purposes of study, planning, and action aimed at the identification and solution of school health problems." [5] This group would be composed of respresentatives from the central administration, subject-matter areas, students, parents, professional groups, custodial staff and others whose duties have particular bearing on the health of the school child. Such a group of individuals, regardless of type or size of school, can play an important part in planning and carrying out the health education program. They can be instrumental in providing the necessary funds, materials, staff, and experiences that make for an outstanding program.

IV. CONTENT AREAS OF HEALTH EDUCATION

There is considerable knowledge and information that may be taught in health education. With all the literature that is available in such forms as textbooks, resource books, pamphlets and promotional material, it is important that content be selected with care. At the present time there is little uniformity in the content of health education courses being taught in the schools throughout the country.

[4]Report of the Committee on Terminology in School Health Education, *op. cit.,* p. 14.
[5]*Loc. cit.*

Content areas in health education should be selected on the basis of many pertinent factors. These include the interests and needs of children in any given locality; attitudes, understandings and behavior of any particular group; type of community in which the school is located; resources available; and the philosophy of the school and community. Health knowledge is important and can be justified only as the pupils apply it to their own lives and the lives of individuals around them. Problems that affect them personally must be selected in preference to detailed information on general health.

There is no one course of study or general health format that may be stated as being the best. Although the basic health needs of all individuals are similar in some respects, the application of specific facts and information will be governed by the local situation.

It has been pointed out that content areas in health education should be selected, to a certain degree, on the basis of the needs and interests of the children being served. Therefore, the question arises as to how such interests and needs can be determined. The American Association of School Administrators[6] suggests seven ways in which this vital information may be obtained. First, interests and needs may be determined through an analysis of health records which every school should keep in a cumulative manner and which contain such valuable information as the results of health appraisal and health counseling. Second, the teacher's observation offers some indication of interests, desires, and health problems. Third, tests of knowledge, attitudes, and habits uncover superstitions and other health problems, together with the accuracy of the health knowledge possessed by the student. Fourth, conferences with parents, teachers, and pupils reveal many health interests and needs. Fifth, a student-interest survey will offer an indication of the interests in the field of health, as the students themselves see them. Sixth, a study of current literature concerned with scientific information in the field of health is essential. New knowledge and new health problems are revealed each day through experimentation and research on the part of the medical and other professions. Finally, a study of the health of the community is imperative, in order to know the health problems that are peculiar to the local setting with its own industrial, housing, sanitation, water supply, and other problems which characterize it.

Although the specific course of study will vary from community to community it is still necessary to recognize that the basic health needs of children and the general content areas of health education are similar. To a great degree, what takes place is the specific adaptation of these general areas to the local situations.

It seems important for the general information of the reader to point out some of the basic health needs of children and also the general health content areas, as listed by leaders in the field. Finally, it seems essential to briefly discuss some of the controversial content areas.

A. Health Needs and General Content Areas for Health Education

Grout[7] points out there are many health needs that are common to children at various age levels, although they may manifest themselves differently. She lists

[6]American Association of School Administrators. *Health in Schools—Twentieth Yearbook.* Washington, D. C.: National Education Association, 1951, p. 175.

[7]Ruth E. Grout. *Health Teaching in Schools.* Philadelphia: W. B. Saunders Company, 1953, p. 28.

and discusses eleven basic health needs with which those interested in health education should be concerned. These are: (1) food and eating, (2) elimination of body wastes, (3) exercise and play, (4) sleep and rest, (5) eyes and ears, (6) teeth, (7) posture, (8) illnesses and disease, (9) accidents and injuries, (10) emotional adjustments, and (11) sex adjustments.

Other leaders in the field of health education, although not specifically listing the needs of school children, have suggested various health topics or health problems that should be covered in health education, thus implying needs in these areas.

Hoyman formulated a Four-Cycle Plan of Health Instruction for the Oregon Schools, which was constructed as a result of state legislation making it mandatory that health instruction be given in certain definite areas in the elementary and secondary schools of the state. The various health content areas, as specified by law, are given major emphasis in health instruction once during each cycle. "Each area is emphasized four times during the 12-year health curriculum." The four-cycle plan is outlined below:

FOUR-CYCLE PLAN OF HEALTH INSTRUCTION IN OREGON SCHOOLS[8]

		Cycle 1 Grades			Cycle 2 Grades			Cycle 3 Grades			Cycle 4 Grades		
Areas	Health Units	1	2	3	4	5	6	7	8	9	10	11	12
I	Structure and Functions of Human Body	x			x			x			x		
II	Personal Hygiene*	x			x			x			x		
III	Physiology of Exercise		x			x			x			x	
IV	Nutrition		x			x			x			x	
V	First Aid and Safety Education		x			x			x			x	
VI	Choice and Use of Health Services and Health Products			x			x			x			x
VII	Communicable Diseases†			x			x			x			x
VIII	Community Health and Sanitation			x			x			x			x
IX	Mental Health‡		‡			‡			‡				x

*This unit also includes instruction in the area, "Effects of Alcoholic Drinks, Stimulants, and Narcotics."
†This unit also includes instruction on the noncommunicable diseases.
‡On the three lower levels, appropriate instruction on mental health is included in the units on "Personal Hygiene." The unit on "Mental Health," recommended for grade 12, also includes instruction on "Family-Life Education."

The Joint Committee on Health Problems in Education of the National Education Association and the American Medical Association[9] discussed what they consider to be the big dozen health problems. These are:

1. Food and Nutrition
2. Exercise, Rest and Sleep
3. Vision and Hearing
4. Mental Hygiene
5. Sex Education
6. Alcohol and Tobacco
7. Colds and Other Respiratory Diseases
8. Other Communicable Diseases
9. Heart Disease and Rheumatic Fever
10. Dental Caries
11. Accidents
12. Cancer

[8]Howard S. Hoyman. *Health Guide Units for Oregon Teachers.* Salem, Oregon: Oregon State Department of Education, 1945.

[9]Joint Committee of National Education Association and the American Medical Association, *Health Education.* Charles C. Wilson (Editor). Washington, D. C.: National Education Association, 1948, pp. 45-46.

These have been listed arbitrarily and not in any definite order, with some dovetailing of the various problems.

Brownell and Williams[10] have prepared what they term a "check list" which has been utilized with success by some teachers and writers in health education. It can be utilized to insure that important health topics are not overlooked. Their check list follows:

1. *Personal regimen.* Food, shelter, clothing, sleep, play, elimination, cleanliness, and similar factors. This area of concentration deals with health matters related to self and for which the person is largely responsible.
2. *Safety.* Personal safety, the protection of others against accidents, and the elements of first aid.
3. *Mental hygiene.* The establishment of emotional stability and control, the causes and outcomes of improper mental health, and the development of personality.
4. *Social hygiene.* Appropriate home and family experiences, proper male and female relationships, and approved sex instruction.
5. *Professional health services.* The work of physicians, nurses, dentists, hospitals, and clinics, and home care of the sick.
6. *Public health.* Health factors and agencies affecting the general public, and the work of public-health organizations.
7. *Temperance.* Moderation and control in all life activities, with special reference to alcohol, tobacco, tea, coffee, narcotics, and other harmful drugs.

Kilander[11] in discussing trends in health education in secondary schools based upon a review of twenty-two state courses of study, points out that the trend is to include instruction in ten major areas. These are:

1. Personal living
2. Community living
3. Sanitation
4. Nutrition
5. Physical activity
6. Safety education
7. First aid
8. Emotional and social health
9. Education for family living
10. Occupational or industrial health

He further points out that some of the various subtopics included under these major areas are:

Cleanliness and grooming
Care of eyes, ears, and teeth
Fatigue, rest, sleep, and exercise
Alcohol and tobacco
Emotions
Recreation and hobbies
Communicable and noncommunicable diseases
Lighting, heating, and ventilation
Periodic health examination and selecting a doctor
Health advertising
Home nursing

[10]C. L. Brownell, and J. F. Williams, *Teachers' Manuals for Health of Our Nation Series.* New York: American Book Company, 1947.

[11]H. F. Kilander, "Trends in Health Education in Secondary Schools," *The Journal of School Health,* XIX: 238-239, November, 1949.

Human reproduction and marriage
World health problems
Anatomy and physiology

Strang and Smiley[12] point out that the most common health problems are concerned with:

growth	fatigue
posture	mental hygiene
exercise and play	smoking
correction of defects including vision	drinking
and teeth	social hygiene
prevention of disease	food
	safety

The American Association for Health Education, Physical Education, and Recreation[13] points out that when several recommended methods are utilized in determining the content of a health course it is found that health problems in the junior high school center around such topics as:

personal health	nutrition
safety education	disease control
first aid	home care of the sick
	sanitation

In the senior high school the health problems that students are interested in center around such topics as:

consumer health education
mental health and personal adjustment
family life education
community health problems
driver education

In examining these various lists of health education topics which have been developed by associations and leaders in the field, one can readily see there is considerable overlapping. The areas of personal health, community health, sanitation, nutrition, safety, first aid, driver education, sex education, home nursing, and mental health appear to be the ones most commonly mentioned. Many of the other topics that are listed can be included under one or more of these headings. For example, exercise, rest, and play could be included under personal health; disease prevention and control could be included under personal and community health or sanitation; alcohol and tobacco under personal health; accidents under safety and first aid; and emotions under mental health. The question of terminology is not as important as the need for covering the various areas in respect to the needs and interests of students in each local situation. However, it would seem important

[12]Ruth M. Strang and Dean F. Smiley. *The Role of the Teacher in Health Education.* New York: The Macmillan Company, 1950, p. 110.
[13]The Joint Committee. *Administrative Problems in Health Education, Physical Education and Recreation,* Washington, D. C.: AAHPER, 1953, pp. 14-15.

for every administrator to check these various lists, representing some of the best thinking in the field, to determine whether or not his particular school is covering all of the essential areas in the field of health education. By so doing he will insure that the basic health education needs of the student are provided for.

B. Controversial Content Areas in Health Education

The question often arises as to whether such controversial subjects as sex, narcotics, or alcohol education should be provided for in health education. The fact that some of these problems are more pronounced in certain communities, and possibly restricted to some population groups, together with the fact that some education might tend to stimulate curiosity, are reasons put forth for not including them in courses of study.

On the other hand, instruction in regard to the ill effects of narcotics and alcohol is required by law in many states. Furthermore, it is felt that if children and youth are provided with the facts, intelligent instruction in these subjects will act as a preventive measure. In the area of sex education, it is believed that the term "sex education" creates opposition among many parents and church groups and consequently should not be used. If it is introduced in the natural process of instruction without undue emphasis, much good can be done.

Some of the best thinking in the field emphasizes the fact that the nature of the instruction will depend upon the local situation. Where a narcotics or alcohol problem exists, there should be provision in the school curricula for the presentation of sociological, physiological, and psychological facts, as well as the legal aspects of such a problem. Students should understand these facts and be guided intelligently in making the right decisions and establishing a sound standard of values.

The State of Nebraska[14] has prepared an instructional guide for Nebraska teachers in which it points out knowledges and understandings to be attained in selected health education content areas. It also lists suggested activities, instructional aids, and supplementary resources. In the area of alcohol and narcotics, for example, it lists the following problems to be considered: Problem A: What are some definitions that need to be understood before the component problems of alcohol and narcotics can be considered? Problem B: What are some points of agreement which have been reached by those who are seeking answers to problems of alcohol? Problem C: What facts do students need to know to evaluate the effects of tobacco on the body? Problem D: What do prospective teachers need to know concerning other types of stimulants and narcotics? In this state teachers are given considerable help in such controversial areas.

Health education is not the only area in which discussions of sex, narcotics, and alcohol should take place. Social studies, biology, general science, physical education, and other classes also have a responsibility. Many phases of these subjects logically fit into certain aspects of these courses. Teachers must appreciate the importance of such instruction and the need for dealing with these subjects objectively on the basis of the facts. It is not necessary for the teacher to take a

---

[14]Departments of Public Instruction, Health and Assistance and Child Welfare. *Health Education for Nebraska Teachers.* Lincoln, Nebraska: Department of Public Instruction, 1951.

definite stand and act in the capacity of a minister preaching on the subject. Instead, if students obtain the necessary facts through research or some other method and then interpret them intelligently, the right answers will be clear. The students make their own decisions, not on the basis of the teacher's position, but on the basis of the facts which they have collected.

In regard to sex education, the emphasis should be more on the moral and sociological aspects rather than only on the biological aspects. The end result should be to have students recognize what is desirable behavior and what constitutes high moral standards, rather than only to become acquainted with a body of factual knowledge such as that concerned with the reproductive organs. Students should be taught to live the finest type of lives possible.   Sex education should not be a separate course, but should be included and discussed in every course where its various aspects arise during regular discussions. Parents and representative community groups should be consulted and asked to participate in any discussions relative to the planning for instruction in this area. It is very important to have well-trained and qualified teachers handling such instruction. If the right type of leadership is provided, the results can be very beneficial to all concerned, but if poor leadership exists, many harmful results can come from such discussions.

V. HEALTH EDUCATION AT THE ELEMENTARY LEVEL

Health education at the elementary level is aimed primarily at having the child develop good health habits and health attitudes, and live happily, healthfully, and safely. This is achieved in great measure by adapting good health practices to the regular routine of school and home living, rather than by dispensing technical, factual knowledge concerning health. The responsibility for the guidance, planning, and stimulation of good health practices and attitudes falls upon the classroom teacher. She is the guiding influence and her understanding of good health will determine to a great degree how effective such a program actually is.

The type of health program offered should be adapted to the child's level and planned in accordance with his or her interests and needs. It should also be remembered that health education is a continuous process and cannot be compartmentalized within a definite subject area or within a class period. It embraces all the activities and subjects that are a part of the child's life.

At the primary grade level the emphasis should be more on the child and his daily routine as affected by certain health practices and attitudes. His various routines and associations at school and at home form the basis for the health emphasis. The importance of a healthful classroom environment is stressed. Such items as cleanliness, eating, use of lavatories, safety, and good mental hygiene are brought out as the child plays, eats, and performs those many experiences which are common to all youngsters of his age.

In the upper elementary years the values of certain health practices are brought out. A planned progression in instruction is developed. Although there is still stress on the actual practices and attitudes concerned with the daily routines and associations, more factual information is incorporated to form the basis for such habits. Furthermore, more and more responsibility is placed on the child for his own self-direction and self-control.

The utilization of trips and textbooks which point up the value of healthful living, interesting and inspiring stories, visual aids, class discussions, and projects can become a part of the experiences of each child so that the need for certain behavior is dramatically and effectively stamped upon his mind and total being.

Since health experiences should be based on the needs and interests of the child, the wise teacher will utilize various means of obtaining accurate information about these needs and interests. Such techniques as talks with parents and pupils, observations of children under various situations, a perusal of health records, a study of the home environment and community together with scientific measuring devices that have been developed to determine health knowledge and attitudes will be utilized. A health education program that is not based on accurate knowledge of needs and interests will fail to accomplish its objective of helping individuals to live a happier and healthier life.

According to the American Association of School Administrators' *Twentieth Yearbook,*[15] the health problems that confront and interest children in the primary grades include such topics as (1) growth and health, (2) nutrition, (3) elimination, (4) exercise, relaxation, rest, and sleep, (5) personal hygiene, (6) prevention and control of disease, (7) care of eyes and ears, (8) medical and dental attention, (9) emotional and social adjustment, and (10) safety. These various subjects would of course be adapted to the child at the primary school age. At the intermediate level the health problems would cover many of the same topics with the information and experiences being adapted to the level of this child. These topics include (1) growth and health, (2) nutrition, (3) exercise, relaxation, rest, and sleep, (4) personal hygiene, (5) care of eyes and ears, and (6) prevention and control of disease.

The Norfolk, Virginia, Public Schools[16] list fourteen basic areas of health instruction for the elementary school:

1. Play and physical education
2. Social hygiene
3. Mental and emotional health
4. Personal hygiene, including diet, rest, and sleep, exercise, clothing, elimination, handwashing, and exposure
5. Experiences in healthful living
6. Communicable diseases, including diseases listed under health service
7. Nutrition
8. Dental hygiene
9. Eye hygiene
10. Posture education
11. Safety education
12. First aid
13. Experiences in health service
14. Foot hygiene

[15]American Association of School Administrators, *op. cit.*, pp. 149-153.

[16]Committee of Teachers and Administrators in the Norfolk Public Schools. *School Health.* A Guidebook in Health Education for the Norfolk Public Schools. Norfolk, Virginia: Department of Health and Physical Education.

Good teaching of health at the elementary level can be judged by four criteria:

1. It meets a felt need; information or help is desired.
2. It acquaints pupils with desirable procedures, based on accepted scientific knowledge.
3. It creates a desire to use knowledge, to practice what has been learned.
4. It provides opportunities and facilities for action.[17]

Along with these four criteria can be listed six commandments for successful health teaching:

1. Consider individual differences.
2. Discourage self-diagnosis and self-medication.
3. Avoid embarrassing pupils.
4. Adapt teaching to pupil's interests, needs, and capacities.
5. Base teaching on real life problems and real people.
6. Use a variety of teaching methods.[18]

If these criteria and commandments are kept in mind by teachers at the elementary level, the health experiences of all children who come under such leadership will be well provided for.

VI. HEALTH EDUCATION AT THE SECONDARY LEVEL

Since many aspects of health education at the secondary level are covered in this chapter under the topics of "Content Areas of Health Education," "Concentrated, Correlated, and Incidental Health Teaching," and "Organization of Classes," this discussion will be limited to a brief summary of some of the points of emphasis in health education at the secondary level.

The structural organization of the secondary level differs from the elementary level. At the elementary level, the classroom teacher takes over-all charge of a group of children. She teaches them in various subjects, stays with them throughout the entire day and has supervision of their activities. At the secondary level, the child has many different teachers. These teachers specialize in subject-matter to a greater degree than they specialize in pupils. There is departmentalization with such subject-matter areas as mathematics, social studies, and English. This structural organization affects health education tremendously.

First, this structural organization points up the need for concentrated courses in health education such as those found in the other subject-matter areas. Health education as a subject should receive equal consideration with the other important subjects in the secondary school offering, in all aspects such as scheduling, facilities, and staff. The minimum time that should be allotted has been stated as a daily period for one semester, at either the ninth or tenth grade level, and a daily period for one semester, at either the eleventh or twelfth grade level.

Second, this structural organization emphasizes the need for a specialist in the teaching of health education. Just as specialists are needed in English and the other subjects offered at the secondary level, so are they needed in the field of health

---

[17]Joint Committee of National Education Association and American Medical Association, *op. cit.*, p. 223.
[18]*Ibid.*, p. 226.

education. The body of scientific knowledge, the training needed, and the importance of the subject make such a specialist a necessity.

Third, this structural organization stresses the need for coordination and cooperation. Health cuts across many subject-matter areas, as well as the total school life of the child. In order that it may be properly treated in the various subject-matter areas such as science, home economics, and social studies, in order that the physical environment and the emotional environment may be properly provided for, in order that health services may be most effectively administered, and in order that close cooperation and coordination between the school and the rest of the community may be obtained, there is an essential need for some type of coordinating machinery. There is a need for a school health council or committee where individuals representing various interests and groups can pool their thinking and bring about cooperative effort. There is a need for some individual to act in the capacity of a health coordinator, to spearhead the movement for cooperation and coordination, and to develop good relationships among the various departments and interests represented in the total school situation, as well as with those in the broader community.

In order to have an effective, sound health education program at the secondary level, the central administration must provide the type of leadership which leaves no doubt as to the importance of health in the lives of the many children who attend the schools. Such administrative leadership will reflect itself from the very top to the very bottom of the school structure and be felt at the grass roots of all community enterprises.

The content covered at the secondary level should also be adapted to the needs and interests of the students in this age group. In the early years of the secondary school it is felt that the stress should be on the personal health problems of the students themselves, how hereditary factors affect their health, how good and poor health manifest themselves, and how health practices affect the attainment of life ambitions and goals. In the later years, the stress should be more on adult living, family living, and community health. Since a majority of the students will not be going to college, this will represent the school's last opportunity to impress them with their health responsibilities—to themselves, their loved ones, and the members of their community. Such items as the importance of family life, environmental factors that affect community life, and the importance of health in achieving adult objectives should be covered.

Health education at the secondary level can represent an experience which will have a lasting effect for the betterment of human lives. The leadership that is provided, the methods that are used, and the stress that is placed upon such an important aspect of living will determine in great measure the extent to which each school will fulfill its responsibility.

VII. HEALTH EDUCATION AT THE COLLEGE AND UNIVERSITY LEVEL

The college and the university also have responsibilities for health education. Health is important to everyone regardless of the type of work he may do.

Years ago the college and university health education offerings consisted mainly of lectures on various aspects of the anatomy and physiology of the human body. These were usually given by medical personnel and were often a collection of uninteresting facts, unrelated to the student's interests and health problems. In more recent years this type of presentation has changed. The emphasis has shifted from the factual medical knowledge to health problems which students themselves encounter in day-to-day living and also to those subjects in which students are especially interested. Consequently, discussions are now held on subjects concerned with family living, personal and community health, mental health, nutrition, the prevention of disease, and related subjects.

Student Health Center, Kent State University, Kent, Ohio.

The Third National Conference on Health in Colleges recommended major health instruction courses appropriate to special groups of students. They also suggested "a minimum of 45 class hours or three to four semester credits" for a basic or general health course in "personal and community health." Other recommended procedures for college health courses are in order of preference: (1) the three or five hour one-semester required or elective course, (2) the two hour per week course for two credits, (3) the two hour course shared with a physical education requirement, and (4) the one hour per week course for one credit. Such a course should meet frequently enough to maintain the student's interest and to cover the subject adequately. Furthermore, the lecture method of presentation should not be the only one used.[19]

In addition to hygiene courses, there is also a need in colleges and universities for courses in marriage and family living, public health, and other problems pertinent to student interests and needs.

VIII. HEALTH EDUCATION FOR ADULTS

Adults are the guiding force in any community. The prestige they have, the positions they occupy, and their interests determine the extent to which any project or enterprise will be a success. Therefore, if the schools are to have an adequate health education program, if the knowledge that is disseminated, attitudes that are developed, and practices that are encouraged are to become a permanent part of the child's being and routine, the adult must be taken into consideration. Unless this is done, the schools' efforts will be of no avail.

There is a great need for parental education and for education in regard to the many health problems which confront any community. Adults are interested not only in children's health problems, but also in the causes of sickness and death in the population and ways in which they can live a healthier life. Adult education is rapidly spreading across the length and breadth of this country. It is important that health education become one of the areas considered in any such program.

Schools should play a key part in adult education programs through the facilities, staff, and other resources at their disposal. They should cooperate fully with the many official and voluntary health agencies, and other interested community groups, in the furtherance of health objectives. Adult education programs in the area of health should be designed to discover community health problems, understand the health needs of children, and understand school health programs. Such discovery and understanding should lead to active participation in meeting health needs and solving health problems. Such a program would also lend itself to growth in respect to health knowledge, attitudes, and practices.

IX. CONCENTRATED, CORRELATED, AND INCIDENTAL HEALTH TEACHING

Three ways of including health education in the school offering are through concentrated, correlated, and incidental teaching. Each of these will be discussed.

A. Concentrated Health Education

Concentrated health education refers to the provision in the school offering for regularly scheduled courses which are confined solely to a consideration of health, rather than a combination with some other subject-matter area. It implies a scheduled time for class meetings and a planned course of study. It is recommended that such courses be given on the secondary school level. Furthermore, such courses should be held for a daily class period at least one semester during the ninth or tenth grade and also during the eleventh or twelfth grade.

It is the general consensus that concentrated health education is a necessity. If the objectives for which the school health program has been established are to

---

[19]Wilson, *Health Education*, p. 270.

be achieved, time must be made available in the curricular offering of the school. Health has been listed as one of the main objectives in the field of education. Therefore, it would seem logical to assume that in order to achieve such an objective proper provisions must be made.

Concentrated health education courses required of all students result in many educational benefits. There is a specialized body of knowledge to impart which can best be given to students in a concentrated manner, rather than by depending upon some other subject to provide this information. It allows for better planning, teaching progression, and evaluation. It further allows for the giving of credit, as is given for any other course which is offered separately. It is more likely to result in health instruction by teachers who have specialized in this particular area and are qualified and interested in participating in such a course. When offered as a separate course it enables boys and girls to be in the same class, as in other subjects. This is not true if it is combined with physical education, where boys and girls are usually in separate groups. It offers greater opportunities for discussion of personal health problems with guidance and counseling in regard to these problems, and for the utilization of teaching methods appropriate to such a course.

The importance of concentrated health education is clearly recognized in the upper six years of school by one superintendent of schools who says, ". . . In the upper six years some of the health instruction may be provided for in other subjects, science and home economics, for example, but there must be at least a one-unit health course taught by a specialist. Only through such a course can justice be done to the extensive content of the complete health education course, since specialists in other subjects have their own objectives to satisfy and can be expected to subordinate satisfaction of health objectives. Moreover, maturing students, particularly those in the senior high school, need the challenge of being exposed to the teaching of a health specialist. Much can be said for diffusing health content through the high school program of studies, so long as diffusion does not result in confusion, if not chaos, and so long as provision is made for an adequate degree of specialization through the one-unit course."[20]

B. Correlated Health Education

Correlated health education refers to the practice of including health concepts in the various subject-matter areas. For example, in the area of history the relationship of the rise and fall of various groups of people could be related to their health and the prevalence of disease as could the increased speed of transportation and the transfer of disease from one country to the other. In the area of English, a study of the works of literature could be selected with a view to pointing up the health problems of individuals during various periods of history. The relationship of music and of art to mental health could be brought out. Mathematics could be used as a tool to figure the costs of various health projects. Science could bring out the health aspects in relation to the structure and functions of the human body. Home economics provides an excellent setting for teaching such things as nutrition

[20]John L. Miller, "An Administrator Looks at the School Health Program," *The Journal of Educational Sociology*, 22: 27, September, 1948.

and personal cleanliness. There is hardly a subject-matter area that cannot be correlated with health education.

Correlated health education should be a part of every school health program. This necessitates definite planning to insure that such an important subject is emphasized at every opportunity. Schools with health coordinators have found that such a person can perform an outstanding job in this area by meeting with teachers in the various subject-matter areas and discussing and planning the contributions they can make to health education. Although correlated health education is very important and should be included in every school, it should not be regarded as a substitute for concentrated health instruction. Even when there is a concentrated health program there should also be a correlated health program which permeates the entire school offering. When both correlated and concentrated health education are provided for, in adequate amounts and in the right manner, the best results are obtained.

C. Incidental Health Education

Incidental health education refers to that education which takes place during normal teaching situations, other than in regular health classes, where attention is focused on problems concerned with health. Such occasions may arise as the result of a question asked by a student; a problem that is raised in class; a personal problem which confronts a member of the class, a family, or the community; or a sudden illness, accident, or special project. It represents an opportunity for the teacher, physician, dentist, or nurse to provide information that is educational in nature. When a child has his eyes examined or chest x-rayed, for example, many questions arise and opportunities are afforded to give the child information which will have a lasting and beneficial value. In many cases this will benefit the health of the child more than information given in more formalized, planned class situations. Teachers and others should constantly keep in mind the necessity for continually being alert to these "teachable moments." When a child is curious and wants information, this establishes a time for dynamic health education. Incidental health education can be planned for in advance. Situations and incidents should be anticipated and utilized to their fullest in the interests of good health.

X. ORGANIZATION OF CLASSES

Many problems arise in connection with the organization of health education classes. Some of the more prevalent of these are concerned with whether boys and girls should meet together or separately, time arrangement, and scheduling.

A. Class Organization

Boys and girls should be scheduled for health classes in a way which is in the best interests of all concerned. This would mean that where health education is a combined program with physical education, and where the boys and girls are in separate classes, it would probably be best to conduct the health classes in a similar manner. On the other hand, if health education and physical education are not combined, it would seem they should be handled in the same manner as any other subject.   This would mean there would be mixed groups.   The fact that the subject matter is health education should not mean separation of sexes.   It should be pointed out, however, that some leaders in the field maintain this concept is wrong and advocate keeping the sexes separate as a means of getting better organization.

It is generally agreed that if boys and girls meet as a mixed group for health education they should continue as a mixed group throughout the entire course. It does not seem wise to have them meet separately when certain topics are considered.   To do so tends to overstress and play up as "hush hush" certain aspects of health education.   This creates confusion and encourages undue curiosity.   It is best to treat the subjects in a natural and educational manner.

B. Time Arrangement

There are many time arrangement patterns being followed in respect to health education.   This is true especially on the secondary level.   A study by Kilander[21] points this up.   Some of the patterns he found to exist in the schools are as follows:

Daily class periods in health instruction:
>   For 1 semester
>   For 2 semesters in different years—usually 1 each in junior and senior high school
>   For 1 whole year

2 or 3 class periods per week (alternating with physical education classes):
>   For 1 semester
>   For 2 semesters (equivalent in time and credit to 1 full semester)
>   For 4 semesters (equivalent in time and credit to 1 full year)
>   For each semester up to 5 years

1 class period per week (usually as a regularly scheduled part of a combined course in health and physical education):
>   For 1 year
>   For several years
>   For each year on the junior and senior high school levels

Integration of health education with other subjects:
>   With physical education-combined grades and credit
>   With other subjects, such as biology and general science—combined grades and credit.

This same study points out that the most common procedure followed in the secondary schools throughout the country calls for two or three class periods a week of health education, although state departments of education most frequently recommend daily class periods for one or two semesters.

---

[21]H. F. Kilander.   *Health Instruction in the Secondary Schools.*   An Inquiry into Its Organization and Administration.   Office of Education, Pamphlet No. 110.   Washington, D. C.:   U. S. Government Printing Office, 1951, p. 11.

The *Suggested School Health Policies—A Charter for School Health* recommends that "specific health courses should be provided in secondary schools and should have a minimum time allotment of a daily period for at least one semester during either the ninth or tenth grade and a similar amount of time in the eleventh grade. Health courses should be placed on par with courses in other areas of instruction and given proportional credit or recognition. Health courses should be given in regular classrooms with classes comparable in size to those in other subject-matter areas."[22]

The Joint Committee on Health Problems in Education of the National Education Association and the American Medical Association reaffirmed this stand when they pointed out that "the trend appears to be toward concentrated health courses, one early in the high school, the other late in the senior high school period."[23]

Kilander supports this statement when he says, "The current trend is to consolidate the hours commonly given to health and safety instruction, where it has been offered during health and physical education time, into one or two semesters in the junior and senior high schools. The recommendations of several national organizations and conferences have been that there be at least one full semester (preferably two, including safety) of daily instruction on both the junior and senior high school levels. A less satisfactory plan is that of two or three hours of instruction weekly for one full year on each level."[24]

XI. RESOURCES

The teacher or other individual interested in obtaining help in planning, organizing, and administering a health education program can consult numerous persons and organizations for guidance and help. There are also many materials available for their use. Within the school itself, such resource help exists in the form of staff members who posssess specialized knowledge such as the school physician, nurse, home economics, and physical education teachers. The community also offers numerous resources, which can enrich the health education program immensely. In addition to the school and community, the state and nation also have rich resources which, in many cases, are available merely for the asking.

The organizations at the local, state, and national levels that offer resources for the field of health education can be listed and discussed under the following headings, (A) Professional Agencies and Associations, (B) Official Agencies, and (C) Commercial Organizations.

A. Professional Agencies and Associations

Under professional agencies and associations can be listed such organizations as voluntary health agencies, medical, dental, and nursing associations, council of

[22]National Committee on School Health Policies. *Suggested School Health Policies*. New York: Health Education Council, 1946, p. 17.

[23]Joint Committee on Health Problems in Education of the National Education Association and American Medical Association, *op. cit.*, p. 243.

[24]H. F. Kilander, "Trends in Health Education in Secondary Schools," *The Journal of School Health*, XIX: 240, November, 1949.

social agencies, and other health education associations. Some of the more prominent are listed here:

1. Voluntary Health Organizations[25]

American Cancer Society	47 Beaver Street	New York 4, N. Y.
American Heart Association	44 East 23 St.	New York, N. Y.
American Red Cross	17th and D St. N.W.	Washington 13, D. C.
American Social Hygiene Association	1790 Broadway	New York 19, N. Y.
American Hearing Society	817 14th St. N.W.	Washington 5, D. C.
Child Welfare League of America	345 East 46th	New York, N. Y.
National Committee for Mental Hygiene	1790 Broadway	New York 19, N. Y.
National Foundation for Infantile Paralysis	120 Broadway	New York 5, N. Y.
National Safety Council	425 N. Michigan Ave.	Chicago, Illinois
National Society for the Prevention of Blindness	1790 Broadway	New York 19, N. Y.
National Society for Crippled Children and Adults	11 S. LaSalle St.	Chicago 3, Illinois
National Tuberculosis Association	1790 Broadway	New York 19, N. Y.

2. Professional Associations[26]

American Academy of Pediatrics	610 Church Street	Evanston, Illinois
American Association for Health, Physical Education, and Recreation	1201 Sixteenth St. N.W.	Washington 6, D. C.
American Dental Association	222 East Superior St.	Chicago 11, Illinois
American Hospital Association	18 East Division St.	Chicago 10, Illinois
American Medical Association	535 No. Dearborn St.	Chicago 10, Illinois
American Nurses Association	2 Park Avenue	New York 16, N. Y.
American Public Health Association	1790 Broadway	New York 19, N. Y.
American School Health Association	228 No. LaSalle St.	Chicago, Illinois
Child Study Association of America	132 E. 74th St.	New York, N. Y.
National Education Association	1201 Sixteenth St. N.W.	Washington 6, D. C.
National Organization for Public Health Nursing	2 Park Avenue	New York 16, N. Y.

B. Official Agencies

Official agencies, such as state departments of health, state departments of
education, and public health departments offer a rich source of help. They offer

---

[25]Joint Committee on Health Problems of National Education Association and American Medical Association, *op. cit.,* p. 331.   (Adapted.)

[26]*Loc. cit.* (Adapted.)

guidance and consultant services, disseminate information and materials in various forms for use in health classes, and make available films and other visual aids.

Government agencies on the national level provide resources in various forms including consultant services, health reports, and grants-in-aid, and publish various materials of interest and use to all those teaching health education.

State colleges and universities, as well as those which are private, should be kept in mind when seeking resources for health. In many such institutions the staffs, with their various specialists, are available for use in the schools. Many times they will conduct workshops and institutes to provide in-service training to local schoolteachers. Many have film libraries and other materials which may be rented at a very nominal fee.

Thought and planning are required in order to use these various resources effectively. The right persons to contact should be known, materials which are borrowed should be returned on time, and consultant services should be handled in a considerate manner.

Some official agencies follow:[27]

Atomic Energy Commission, Washington 25, D. C.

Department of Agriculture, Washington 25, D. C. (Bureau of Animal Industry and Bureau of Home Economics and Human Nutrition)

Department of Commerce, Bureau of the Census, Washington 25, D. C.

Department of Health, Education and Welfare, Washington 25, D. C. (Office of Education, Office of Special Services, Public Health Service and Social Security Administration)

Department of the Interior, Bureau of Mines, Washington 25, D. C.

Department of State, Washington 25, D. C.

Executive Office of the President, National Security Resources Board, Civilian Defense Office (Federal Civil Defense Administration), Washington 25, D. C.

Government Printing Office, Superintendent of Documents, Washington 25, D. C.

Midcentury White House Conference on Children and Youth, Washington 25, D. C.

State boards of health, located in the state capitals.

State departments of education, located in the state capitals.

State universities and colleges

Tennessee Valley Authority, Health and Safety Division, Knoxville, Tennessee.

World Health Organization, Palais des Nations, Geneva, Switzerland.

C. Commercial Organizations

There are many commercial companies that dispense health materials. Although this material should be evaluated with care, much of it will prove helpful in the field of health education. Some of the commercial companies are listed:[28]

The American Institute of Baking, 400 East Ontario, Chicago 11, Illinois

The Cereal Institute, 135 South LaSalle Street, Chicago, Illinois

---

[27]American Association of School Administrators, *op. cit.*, pp. 459-460.

[28]Adapted from Turner, Clair E. *School Health and Health Education*, ed. 2, St. Louis: The C. V. Mosby Company, 1952, p. 414.

General Mills, Inc., 400 2nd Avenue South, Minneapolis, Minnesota

The Evaporated Milk Association, 307 North Michigan Avenue, Chicago, Illinois

The Florida Citrus Fruit Commission, Lakeland, Florida

Health Information Foundation, 420 Lexington Avenue, New York 17, New York

The Milk Industry Foundation, Chrysler Building, New York, N. Y.

The National Association of Manufacturers, 14 West 49th Street, New York 20, New York

National Canners Association, Home Economics Division, National Canners Building, Washington, D. C.

The National Livestock and Meat Board, 407 South Dearborn Street, Chicago 5, Illinois

Sunkist Growers, Box 2706, Terminal Annex, Los Angeles 54, California

The United Fresh Fruit and Vegetable Association, 777 14th Street, N.W., Washington, D. C.

The Wheat Flour Institute, 309 West Jackson Boulevard, Chicago 6, Illinois

QUESTIONS AND EXERCISES

1. What is the relationship of health education to the total school health program?

2. Write an essay of 250 words citing evidence to show the need for health education.

3. What part do the superintendent and principal play in the development of a desirable health education program for the schools?

4. If a physical education person is teaching health education, what should be his or her qualifications in order to do an acceptable job?

5. Identify: (a) health coordinator, (b) school health council, (c) health services, (d) concentrated health teaching, (e) incidental health teaching, (f) four-cycle plan, (g) Joint Committee on Health Problems, (h) official agencies, and (i) problem-solving activities.

6. How should health education classes be organized?

7. What are eight content areas in health education? Which do you feel are most important in your school? What are the controversial content areas?

8. How does health education vary at the elementary, junior high school, senior high school, and college levels?

9. What are the resources available to individuals in the area of health education?

SELECTED REFERENCES

American Association of School Administrators. *Health in Schools—Twentieth Yearbook.* National Education Association, 1951.

American Medical Association. *Physicians and Schools.* Donald A. Dukelow and Fred C. Hein, Editors. Report of the Fourth National Conference on Physicians and Schools. Chicago: the Association, 1953.

Brownell, Clifford Lee. *Principles of Health Education Applied.* New York: McGraw-Hill Book Company, Inc., 1949.

Byrd, Oliver E. *Textbook of College Hygiene.* Philadelphia: W. B. Saunders Company, 1953.

Chenoweth, Laurence B., and Selkirk, Theodore K. *School Health Problems.* New York: Appleton-Century-Crofts, 1953.

Coops, Helen Leslie. *Health Education in Elementary Schools.* New York: A. S. Barnes and Company, 1950.

Department of Health, Education and Welfare. *Better Health for School-Age Children.* Washington, D. C.: The Office of Education, the Department, 1951.

Etheredge, Maude Lee. *Health Facts for College Students.* Philadelphia: W. B. Saunders Company, 1953.

Fields, Morey R., and Edgerton, Avis E. *Teachers' Guide for Health Education.* New York: Remsen Press, 1949.
Grout, Ruth E. *Health Teaching in Schools.* Philadelphia: W. B. Saunders Company, 1953.
Hoyman, Howard S., "Basic Issues in School Sex Education," *The Journal of School Health,* XXIII: 14, January, 1953.
Hoyman, Howard S. *Health-Guide Units for Oregon Teachers.* Salem, Oregon: Oregon State Department of Education, 1945.
Joint Committee on Health Problems in Education of the National Education Association and American Medical Association. *Health Education.* Charles C. Wilson, Editor. Washington, D. C.: National Education Association, 1948.
Kilander, H. F. *Health Instruction in the Secondary Schools—Its Organization and Administration.* Office of Education. Pamphlet No. 110. Washington, D. C.: U.S. Government Printing Office, 1951.
Kilander, H. F., "Trends in Health Education in the Secondary Schools," *The Journal of School Health,* XIX: 237, November, 1949.
Kirkendall, Lester A. *Sex Education as Human Relations.* New York: Inor Publishing Company, 1950.
Krueger, Walter W. *Personal Hygiene.* Philadelphia: W. B. Saunders Co., 1950.
Lamkin, Nina B. *Health Education in Rural Schools and Communities.* New York: A. S. Barnes and Company, 1946.
Langton, Clair V. *Orientation in School Health.* New York: Harper & Brothers, 1941.
Los Angeles City Schools. *Experiences in Health Education for Elementary School Children.* Los Angeles: Los Angeles City School Districts, Division of Instructional Services. Publication No. 566, 1953.
Metropolitan Life Insurance Company, Health and Welfare Division. *The School Health Program.* School Health Monograph No. 12. New York: Metropolitan Life Insurance Company, 1 Madison Avenue, 1952.
Miller, John L., "An Administrator Looks at the School Health Program," *The Journal of Educational Sociology,* 22: 26, September, 1948.
National Committee on School Health Policies. *Suggested School Health Policies—A Charter for School Health.* New York: Health Education Council, 1946.
National Education Association. The Department of Elementary School Principals. *Health in the Elementary Schools.* Washington, D. C.: the Association, 1950.
National Tuberculosis Association. *A Health Program for Colleges.* A Report of the Third National Conference on Health in Colleges. New York: the Association, 1948.
Oberteuffer, Delbert. *School Health Education.* New York: Harper & Brothers, 1954.
Rugen, Mabel E., "Working Together for Better Health Education," *The Journal of Educational Sociology,* 22: 51, September, 1948.
Schneider, Elsa and McNeely, Simon A. *Teachers Contribute to Child Health.* Office of Education Bulletin 1951, No. 8. Washington, D. C.: U.S. Government Printing Office, 1951.
Schutz, Dorothy L., "An Evaluation of the Free Health Publications Available for Use With Children in Grades One and Two," *The Journal of School Health,* XX: 8, January, 1950.
Sharman, Jackson R. *Introduction to Health Education.* New York: A. S. Barnes and Company, 1948.
Sheele, Leonard A., "The School and National Health," *The Journal of Educational Sociology,* 22: 31, September, 1948.
Steinhaus, Arthur H., "Health Education in the United States," *Journal of School Health,* XIX: 292, December, 1949.
Strang, Ruth M., and Smiley, Dean F. *The Role of the Teacher in Health Education.* New York: The Macmillan Company, 1950.
The Joint Committee (Editors.) *Administrative Problems in Health Education, Physical Education and Recreation.* Washington, D. C.: American Association for Health, Physical Education and Recreation, 1953.
Turner, Clair E. "Health Education and Community Organization," *Journal of School Health,* XIX: 246, November, 1949.
Turner, C. E. *School Health and Health Education.* St. Louis: C. V. Mosby Company, 1952.
"Voluntary Health Agencies and the Schools," An Official Report. *The Journal of the American Association for Health, Physical Education and Recreation,* 20: 73, February, 1949.
Williams, Jessie F., and Abernathy, Ruth. *Health Education in Schools.* New York: Ronald Press, 1949.
Wilson, Charles C. "Teacher Contributions in School Health," *The Journal of Educational Sociology* 22: 14, September, 1948.

Chapter XV

THE SCHOOL HEALTH SERVICES PROGRAM

The health of school children is a most important consideration for educators, parents, physicians, and others who desire to develop a fit populace. A good school health services program is an essential in the achievement of this goal. Without satisfactory health services, the health of school children cannot be adequately developed, maintained, and protected.

The history of health services shows that in early schools the stress was mainly on providing sanitary facilities and a clean environment. This was accomplished through a system of inspections and procedures. As more thinking has been given to this subject, however, there has been increased attention focused on those measures essential to the maintenance and improvement of the child's health. As a result, physicians, dentists, and other specialists have become more closely related to the schools. In turn, this has meant better detection of health defects, a more complete follow-through to insure the correction of such defects, more adequate means for preventing and controlling communicable disease, an increased realization of the potentialities of the medical examination as an educational tool, and more attention to the eyes, throat, ears, nose, and teeth. As the need for better health services was recognized by the public at large, state laws were passed to provide these services. These laws required such procedures as periodic medical examinations and regular checking of vision and hearing. They also stressed the need for school nurses, who were trained not only in their particular area but also in the field of education. Today, there is a feeling that in order to adequately develop and educate the "whole" child, health services must be an essential part of the school program.*

According to the Report of the Committee on Terminology in Health Education, of the American Association for Health, Physical Education and Recreation, and the American School Health Association,[1] school health services cover a broad area. They include the school procedures established to:

1. appraise the health status of pupils and school personnel;
2. counsel pupils, parents, and other persons involved concerning appraisal findings;
3. encourage the correction of remediable defects;

---

*For a discussion of the establishment of priorities in the various aspects of the health service program, the reader should consult *Priorities in Health Services for Children of School Age*, a publication of the Office of Education, Washington, D. C., 1949.

[1]Report of the Committee on Terminology in Health Education, American Association for Health, Physical Education and Recreation, and American School Health Association, *Journal of School Health*, XXI: 170, May, 1951.

4. help plan for the health care and education of handicapped (exceptional) children;
5. help prevent and control disease;
6. provide emergency care for the sick and injured.

These school health services, as outlined by this national committee will form the basis for the discussion to follow.

I. THE PLACE OF HEALTH SERVICES IN THE SCHOOLS

Health services is one phase of the total school health program. The other two areas, healthful school living and health education, have been discussed.

The health services program must be well publicized so that educators and the public in general will understand why such services are essential. Only as this need is understood will there be adequate planning and provision for such services.

The Joint Committee of the American Medical Association and the National Education Association[2] have listed the following as reasons why school health services should exist.

1. They contribute to the realization of educational aims.
2. They minimize hazards of school attendance.
3. They facilitate adaptation of school programs to individual capacities and needs.
4. They help children secure the care they need.
5. They possess inherent values for health education.

Health services contribute to the realization of educational aims. Educational committees, conferences, and other important groups have continually listed health as one of the objectives of education. Health services are necessary to attain this objective. Certainly it is just as important that our educational systems turn out healthy children as it is to turn out graduates who are well informed in such areas as mathematics, English, and geography. Life's goals cannot be accomplished successfully with mere facts. Health is a very important consideration.

Health services minimize hazards of school attendance. They make it possible for the child to participate in the various school offerings under safe conditions. Through emergency care, it is possible to reduce greatly the harmful effects of injuries in the event of accidents. Adequate precautions are taken against the spread of communicable disease. Medical examinations identify health defects, making for safer participation in athletics and other school activities. These are only a few of the many hazards that can be removed or minimized through effective health services.

Health services help children to better adapt to the school program. Through careful and regular checking of vision and hearing and correction of defects, children will adjust better to their responsibilities. Deficiencies, defects, and weaknesses which are prevalent will be noted and provided for. Such information will

---

[2]Joint Committee of American Medical Association and National Education Association. *School Health Services.* Charles C. Wilson, Editor. Washington, D. C.: National Education Association, 1953, p. 2.

make for a better and more complete understanding of the child. As a result, it will help the child to grow and develop in a desirable manner.

School health services provide a convenient location where matters in reference to the health of the entire population of a particular community can receive attention. The school is one of the few places where all the children in a community congregate. As such, it provides a point for focusing attention on the health needs of all children, for proper referral of individuals needing corrective work, and for the elimination of certain defects. Through the school the attention of the whole community can be focused on health problems that need attention.

School health services have potentialities for educating the parents as well as the children. They have potentialities for developing proper attitudes toward health, developing proper habits, and imparting scientific information. Through the medical examination, for example, the teacher, nurse, physician, and others are provided with an opportunity to educate children and parents about various aspects of human bodies and practices that make for a truly healthy person.

The nature and scope of the school health services program in New York State, together with some deterrent factors and achievements, are summarized here in order to give the reader an indication of what one state is doing in this area.

In 1913 the Legislature placed responsibility on the Commissioner of Education for carrying out the provisions of the Education Law, article 19, sections 901-12. In 1937 the law was augmented and reinforced by the Commissioner's Regulations governing School Health Service and by Department Regulations fixing responsibility for administrating the above law and regulations on the Bureau of Health Service. In accordance with the above law and regulations, the following areas represent the State's program in School Health Service:

A. Essential Phases of School Health Service
 1. Annual and subsequent medical examinations
 2. Notification of parents regarding child health status
 3. Annual testing of all pupils for vision and hearing
 4. Dental hygiene examinations and Dental Health Education
 5. Communicable Disease Control in cooperation with parents and Public Health authorities
 6. Recording and reporting
 7. Follow-through of each individual pupil with his parents until needed medical and dental care is secured
 8. Health guidance of the individual pupil, his parents, and teachers
 9. First-aid care in school emergencies
 10. Sanitation and safety of the school plant
 11. In-service training of school administrators and Health Service personnel
 12. Evaluation of programs as a basis for planning, organization, and coordination
 13. Cooperate with all state and community agencies concerned with child health

B. Deterrent Factors
 1. Lack of medical and dental treatment facilities in some upstate areas
 2. Lack of sufficient training facilities in New York State for dental hygiene teachers
 3. Assignment of school nurse-teachers to duties not requiring such professional preparation
 4. Lack of adequate Health Service for preschool children
 5. Insufficient School Nursing Service employed by boards of education

C. Present Achievements by Local School Authorities
1. 94.5 per cent of pupils enrolled now receive an annual health examination
2. In cities and villages 73.8 per cent of children with defects receive needed medical care. In central schools 55.1 per cent and in union free schools 61.8 per cent receive recommended treatment.[3]

II. THE RESPONSIBILITY FOR SCHOOL HEALTH SERVICES

The question is frequently raised as to whether school health services should fall within the province of school personnel or public health department personnel. Both the school and the public health department are vitally interested in seeing that such services are provided. Both have specialized personnel who can render important contributions to the successful administration of health services. The school is especially interested in the educational aspects of such services and the vast potentialities they have for educating the children and public. It has personnel who are specially trained in educational methods and techniques. In many communities it also has physicians on the staff who perform medical examinations and other health services. On the other hand, the public health department has specialists in sanitation, epidemiology, and other areas pertinent to the health services program.

Since both the school and the public health department have interests in health services, each local community should decide how such a program can best be carried out. In some communities the public health department is better staffed and qualified to perform many of the health services. In other communities the school has the better staff and other requisites. In many cases, health services should be a cooperative endeavor, where the health department and the school work together, sharing their resources and planning a program in the light of these conditions.

Kilander found in surveying health services in 2,886 cities, that "60.2 per cent were administered by the Board of Education; 10.9 per cent by the Board of Health; 23.0 per cent jointly by Boards of Education and Health; and 5.9 per cent by other authorities."[4]

III. EDUCATION VERSUS TREATMENT

With the school becoming an increasingly important social organization of the community, the question often arises as to whether it should provide treatment as part of its health services program. The philosophy on which the school program is based establishes it mainly as an agency concerned with education. The educational aspects of the health services program represent the major contribution of the schools. By identifying health defects, making referrals to medical, dental, and other experts, by counseling, providing for emergency care, making special provisions for the handicapped, and establishing and encouraging measures to prevent and control communicable diseases, the school is carrying out its responsibilities in health services. However, in some communities, as a result of agreement and

---

[3]The State Education Department, Bureau of Health Service, *The School Health Service Program.* Albany, New York, Fitness Conference—May 14, 1951.
[4]H. F. Kilander. *Health Services in City Schools.* Bulletin 1952, No. 20, Washington, D. C. U. S. Government Printing Office, 1952, p. 11.

consultation among public health, medical and dental professions, educators, and others, provisions have been made to provide dental treatment, occupational therapy, and other services. Such programs are exceptions to the rule, however, and usually are initiated as a result of a need for expediency and because it is felt that such a practice is the best way to handle certain health problems. Treatment is not usually a part of the school health program.

IV. SCHOOL HEALTH SERVICES

The rest of the chapter will be concerned with a discussion of the various health services that have been listed by the Committee on Terminology in Health

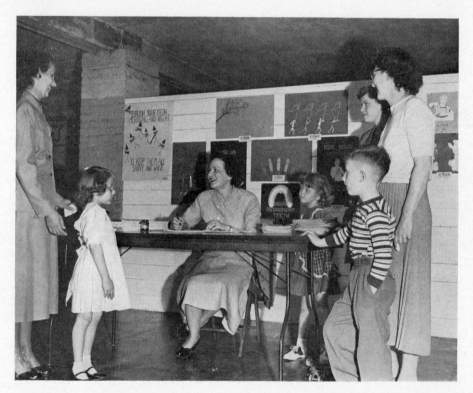

The cooperation of many individuals is needed to do an acceptable job in health service. (Courtesy of Indiana State Department of Health.)

Education of the American Association for Health, Physical Education and Recreation and the American School Health Association. These health services are (1) health appraisal, (2) health counseling, (3) correction of remediable defects, (4) care and education of the exceptional child, (5) prevention and control of communicable diseases, and (6) emergency care. They will be considered in respect to how they fit into the total school health program. Some of the various techniques that are used and administrative problems that arise, together with acceptable procedures to be followed will be discussed.

A. Health Appraisal

Health appraisal is that phase of school health service which is concerned with evaluating in as objective a way as possible, through examinations, observations, and records, the health of the "whole" child. It is not limited to medical examinations as some have erroneously believed.

The cooperation of many individuals is needed to do an acceptable job in health service. Teachers, administrators, physicians, dentists, psychologists, public health officials, social workers, parents, and lay leaders must all work together. Through the active cooperation of all, the necessary plans will be made for continuous evaluation and appraisal. If a health council exists, this body can play a major role in coordinating the various aspects of the program.

Planning should involve desirable facilities and procedures for health appraisal. There should be provision for privacy and quiet so that the best type of examinations and other techniques can be used in an acceptable manner.*

The aims of health appraisal have been well stated in the American Association of School Administrators' twentieth yearbook.

1. To identify pupils in need of medical or dental treatment.
2. To identify pupils who have problems relating to nutrition.
3. To identify pupils who are poorly adjusted and in need of special attention at school or of treatment by a psychiatrist or a child guidance clinic.
4. To measure the growth of pupils and to assist them in attaining optimum growth.
5. To identify pupils with nonremediable defects who may require modified programs of education—for example, the crippled, partially sighted, hard-of-hearing, mentally retarded, and those with speech defects.
6. To identify pupils who need a more thorough examination than is usually provided at school—for example, X-Ray examination, examination by a specialist, or a laboratory examination of one kind or another.
7. To identify pupils who may be cared for best apart from the regular school situation—for example, the blind, deaf, and tuberculous.[5]

The techniques used in health appraisal that will be discussed here include medical, psychological, and dental examinations, screening for vision and hearing, teacher observations, and health records.

1. Examinations.—Examinations are effective means of health appraisal.

a. *Medical Examinations.*—There are many important considerations for the administrator to keep in mind if medical examinations are to fulfill their objective. The following are some administrative guides.

(1) *Types:* Both periodic and referral examinations should be given to school children. The *periodic* is the medical examination which is given at stated intervals while the child is in school. *Referral* examinations are those which are given to children who have health problems needing special attention and who have been referred to the proper professional source. Such children may be referred to the physician as a result of teacher's observations, screening examinations, health records, notations, or other indications that special attention is needed. The *examination of athletes* is also a type of medical examination that needs to be considered.

*A description of the health room is included in Chapter XII.
[5]American Association of School Administrators. *Twentieth Yearbook. Health in Schools.* Washington, D. C.: National Education Association, 1951, p. 261.

(2) *Planning:*   Medical examinations require planning.   Young children should be informed as to their nature and purposes.   The teacher can play an important role in explaining some of these purposes and procedures.   Desirable attitudes can be developed so that children and parents look forward to such an event with interest and anticipation.   The various instruments that are used, such as the stethoscope, can be shown and discussed.   If the proper atmosphere is created the child will not be afraid or uneasy.   Planning should also take into consideration the provision of adequate facilities, having parents present, and making available the necessary health records.

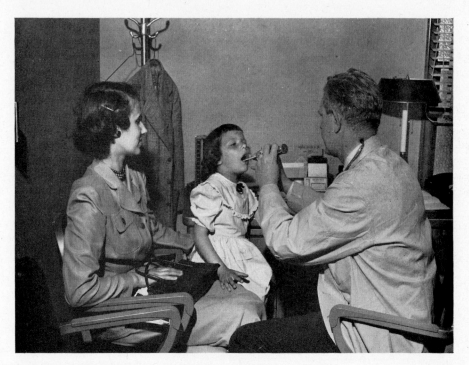

The family physician conducts the medical examination.   (Courtesy of Indiana State Department of Health.)

(3) *Frequency:*   At least four periodic medical examinations should be given during the time a child is in the elementary and secondary schools.   There should be a minimum of one examination at time of entrance to school, one at the intermediate grade level, one at the junior or early high school level when the student is entering the adolescent period, and one toward the termination of the high school period.   Referral examinations should be given at any time when health problems are detected.   There is also a need for more medical examinations for students who are engaging in the athletic phase of the physical education program and for those whose health conditions are such that the physician recommends examinations at more frequent intervals.

(4) *Examiner:*   There is a trend toward having the family physician conduct the medical examination.   It is felt that through a more complete knowledge of

the family history and a closer personal relationship, a better job can be done. However, since some families do not have their own physicians, since it means an additional outlay of funds, and for other reasons, many schools must rely on a school physician to administer the examination. The procedure that is utilized in each community should be a local prerogative and based upon the type of examination that will produce the best results.

(5) *Personnel in attendance:* The personnel that should be in attendance at the medical examination would include the physician, nurse, child, teacher, and parents at the elementary level. At the secondary level, the child should have progressed to the point where he or she assumes the responsibility for his own health and so the need for parents at the examination is not as great. Special attention should be given to sending a written invitation to parents listing the date and time of the examination. The presence of parents at these medical examinations provides an excellent opportunity for educating them in regard to their child's health, as well as their own.

(6) *Setting:* The place where the examination is held should be conducive to good results. The physical and the emotional atmosphere should receive attention. There should be privacy for disrobing, so that interruptions will not occur, and quiet so that distractions will be reduced to a minimum. The examination room should also provide ample space for personnel, equipment, and supplies and should be attractive.* Tensions, hurry, and excitement should be reduced to a minimum. The entire setting should breathe friendliness and informality.

(7) *Records available:* Essential health records should be brought up to date and be available at the time of the examination. These would include students' health cards, vision and hearing records, height-weight statistics, accident reports, and any other information that will help the physician to better interpret the results of the examination.

(8) *Scope:* According to the twentieth yearbook of the American Association of School Administrators, the "periodic school medical examination will include inspection or examination of at least the following:

eyes and lids	ears: canal and drums
nose	teeth and gums
throat and mouth	lymph node and thyroid gland
heart: before and after	lungs
exercise	scalp and skin
nutrition	bones and joints
posture	nervous system
feet	inguinal and umbilical region
speech	for hernia in males[6]
behavior attitudes	

(9) *Time:* The examination that is administered by the school physician should be of sufficient length to detect any health defects and also make the experi-

---

*See p. 221 for description of health suite.
[6]*Ibid.,* pp. 282-283.

MASSACHUSETTS DEPARTMENT OF PUBLIC HEALTH - MASSACHUSETTS DEPARTMENT OF EDUCATION

Family Physician's Report of School Health Examination

NAME OF PUPIL _____

PREVIOUS DISEASES AND OPERATIONS

RECORD OF IMMUNIZATION

PHYSICAL EXAMINATION

Height _____   Thyroid _____
Weight _____   Lymph glands _____
Nutrition _____   Breasts _____
General body type _____   Lungs _____
Posture (remark on presence or absence   Heart _____
 of scoliosis and lordosis, and define   Blood pressure _____
 scoliosis as functional or organic)   Pulse rate at rest _____ After exercise _____
_____   2 minutes after exercise _____
                                      Abdomen _____
Skin _____   Hernia _____
Eyes _____   Pilonidal sinus _____
Ears _____   Genitalia _____
Nose _____   Skeleton _____
Mouth _____   Feet _____
Teeth _____   Reflexes _____
Pharynx _____

LABORATORY TESTS

Date   Test   Result   Urinalysis: _____ Date _____
_____ Tuberculin _____   Specific gravity _____
_____ Chest X-ray _____   Albumin _____
_____ Hemoglobin _____   Sugar _____
                                      Microscopic _____

Is this child capable of carrying a full program
 of school work including gymnastics and athletics?   Yes _____ No _____
Must the school program be modified to meet the needs
 of this child?   Yes _____ No _____
 By restriction of use of stairs?   Yes _____ No _____
 By special seating accommodations?   Yes _____ No _____
 Other (specify) _____

Does the pupil have any irremediable defects?   Yes _____ No _____

REMARKS:

Date _____   Signature of Physician _____

ARD OF EDUCATION

CITY OF NEW YORK

PUPIL'S MEDICAL REPORT

DEPARTMENT OF HEALTH

ne..Date of Birth.................................
     Last Name   First Name

ress..School...................................... Borough.................... Class................
    Street   Boro or Town   Apt.

Smallpox Vaccination.................**Diphtheria Immunization***.............**Supplementary Diphtheria Toxoid***............
                   Year   Year   Date

Significant family history (e.g. rheumatic fever, tuberculosis, diabetes, hypertension, convulsive disorder)............................

Significant personal history (e.g. rheumatic fever, convulsive disorder, otitis media, pneumonia, other serious illnesses, operations) giving dates where possible...

Please indicate below by a check (√) in the column on the left any positive findings on physical examination or any handicapping disability and describe fully in section on right:

Skin	
Eyes†	
Ears†	
Nose and Throat	
Mouth	
Neck	
Heart	
Lungs	
Abdomen	
Hernia	
Extremities	
Nutritional Status	
Other (identify)	

DESCRIPTION:—

TREATMENT ADVISED:—

† *If vision and hearing have been tested please indicate score.*

Is there any specific time you wish to see this pupil again? ☐ Yes. If so, when...☐ No

Do you recommend any modifications in this pupil's program? (See letter on reverse side.)

Recommendation for Physical Activity in School (Use √)

☐ Full physical activity..

☐ Modified physical activity, because of..

Note: If modified program is recommended, the pupil will not be permitted to participate in any activity to the point of fatigue or breathlessness. The Department of Health reserves the right to re-examine all pupils for whom restriction of physical activity is recommended.

For High School Pupils Only

This pupil is being trained for...

From your knowledge of the pupil is this suitable? ☐ Yes ☐ No

Your suggestion as to change of vocation...

Date of examination...................................., 19....... ....M.D.
                                              Signature of Physician

(Physician: Please print or type your name, address   ....
and telephone number in spaces provided.)   Physician's Address

            Physician's Name   Physician's Telephone Number

e Department of Health recommends the usual course of injections of diphtheria toxoid for children under ten years never before immunized.
e supplementary injection of 0.2 cc diphtheria toxoid is recommended for children immunized three or more years prior to the date of this
amination, unless they have had a negative Schick Test within six months.

55-215M-7-51

HEALTH RECORD

Parents or Guardians—Mr. and Mrs.

Occupation of Father   Session Teacher

Occupation of Mother   Family Doctor   Family Dentist

MEDICAL EXAMINATION		1	2	3	4
1. Date of Examination					
2. Age					
3. Weight					
4. Height					
5. Hearing	Rt.				
	Lt.				
6. Eyes	Rt.				
	Lt.				
7. Test with glasses		Yes No	Yes No	Yes No	Yes No
8. Ring Worm					
9. Plantar Warts					
10. Hair					
11. Personal Hygiene					
12. Pulse before exercise					
13. Pulse after exercise					
14. Heart					
15. Lungs					
16. Tremor					
17. Abdomen					
18. Hernia					
19. Ears					
20. Nose					
21. Tonsils					
22. Adenoids					
23. Teeth					
24. Thyroid					
25. Glands					
26. Nutrition					
27. Skin					
28. P. E. Classification					
Unrestricted (A or B)					
Partially Restricted (C)					
Rest Only (D)					
Permanent Excuse					
Temporary Excuse					
29. Swimming					
Permanent Excuse					
Temporary Excuse					
Doctor's Initials					

HISTORY OF DISEASE

Chicken Pox | St. Vitus Dance | Diphtheria | Measles | Mumps | Pneumonia | Scarlet Fever | Rheumatic Fever | Whooping Cough | Tonsilitis | Hay Fever | Asthma | Date of Vaccination for Small Pox | T. B. in Family? | Date of Skin Test

Headaches:
Never
Occasionally
Frequently

Menstruation
Regular
Irregular
Dysmenorrhea

Operations:
Tonsils
Others:

Injuries

Postural Findings Scoliosis	L	R	L	R	L	R	L	R
Shoulder High								
Hip High								

Feet:
Pronation								
Long. Arch								
Transverse Arch								
Head Forward								
Round Shoulders								
Hollow Back								
Abdomen								
Body Balance								
Posture Grade								
Corrective Gym								

COMMENTS:

Explanation of Terms: "O"—Normal; "X"—Slight Defect; "XX"—Moderate; "XXX"—Marked.

Girl's health record. Highland Park High School, Highland Park, Illinois.

ence educational in nature. The minimum average time per student should be fifteen minutes or four per hour.

(10) *Priorities:* An American Public Health Association committee recommends the following priorities for medical examinations in secondary schools.

   a. Pupils who have returned to school without a medical certificate after prolonged or frequent absence.
   b. Pupils referred by the school staff.
   c. Pupils entering school for the first time.
   d. Pupils leaving school before the next scheduled health examination. (N.B. This should include examinations for employment certificates where required.)
   e. Pupils entering junior high school.
   f. Pupils ready to graduate from senior high school[7]

(11) *Examination of Athletes:** Administrative guides for athletic examinations are as follows:

(a) Medical examinations should be administered to all engaged in athletics, previous to actual participation and as they are needed during the time the sport is in progress. This refers to all forms of strenuous athletics whether it be interscholastic, intramural, or part of the class program.

(b) There should be adequate provision for medical service at all athletic contests.

(c) A physician's recommendation should accompany any athlete returning to competition after a period of illness.

(d) Examinations conducted for participation in athletics should preferably be conducted by the family physician. In instances where this is not feasible, the school physician should perform this service.

b. *Psychological Examinations.*—With the increased emphasis on mental health, various psychological examinations are being used more extensively. These examinations, however, represent only a very small part of the school mental health services that should be available. Mental health programs are concerned with helping children to adjust satisfactorily to the school environment, detecting individual behavior problems, aiding the teacher, parent, and others to better understand human behavior, and helping in every way possible to appraise personality, discover mental handicaps, emotional difficulties, and maladjustments.

Psychological examinations and tests which appraise such factors as pupils' abilities, attitudes, personalities, intelligence, and social adjustment offer techniques for obtaining much information. The administration and interpretation of the findings of such techniques should be handled by qualified individuals.

c. *Dental Examinations.*—Administrative guides governing school dental services are as follows:

(1) *Emphasis:* The emphasis in school dental services should be on health education. Children and parents should develop proper attitudes toward dental

---

*See also "Health Safeguards" in Chapter XVIII.

[7]Report of the Committee on Health Service Programs for Secondary Schools. *Suggested Standard for Health Services in Secondary Schools. American Journal of Public Health Year Book,* 42: 143, May, 1952.

caries and oral hygiene. Periodically, they should consult their family dentist for the necessary examination, care, and advice.

(2) *Personnel:* The personnel in the school particularly concerned with dental health include the teacher, the nurse, physician, and dental hygienist. The staff will depend upon the community philosophy concerning dental care. If the emphasis is upon education, it will be different than if it is on treatment. When a dental hygienist is a member of the school staff, she often has a variety of duties, including acting as a resource person for classroom teachers regarding dental health, making topical applications of sodium fluoride, cleaning children's teeth, and administering limited dental inspections or examinations.

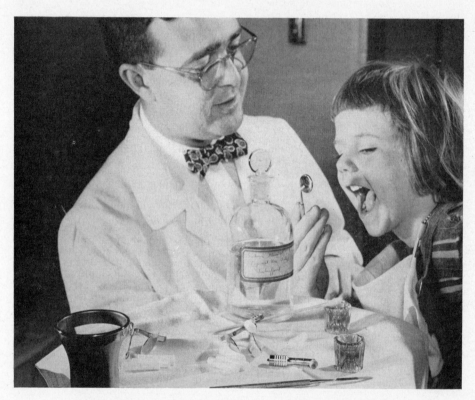

Dental inspection. (Courtesy of Indiana State Department of Health.)

(3) *Nature:* A difference of opinion exists as to whether or not schools should provide dental examinations or inspections for pupils. Those in favor of such a practice point to its value as a motivating device to encourage parents and children to visit the dentist. Furthermore, they say it helps children in the low-income classes and focuses attention on the dental needs of children. Those not in favor of such a practice argue that as a result of school examinations children and parents visit their dentist less often and in some cases even substitute this examination for regular dental care. They further point out that it is the responsibility of everyone to make provision for his own dental care and that the school

is not the agency responsible for providing such a service. The question of the school's responsibility should be decided in each local community through conferences with dentists, educators, parents, and others interested in the problem. It can then be resolved in a manner that will best meet the needs of the children.

(4) *Scope:* The scope of the school dental program usually concerns itself with the dental examination or inspection, limited to the conditions stated above, and prophylaxis or cleaning. In addition, there are a few schools that treat emergency cases and provide other dental care for children of parents who cannot afford such services.

(5) *Dental problems:* The problems concerned with dental health are dental caries, or decayed teeth; malocclusion, a condition in which the teeth do not uniformly fit together when the jaws are closed; and periodontal diseases in which the tissues surrounding the teeth become infected, such as gingivitis or inflammation of the gums, or Vincent's infection or trench mouth. Although dental caries is the most common problem, the others should receive due consideration.

FORM 79 5M 8-48 ⊕

New Trier Township
High School

DENTAL CERTIFICATE

Winnetka
Illinois

This is to certify that I have examined the teeth of

STUDENT'S NAME_____ADVISER_____
            (Last)   (First)

RECORD OF EXAMINATIONS

Date	Clean	Under Repair	Under Treatment	Remarks	Dentist's Signature

Dental caries can best be prevented and controlled through good dental hygiene which includes frequent brushing, especially after eating; reducing sugar intake; topical fluoride applications which, it is estimated, can cut down dental caries by about 40 per cent; and fluoridation of water supplies which experiments have shown reduce dental caries from 40 to 60 per cent.

(6) *Educational implications:* The educational implications of dental health services are far reaching. Pupils and parents can be motivated to practice good oral hygiene and to visit their dentist regularly. The proper attitudes can be developed, resulting in good dental habits.

2. Screening for Vision and Hearing Defects:

a. *Vision:*

(1) *Vision health services:* The vision health services program in the school is concerned with the examinations given by physicians and appraisal of visual acuity. The appraisal of visual acuity is accomplished through continuous observations by the teacher and screening examinations. Both are necessary for the continual and satisfactory appraisal of the vision of school children.

(2) *Frequency of Screening Tests:* Tests of visual acuity should be given annually. The optimum time for such screening is immediately after the opening of school in the fall. They can be given to children in the early grades, as soon as they are old enough to cooperate satisfactorily. If possible, there should be a complete eye examination before the child enters school.

(3) *Administration of screening tests:* The teacher, after proper instruction and training, is qualified to administer various screening devices for vision. These devices, however, are only for purposes of detecting those individuals who need special care in respect to their vision. Their use is not a diagnostic technique.

(4) *Selection of screening devices:* The particular device that is utilized for checking visual acuity, together with the plans for appraisal, should be selected and arranged through conferences of school administrators, teachers, nurses, physicians, ophthalmologists, and optometrists.

It has been found that with young children, the Snellen E. chart seems effective. For older children, the Snellen and Massachusetts Vision Tests have received wide recommendation. These devices should be administered according to prescribed instructions and pupils should be properly prepared for the examinations.

If needed, there are techniques for determining color acuity such as the Holmgren test, and for determining muscle balance such as the "cover test."

(5) *Referrals:* The results of the screening examinations should be recorded and studied. In the light of these results and the teacher's observations, children with difficulties should be referred to the proper place for an eye examination. According to the Joint Committee of the National Education Association and the American Medical Association, "parents should be urged to secure eye examinations for children who are in the following categories. (a) Those who consistently exhibit symptoms of visual disturbance, regardless of the results of the Snellen test, (b) Older children who have a visual acuity of 20/30 or less in either eye, with or without symptoms, and (c) Younger children (seven years of age, or less) who on a re-examination have a visual acuity of 20/40 or less in either eye, with or without symptoms."[8]

(6) *Teacher's observations:* The teacher as well as the parent should be alert to visual difficulties and problems among children. By being aware of certain actions and manifestations of the child from day to day under varying situations, it is possible to detect many eye difficulties which should be referred for examination. Many of these eye difficulties might go unnoticed unless the alert teacher or parent is aware of certain characteristics which indicate vision problems.

---

[8]Joint Committee. *School Health Services, op. cit.,* p. 77.

The Joint Committee[9] has listed certain manifestations of visual difficulty in children before they begin to read and after reading activities have begun.

Before the child begins to read:
Attempts to brush away blur
Blinking more than usual
Frequent rubbing of the eyes
Squinting when looking at distant objects
Frequent or continuous frowning
Stumbling over small objects
Undue sensitivity to light
Red, encrusted, or swollen eyelids
Recurring styes
Inflamed or watery eyes
Crossed eyes

After reading activities have begun:
Holding a book too far away from or too close to the face when reading
Inattention during reading periods, chalkboard, chart or map work
Difficulty in reading or in other work requiring close use of the eyes
Inability, or lack of desire, to participate in games requiring distance vision
Poor alignment in written work
Tilting head to one side or thrusting head forward when looking at near or distant objects
Irritability when doing close work
Shutting or covering one eye when reading

b. *Hearing.*—Administrative guides for conduct of health services in regard to hearing are as follows:

(1) *Scope:* The main responsibility of the schools in respect to auditory health services is to detect those pupils with hearing difficulties, as early as possible. This can be accomplished through such means as teacher observations and screening tests. A counseling and follow-through program which aims at remedying the defect should also be a part of the total plan.

(2) *Frequency:* Continuous observations should be a part of the school routine. Annual screening tests during the elementary years and one every two years at the secondary level are recommended. There should be a minimum of three tests during the first eight years of school. It is also recommended that a preschool test of auditory acuity should be given wherever possible.

(3) *Techniques:* The most common techniques for screening auditory acuity are as follows: The group audiometer is a common device to screen out children with hearing defects. This device is not recommended for children lower than the third grade. Individuals with suspected hearing losses of 9 or more Sensation Units in one or both ears should be given retests to check results or the pure-tone audiometer test for more accurate screening.

Younger children under the third grade level can be screened with such tests of hearing acuity as the "Peep Show" and Skin Response test.

The pure-tone audiometer is recommended as one of the most effective techniques. This is a more accurate instrument and allows for checking of either or both ears.

[9]*Ibid.*, p. 71.

In some schools it may be impossible to have access to an audiometer. In such cases the whisper test may be utilized to detect the most serious cases of hearing loss. This technique requires that the pupil stand 20 feet from the one administering the test, and repeat whispered numbers or words. The watch tick test is also used.

(4) *Referrals:* A hearing loss of 9 or more Sensation Units in one or both ears indicates unsatisfactory hearing, when the group audiometer is used. In such cases re-checks should be made to determine accuracy of screening. If results are consistent, parents should be informed and encouraged to follow through with more complete examination.

Pure-tone Audiometer.   (Courtesy of Indiana State Department of Health.)

When using the pure-tone audiometer it is recommended that a "hearing loss of 15 decibels at two or more tones in the speech range, or of 20 decibels in the higher tones, is reason for referring a pupil for otological examination."[10]

In using the whisper test any child who must be four feet or less from sound in order to hear the whispered numbers or words is a suspect and should be referred for further examination.

Teachers who observe mouth breathing, ear discharge, or other abnormalities or characteristics which might arouse suspicion of hearing loss should refer the case to the proper authorities.

---

[10]American Association of School Administrators, *op. cit.,* p. 278.

(5) *Teacher's observations:* The teacher can play an important part in continually observing the child for indications of hearing loss. She also is a key person in administering screening techniques. She should be watchful for such mannerisms as speech difficulties, requests for repetition of questions, turning of head to better hear what is said, and inattention, together with such noticeable characteristics as discharging ears, earaches, and other departures from the normal makeup of the child. Through such observations the teacher will detect individuals who need to be referred for more careful study and examination. All teachers should be alert for such manifestations.

(6) *Personnel:* Teachers, nurses, or technicians may be utilized in administering the various screening devices. All should be well trained in the use and purpose of such instruments. They should recognize that these are screening instruments and not diagnostic devices. There should be a careful check to determine that the instruments are in good working order and yield accurate results.

(7) *Sources for Further information:*

> American Medical Association, 535 North Dearborn Street, Chicago,
>   Illinois. Council on Physical Medicine and Rehabilitation
> The American Academy of Ophthalmology and Otolaryngology.
> American Hearing Society, 817 14th Street N.W., Washington 5, D. C.

3. Teachers' Observations.—Teachers' observations are of great importance in detecting health needs of school children. Furthermore, they increase in importance in the absence of nurses and doctors. Although this subject has been discussed previously, it is of such great importance that it is considered again here in more detail. Teachers, through observations of the appearance and behavior of pupils from day to day, become very well acquainted with each individual child. Any deviations from normal in appearance and in action will be detected very quickly by the alert teacher. For many of the health needs this provides the only means of discovering problems. Very often they would not be detected through medical examinations and other health services. Therefore, the teacher's role in health services, through her continual association and observation of children, is a major one. Such observations, after careful examination by nurses and physicians, may disclose various deficiencies. They may show that some children are maladjusted socially and emotionally, are undernourished, in the early stages of a communicable or other disease, have some physical defects, neurological difficulties, or have developed poor health habits. Along with referral to nurses and physicians, the parents should also be informed of such discoveries. It should be re-emphasized that in no case does the teacher diagnose. Instead, she refers the matter to the nurse, physician, and parent for further action.

The oft quoted report from the health manual of the Massachusetts Department of Education and Department of Public Health,[11] lists the various physical and behavior conditions for which the teacher should be alert in regard to the children with whom she associates each day.

---

[11]Commonwealth of Massachusetts. *Health in the Schools—A Manual of the School Health Program.* Boston: Massachusetts Department of Education with the collaboration of Massachusetts Department of Public Health, 1951, pp. 23-24.

1. EYES
   a. Styes or crusted lids
   b. Inflamed eyes
   c. Crossed eyes
   d. Repeated headaches
   e. Squinting, frowning, or scowling
   f. Protruding eyes
   g. Watery eyes
   h. Rubbing of eyes
   i. Excessive blinking
   j. Twitching of the lids
   k. Holding head to one side

2. EARS
   a. Discharge from ears
   b. Earache
   c. Failure to hear questions
   d. Picking at the ears
   e. Turning the head to hear
   f. Talking in a monotone
   g. Inattention
   h. Anxious expression
   i. Excessive noisiness of child

3. NOSE AND THROAT
   a. Persistent mouth breathing
   b. Frequent sore throat
   c. Recurrent colds
   d. Chronic nasal discharge
   e. Frequent nose bleeding
   f. Nasal speech
   g. Frequent tonsillitis

4. SKIN AND SCALP
   a. Nits on the hair
   b. Unusual pallor of face
   c. Eruptions or rashes
   d. Habitual scratching of scalp or skin
   e. State of cleanliness
   f. Excessive redness of skin

5. TEETH AND MOUTH
   a. State of cleanliness
   b. Gross visible caries
   c. Irregular teeth
   d. Stained teeth
   e. Offensive breath
   f. Mouth habits such as thumb-sucking

6. GENERAL CONDITION AND APPEARANCE
   a. Underweight—very thin
   b. Overweight—very obese
   c. Does not appear well
   d. Tires easily
   e. Chronic fatigue
   f. Nausea or vomiting
   g. Faintness or dizziness

7. GROWTH
   a. Failure to gain regularly over 3-months' period
   b. Unexplained loss in weight
   c. Unexplained rapid gain in weight

8. GLANDS
   a. Enlarged glands at one side of neck
   b. Enlarged thyroid

9. HEART
   a. Excessive breathlessness
   b. Tires easily
   c. Any history of "growing pains"
   d. Bluish lips
   e. Excessive pallor

10. POSTURE AND MUSCULATURE
    a. Asymmetry of shoulders and hips
    b. Peculiarity of gait
    c. Obvious deformities of any type
    d. Anomalies of muscular development

11. BEHAVIOR
    a. Overstudious, docile, and withdrawing
    b. Bullying, overaggressive, and domineering
    c. Unhappy and depressed
    d. Overexcitable, uncontrollable emotions
    e. Stuttering or other forms of speech difficulty
    f. Lack of confidence, self-denial, and self-censure
    g. Poor accomplishment in comparison with ability
    h. Lying (imaginative or defensive)
    i. Lack of appreciation of property rights (stealing)
    j. Abnormal sex behavior
    k. Antagonistic, negativistic, continually quarreling

4. Health Records.—Some administrative guides in connection with health records are as follows:

(1) As part of the over-all school record, there should be a health record which contains a complete appraisal of the child's health. This should include such items as health history, vision and hearing data, teacher's observations, results of various medical, psychological, dental, and other examinations that are given, reports of all conferences held with student, health defects that have been corrected, and any other information that has a bearing on the health of the child.

(2) The health record should follow the student wherever he goes—when he moves from one community to another or when he is transferred from one school to another.

(3) The records should be cumulative in nature, pointing out the complete health history of the child, together with a continuous appraisal of his health.

(4) The health record should be made available to school, medical, and other personnel who are concerned with and work toward the maintenance and improvement of a child's health. Professional ethics should govern the handling of such information.

(5) The health record, if kept up to date and accurate, will prove a very useful and effective device in furthering the health of all school children.

a. *Health Histories:*

(1) The history of the child's health should be in recorded form as an aid to teachers, nurses, physicians, and others in order to better understand the total picture of the child's health.

(2) This record should be kept on a prepared form and should contain a complete history of communicable diseases, operations, accidents, immunizations, dental history, emotional maladjustments, physical abnormalities, nutritional problems, menstruation, and any other factors which would be of help in better interpreting the total health picture.

(3) The health history should be brought up to date before the medical examination is given so that the examining physician may use it as an aid.

b. *Height-Weight Records.*—Administrative guides in connection with height-weight records are as follows:

(1) The teacher, or children under supervision, should measure and record the height and weight of pupils at least three times a year. It is recommended that this be done at the beginning, middle, and toward the end of the year.

(2) Height-weight records should not be utilized as a device to diagnose such elements as nutritional status. Instead, they should be used as indications that some health problems may exist if, for example, a child's weight does not increase during any three-month period. They are best utilized, not when compared against the height and weight of other children, but when used as a comparison and history of a child's own growth from time to time.

(3) Height-weight records provide an interesting and worth-while phase of health education since pupils are interested in observing their growth and become curious as to some of the reasons that encourage or deter growth.

c. *Accident Records.**—Accident records, as a means of health appraisal, provide information as to reasons for physical abnormalities and emotional maladjustment that may occur in children. They also provide a medium of promoting safety. They should be carefully kept and contain complete information.†

B. Health Counseling

In the light of the findings gathered through appraisal techniques, health matters are discussed with pupils and parents. Such problems as the need for medical and dental treatment, better health practices, diagnostic examinations, special services and analyzing behavior problems are discussed. Through such counseling procedures a better understanding of the health of children and adults is brought about.

Health counseling is an important phase of the total health services program. As health needs and problems are revealed through medical examinations and other techniques, it is essential that defects be corrected, advice given, and a planned procedure established to provide for these needs and eliminate the problems. Health counseling by qualified persons can help in achieving these goals.

1. Purposes.—One general objective of health counseling is to provide pupils and parents with a better understanding of their health needs and the procedures that should be followed in order to satisfy these needs. Also, health counseling serves as a device for health education. Through conferences and discussion regarding health problems it is possible to develop sound health attitudes. Facts are presented which indicate the need for following acceptable health practices. The parent and child are motivated to alter their behavior in accordance with acceptable health standards. In addition, health counseling can help to develop a feeling of responsibility in pupils and parents for the correction of health defects and for promoting school and community health programs.

The specific purposes or objectives of health counseling as listed by Schwebel and Harris[12] are three in number. The first purpose is that of *acceptance of self.* The authors point out that a realistic appraisal of self is needed for the maintenance of high health standards. Since behavior is based on how one views himself and the world at large, it is important that the individual see himself and the world in true perspective. He must see himself in respect to all his needs, defects, and problems. When this goal is realized, planning can take place and help can be given. The health counselor must achieve this objective in order to accomplish the desired results.

The second objective is that of *solving the problem at hand.* After the first objective has been realized, the individual is ready to progress further. He understands himself. He is receptive to counseling recommendations which will help to make life more satisfying. He more clearly recognizes his needs and is interested in meeting them. He sees to it that remediable health defects are corrected and good health habits are established.

The third objective is concerned with *skill in handling future problems.* Counseling is a continuous process with educational implications. It is not centered

---

*For further discussion of accident records see Chapter VIII on Legal Liability.
†See also pp. 149, 151.
[12]Milton Schwebel and Ella Freas Harris. *Health Counseling.* New York: Chartwell House, 1951, pp. 22-28.

solely on the immediate problems at hand, but instead is concerned with establishing an atmosphere of understanding whereby the counselor is consulted in the future when new problems arise. Furthermore, the counseling should result in the student's doing some self-appraisal, to determine his own needs and how his community can help in meeting these needs.

In utilizing counseling as part of the health services program, it should be clearly recognized at the outset that it is not a cure for all ills. There are limitations. Counselors cannot always change individuals. This has been true, for example, of some handicapped individuals who are subject to pity, ridicule, or scorn by their fellow beings. Counselors can only help individuals to understand themselves, realize their potentialities, live out their natural lives in a happy and productive manner. In some individuals, however, the social and physical environments have left their stamp so indelibly that counseling can do only a limited amount of good.

2. The Counselor.—The classroom teacher, school principal, physician, nurse, physical education teacher, social worker, recreation leader, guidance person, and others have potentialities as counselors in the field of health. All have relationships with students which place them in a position to offer helpful advice and guidance. Whether or not they carry out such responsibilities effectively will depend on certain basic requirements.

Basic requirements for the counselors are concerned with their interest in people, personality, and competency in counseling skills.

To be effective, a counselor must be interested in people, from the standpoint of service. The desire to help others live a happy and successful life and to help eliminate those problems which handicap the achievement of such goals must predominate in the counselor's mind. If this characteristic exists, it will serve as one of the major requisites for good counseling.

A second basic requirement is the counselor's personality. Counseling procedure involves divulging personal problems and other matters which are brought out only when there is good rapport between the counselor and student or parent. Personality is a key to the establishment of a warm and cooperative counselor-client rapport. The counselor's personality must reflect such essentials as friendliness, interest in others' problems, and the desire to help. He must be a good listener and respecter of the views of others. A good counselor does not talk down to the pupil but confers with the student in an atmosphere of mutual understanding and respect.

A third requirement is competency in counseling skills. As in all specialized services, there are certain competencies which are essential to doing a good job. Studies have shown that the person who has developed competency in counseling gets more effective results and does a better job than the unskilled individual. Skills are necessary in establishing rapport with clients, understanding the implications of behavior patterns, communicating with students, analyzing pupil problems, conducting group discussion, administering conference procedures, and preparing records. These skills represent a basic requirement for all who wish to do the best job possible in respect to health counseling.

3. Conference Method.—The conference method of counseling which brings about a face-to-face relationship between the counselor, the pupil, and the parent is the best method for achieving desirable results. The use of written notices and standard forms is not recommended because of the possibility of misinterpretation and the lack of a clear understanding of the problems involved.

The success of the conference method will depend on the skill and the degree to which the counselor has planned for the conference. It is essential that the counselor have all the necessary records at hand, together with a complete understanding of the community, home, and problems surrounding the pupil in question.

The counselor must establish the proper relationship among the individuals who are present. A friendly and understanding atmosphere is necessary for the achievement of the desired results. The discussion of health matters must be carried on effectively and in a sound manner so that the pupil and parent will recognize the problems that exist and endorse the action that must be taken.

When the conference comes to an end there should be a common understanding among the counselor, pupil, and parent as to the next steps to be taken in the elimination of the health problems.

C. Correction of Remediable Defects

Two phases of school health services have been discussed. The child's health must first be appraised. Secondly, there must be a counseling procedure whereby the pupil and his parents are informed of health needs and problems so that the necessary action can be taken. After health appraisal and health counseling have been accomplished, the job is not completed. Next there must be a follow-through to see that remediable defects are corrected.

Children have many health defects that can be corrected. Dental caries is an example. It has been estimated that about 50 per cent of two-year-old children have one or more teeth that are carious. When they start school the number has risen to three and the number increases as the child progresses in school. Another study concerned with vision defects showed that 16.3 per cent of elementary school children needed to have eye examinations because of refractive errors.[13] Laxity in the correction of remediable defects seems to be especially prevalent in respect to teeth and eyes. There are also many other defects that can be corrected in the areas of malnutrition, hearing, speech, postural defects, diseased tonsils and adenoids, and emotional disorders.

The school has the responsibility for not only detecting such defects, whenever possible, but also putting forth every effort to see that they are corrected. As pointed out by the American Association for Health, Physical Education, and Recreation, "The school's responsibility may be summarized in these words: to help every child attain the highest possible well-being; to see that no child is deprived of growth by reason of physical handicaps, defects, or anomalies which might constitute an obstacle to growth; to bring to bear measures of detection and follow-through leading to treatment, correction, or other helpful adjustment; and to guide parents, school staff, children, and all others involved to a greater under-

---

[13]Joint Committee. *School Health Services,* pp. 67, 110.

standing of the important factors related to better total health."[14] This statement places upon the school a great responsibility for seeing that all remediable defects are provided for. The fact that this has not always been done in the past was shown by certain studies which analyzed the records of medical examinations given during World War II. It was found that many of the defects listed in these services examinations had previously been detected in school health appraisals. However, since there had been no successful follow-through and correction, the defects still existed.

1. Community Philosophy.—The philosophy in respect to the methods which will be used to correct remediable defects will depend upon the community and the public at large. Although it is generally believed that the school should be concerned with educating parents and the public as to the importance of correcting such defects, rather than with becoming a treatment agency, this belief and practice do not exist in all communities. Basically, the schools should not treat. They are not equipped with the personnel, facilities, and other necessities for such a purpose. However, it is a community prerogative to decide such an issue. As a result, in some communities the school provides for the correction of dental, nutritional, postural, and other defects. In other communities this is considered a parental responsibility, and the school takes over only when indigent parents cannot afford such services. In many communities the school does not treat in any way. The community must decide which method is most effective for the correction of defects.

2. Getting Results.—To obtain the best results in the correction of remediable defects there must be planning, conferences, and accurate record keeping.

The teacher, nurse, health counselor, principal, and school physician should play active roles in planning such a program. A written plan should be developed and distributed so that all will be acquainted with the procedure that is to be followed. The responsibility for record keeping, home visitation, checking periodically to see if defects have been corrected, and all other essential phases of the plan should be clearly designated. Good results will not be obtained if planning is a "hit-and-miss" affair. It will be effective only if it is done in advance of the detection of defects. If necessary, it should also be reviewed and amended periodically.

A second requisite for getting results is home and school conferences. As has been previously pointed out, written notices are cold and formal and do not achieve the desired results, as do personal conferences. If possible, the parents should come to the school for such purposes, as it helps to give the school prestige. However, where parents are reluctant to come to school, there should be visits to the home, preferably by the nurse. This also affords an opportunity to observe home conditions which affect the health of the child. At these conferences or visitations every attempt should be made to interest the pupil and the parent in the correction of the defects.

Two of the main reasons why health defects are not corrected are lack of money to provide the necessary service and indifference on the part of both pupil

[14]American Association for Health, Physical Education and Recreation. *Administrative Problems in Health Education, Physical Education and Recreation.* Washington, D. C.: The Association, 1953, pp. 5-6.

and parent. Conferences should aim at eliminating the indifference and attempting to provide the ways and means when the money problem exists. In most communities there are charitable organizations, civic groups, or others who will be happy to defray such expenses.

A third requirement for getting good results is accurate record keeping. As a part of health appraisal the defects should be properly recorded. It is essential to keep a record of all conferences and home visitations. Progress that has been made should be noted. Accurate and complete records will make it possible to know the current status of each pupil.

3. Community Resources.—Community resources should be tapped for aid in the correction of remediable defects. Public clinics, welfare agencies, and voluntary organizations should be utilized to give aid to indigent families where financial status prevents such treatment. A list of the hospitals, specialists, and clinics for various types of treatment could be provided when parents want additional information. In most cases it is better to suggest the names of several specialists rather than just one.

The school should work cooperatively with the various community agencies interested in this work. In some cases, time during the school day might be provided for students who must have treatment. Literature and other information prepared by various community agencies might be distributed. Meetings between leaders in the school and community agencies might be held to plan a program. A community health council is an ideal place for discussing and formulating plans for the correction of remediable defects. By mobilizing and utilizing community resources, remediable defects will be corrected.

D. Care and Education of Exceptional Children

The term "exceptional" refers to those children who are handicapped mentally, physically, socially, or emotionally, and also to those who are gifted intellectually or in other ways.

A democratic society rests on the premise that all individuals should have equal opportunities to develop the various talents which they possess. This means that all children and youth in our schools should be granted the right to have an education which is adapted to their particular physical, mental, social and emotional endowments. Therefore, whether an individual is gifted, normal, or handicapped, he should have the right to pursue the educational program which is best adapted to his particular needs and which enables him to achieve his potentialities as a human being. This is an important consideration in a democratic society that recognizes the worth of each individual and his right to "life, liberty and the pursuit of happiness."

One deterring factor to the care and education of exceptional children has been the cost. For example, in Cleveland, braille and sight-saving classes in the elementary schools cost $700.16 per pupil in 1950, whereas regular classes cost $197.40 per pupil. However, such expenditure of funds may be a saving in the long run as the handicapped become self-supporting. It is money well spent.

In any discussion of the care and education of the exceptional child, it would seem important to consider (1) identifying the exceptional, (2) discovering the exceptional, (3) adapting the educational program to the exceptional, and (4) discussing the personnel that should be concerned with the care and education of the exceptional.

1. Who Are the Exceptional Children?—The American Association of School Administrators classifies exceptional children in four categories.

(1) Children with superior intellectual capacity or with special talents in high degree.

(2) Children who are mentally retarded.

(3) Children with problems growing out of physical defects, disorder, or disease.

(4) Children who are emotionally disturbed or socially maladjusted.[15]

The number of exceptional children is quite astounding. A few years ago one estimate[16] stated that for every one thousand school population between ages 5 and 19 there are 20 mentally retarded children, 2 who have vision handicaps, 15 deaf or hard of hearing, 10 who are crippled, 15 of lowered vitality, 15 speech defective, 2 epileptic, and 25 who are emotionally disturbed or socially maladjusted. The report also pointed out that there are 20 who are mentally gifted.

The National Society for the Study of Education more recently estimated that from 10 to 12 per cent or approximately four million children of elementary, junior high school, and senior high school ages would fall into the classification of "exceptional" and would need special health services.

The prevalence of exceptional school children is evident in every community. These children should be identified, referred for special services, and the educational program adapted to their needs and abilities. This is an important responsibility in the area of health services. To shirk such a responsibility is to ignore the welfare of a great segment of American children.

2. Discovering the Exceptional Child.—It is very important that each school develop a planned procedure for determining those pupils who are exceptional. It is very simple to identify some cases, such as those that are crippled, defective in their speech, or socially maladjusted. However, in others, where cardiac defects or tuberculosis causes the handicap, it is not as easy. Therefore, it is important to establish a planned program. This can take several forms.

The exceptional child may be identified through the various phases of health appraisal that are conducted as part of the health services program. Through a thorough medical examination, the cardiac-handicapped, for example, will be identified; through a psychological examination the mentally or emotionally maladjusted pupil will be singled out; and through screening procedures, those with vision and hearing handicaps will be known.

The health history which should be a part of every student's health record is another source for information leading to the identification of exceptional characteristics. A health history that lists all the significant diseases, accidents, and other aspects of the health history of a child should also list any exceptional characteristics that exist.

---

[15]American Association of School Administrators, *op. cit.*, p. 214.

[16]U. S. Office of Education, Federal Security Agency. *Needs of Exceptional Children.* Leaflet No. 74. Washington, D. C.: Superintendent of Documents, Government Printing Office, 1944. p. 4. (Adapted.)

Teachers' observations also play a very important part. Through continuous observations on the part of a teacher, deviations from normal behavior will be identified. The individual who is listless might require further examination, display of exceptional talent might indicate a genius in the class, or a child who finds it difficult to keep up with other boys his age in physical education activities should have further attention. Many of the children who fall into the exceptional group will have to be identified by teachers who work with them every day, if they are to be singled out for special help.

Conferences with parents, teacher conferences with the school nurse, certain classroom tests, and reports from family physicians will help to identify exceptional individuals.

All of these methods should be carefully considered as potential media for identifying the many exceptional children that are regularly attending the public schools.

3. Adapting the Educational Program to the Exceptional Child.—Some administrative guides for adapting the educational program and caring for the exceptional child are as follows:

(1) The school, as a general rule, should not undertake the treatment of the handicapped. However, it should do everything within its power to see that the necessary medical care is provided those who need such service. Through its referral service the school can carry out this responsibility.

(2) Exceptional pupils should be treated as individuals and consideration given to each case, rather than dealt with as groups of children with similar characteristics.

(3) Whether or not the exceptional individual is part of the regular group in the school situation, a part of a separate group, or in a separate school will depend upon the individual. The decision should be based on the question of which situation will allow the greatest possibility for improvement of the child's condition and for his total growth and development.

(4) Special classes will aid certain individuals. One source has listed the following:

> Children who are *hard of hearing* or who have *speech defects*. They can be helped by part-time special classes or individual periods of instruction in speech or lip-reading.
>
> Children with *marked defects in vision*. Sight-saving classes may be organized for those whose vision is 20/70 or worse in the better eye after correction or who have other eye conditions that make it desirable to reduce eye work.
>
> Children who are *severely crippled*. This may involve provision of physical therapy and special programs of physical education.
>
> Children unable to attend school—*the home-bound*. This may include children who are convalescing from severe or prolonged sickness, such as rheumatic fever. Some severely crippled children will be in this group.
>
> Children with intelligence quotients ranging from 50 to 70—*the mentally retarded*. These children need a program different from that of intellectually normal children.[17]

---

[17]Joint Committee on Health Problems in Education of the National Education Association and the American Medical Association. *Health Education*. Charles C. Wilson, Editor. Washington, D. C.: National Education Association, 1948, p. 106.

(5) There is a need for an adequate supervisory program in connection with special classes for exceptional children. Good supervision will ensure periodic examinations to determine the status of the individual in respect to his exception, make sure that the program is as much like a regular school program as possible, and see that the child is returned to the regular class with normal children as soon as possible.

The school should do everything within its power to help obtain the necessary medical care for the handicapped child. United States Office of Education, Department of Health, Education, and Welfare.

(6) There are many different courses of action for the education and care of the exceptional. A few methods for making provisions for the various classifications are listed. This listing, however, is in no way complete, and special resources should be consulted for a more complete description of the school's responsibility.

The *deaf,* when so classified by a competent specialist, are those that have a hearing loss of 70 decibels or more. Generally, they should be placed in special schools.

The education and care of the *hard of hearing* will vary with hearing loss (slight—loss of 20-30 decibels, mild to moderate—loss of 30-40 decibels, moderate to severe—loss of 40-70 decibels, and severe—loss of more than 70 decibels).[18] Provisions can be made, such as special arrangements for seating and instruction, hearing aids, speech and lip reading, special classes and special schools.

The *blind* (20/200 in better eye with glasses) may be provided for either by a special school or by special classes where braille is used.

The orthopedically handicapped child. United States Office of Education, Department of Health, Education, and Welfare.

The *partially sighted* (between 20/70 and 20/200 with glasses) can be provided for by proper fitting of correct glasses, sight-saving classes, provision within regular classroom, proper seating, advantageous scheduling of classes and special materials such as typewriters.

The *orthopedically handicapped child* should be cared for in regular classes, whenever it is possible. Special provisions for children handicapped in this group

[18]Joint Committee. *School Health Services,* p. 188.

include: "(a) transportation in school buses with an attendant, (b) physical and occupational therapy, (c) speech therapy, if needed, and (d) general health supervision by the teacher under the general direction of the school medical adviser and nurse, if such are available."[19]

The *speech defective's* first need is a complete examination with medical and surgical care, if necessary, to remove the cause of the speech defect. Speech defects such as stuttering, stammering, and phonetic difficulties can be aided through work with a speech correctionist, especially in the case of young children. Special classes are not needed; the student can attend regular classes and get the necessary treatment at a speech clinic or other place.

Malnourished and *undervitalized* children will usually be cared for on both an individual and a community basis. Health education aimed at raising the nutritional status of the home, a careful perusal of health histories to identify the causes, adjustment of school program, and in some cases provision for special rest rooms will contribute to the solution of the defects.

The *mentally retarded* child (50-70 intelligence quotient) should have a program which stresses, according to his individual abilities, proper health, safety, and social habits; information and skills essential to constructive community living, such as care of children, proper maintenance of the home and the community health resources that are available; and skills for creative and leisure-time activities which will lead to cultural development.[20]

The *mentally gifted child* (I.Q. of approximately 140 or over) has been helped in at least four ways, (1) advancement in school levels according to his ability to achieve higher standards, (2) enrichment of his curriculum so that it is adapted more to his abilities, (3) attendance in special classes, and (4) addition of elective courses.[21]

Cardiac-handicapped children should be provided for after complete examination by competent medical personnel. A few will require special classes, others will require modified programs, and some will need instruction to help them understand and live within certain restrictions.

The *tubercular-handicapped* child, if he has a case of active tuberculosis, should not be in school. The school programs for children who have had the disease should be adapted to their needs. This should be done in consultation with the appropriate medical person. This may mean only part-time attendance at school, provision for rest periods, limited physical activity, and special transportation.

The *emotionally atypical* should be provided for in relation to their maladjustments. Some will need the help of a qualified psychiatrist. Others will be helped by the guidance counselor or teacher. In most cases the teacher can play a key role in providing an emotional atmosphere where the child reacts favorably to the group.

The *socially exceptional* should also be provided for in relation to the extent of their maladjustments. A few of the most severe cases will need confinement to

[19]*Ibid.*, p. 194.
[20]*Ibid.*, p. 203.
[21]*Ibid.*, pp. 206-207.

institutions; the rest will need rehabilitation, care, or developmental opportunities to restore them to normalcy.

The national committee on school health policies points out other ways that the school can make special provisions for handicapped pupils.

> Specially constructed chairs and desks—for the orthopedically disabled children.
> Appropriate seating arrangements—"down front" for children with vision or hearing defects.
> Scheduling of classes all on one floor.
> Rest periods and facilities (cots) for resting—for children with cardiac and other impairments.
> Permission to attend school for only part of the day.
> Adaptation of physical education requirements.
> Transportation to and from school.[22]

Such provisions enable many handicapped pupils to attend regular classes.

4. Personnel.—The teachers who work with exceptional children should be well trained for their duties. Whether or not the child is able to adjust satisfactorily to the group, improve, and be educated and cared for in a desirable manner will depend to a great degree upon the teacher.

Teachers should be well prepared for the particular grade or subject to which they are assigned. In addition, they should be trained to work with exceptional children with specific disabilities. The nature or type of disability will determine the training needed. The teacher should be emotionally stable and have the type of temperament which is suitable for working with abnormal children. The size of classes for exceptional children should be smaller than for regular classes. If progress is to be achieved, the individual approach must be applied as much as possible.

In addition to the teacher, there are other individuals in the school and community who can render contributions to this phase of the health service program. Where they are part of the school staff, the nurse, guidance director, school physician, psychologist, social worker, and director of special education should work closely with the teacher and school administrator in planning the program. Other individuals such as ophthalmologists, psychiatrists, orthopedists, speech correctionists, otologists, directors of agencies dealing with the handicapped, and members of state departments of health and education should be utilized for advice, planning, referrals, in-service education and other contributions to this phase of the health service program.

E. Communicable Disease Control

Wherever children congregate there is the possibility of spreading disease. The school, as a place for children and youth to congregate, is unique in that the law requires attendance. Therefore, if it is compulsory to go to school, there should also be certain protective measures and precautions taken to ensure that everything is done to guard the health of the child. This includes the necessary procedures for controlling communicable disease.

---

[22]National Committee on School Health Policies. *Suggested School Health Policies.* New York: Health Education Council, 1946, p. 37.

The problem of communicable disease control can be discussed under two main headings, first, responsibility and second, the various measures that should be applied in the school situation.

1. Responsibility.—The legal responsibility for communicable disease control rests with state and local departments of health. This means that public health officials have control over school personnel in this matter. In most cases, however, this is a case of cooperation rather than compulsion. School officials should work closely with public health officials so that cases of communicable disease are reported and proper measures taken to prevent other children from contracting the disease.

Three ways in which communicable disease control is administered by school and public health authorities are as follows:

1. A public health department that assumes direct responsibility for community health measures but not for health examinations of school children, customarily employs physicians or nurses, or both, and the principal responsibility for all school functions is carried on by them. Even the primary responsibility for communicable disease control is often delegated by the health department to the school medical personnel who operate under health department rulings but under school administration.

2. A public health department which is responsible for all school health services as well as community health measures. In such instances, school health examinations and all medical school health functions are carried on by health department personnel working cooperatively in the schools but under the direction of the local health officer.

3. A cooperative arrangement and joint responsibility. In such instances personnel paid by one agency may be loaned to another, such as health department personnel loaned to schools and vice versa.[23]

The principles of communicable disease control underlying all three patterns are as follows:

1. Responsibility for the administration of quarantine and other control measures is vested by law in the public board of health, but many detailed procedures may need to be carried out by school authorities and personnel in cooperation with the board of health.

2. Home supervision of communicable diseases is necessarily carried out by the board of health. Therefore, close cooperation must be established by school authorities with the board of health in order to coordinate home and school procedures.

3. Wherever public schools administer their own communicable disease measures and private and parochial schools are served in similar capacity by the board of health, the program must be consistent and well coordinated to avoid community confusion, lack of cooperation, and resentments based upon real or fancied discriminations.

4. If the communicable disease program is administered by the board of health, it must be carefully coordinated with school schedules and the operations of school plants, and there must be opportunities for classroom teachers to familiarize themselves with communicable disease control procedures and with their duties in relation thereto.[24]

---

[23]American Association of School Administrators, *op. cit.,* p. 346.
[24]*Ibid.,* p. 347.

The responsibility for communicable disease control falls upon many individuals. These include public health personnel, school administrative personnel, nurse, school physician, teacher, custodian, and the parent. The teacher, parent, and school nurse must be continually vigilant to notice symptoms of various communicable diseases, isolate such individuals immediately, and refer these cases to the school or family physician. There must be close cooperation among these three. All three play key roles in the control of communicable diseases. If the parent plays his or her role effectively and the child is isolated immediately, he will lessen considerably the exposure of other individuals to disease. If the child is in school, the alert teacher and nurse will take the necessary precautions.

The superintendent, principal, and other administrative officers have the responsibility for establishing policy, working cooperatively with public health officials, providing encouragement and in-service training for teachers, and developing among parents and the public in general an understanding which will be most conducive to communicable disease control.

The custodian, through his or her control over the sanitation of the equipment and facilities, can perform his responsibilities so effectively that a healthful environment is always in evidence and thus the spread of diseases decreased.

The school physician should advise the teacher, nurse, administrative officers, and others who are closely related to the whole problem of communicable disease control as to the necessary measures that should be provided. Through his specialized knowledge, he can contribute much toward the establishment of an effective and workable plan.

2. Control Measures.—There are many control measures that every school should follow to prevent the spread of disease. Some of the more important of these measures are discussed.

a. *Healthful Environment.**—The American Association of School Administrators has outlined the provisions for a healthful environment which are necessary for the control of communicable disease.

> (1) Sufficient classroom, gymnasium, locker room, and playground space to avoid undue crowding.
> (2) Adequate toilet and washroom facilities readily available to maintain the cleanliness of the hands which is most important in preventing the spread of the communicable diseases of childhood, and cleanliness of body which may influence spread of skin diseases and vermin.
> (3) Proper ventilation and heating to prevent either rapid chilling or overheating of the body, with consequent reduction of resistance to the communicable diseases.
> (4) Safe running water, as a precaution against intestinal diseases such as typhoid, dysentery, and acute nonspecific intestinal infections.
> (5) Drinking fountains that are properly designed from the standpoint of both sanitation and safety.
> (6) Use of pasteurized milk as a safeguard against milk-borne diseases.
> (7) A system of exclusions and control of readmissions which effectively isolates children suspected of communicable diseases from healthy children.
> (8) Abandonment of emphasis on perfect attendance by pupils.

---

*See also Chapters XII and XIII.

(9) A policy toward teacher absences that does not put a premium on perfect attendance by teachers, thereby keeping them in school when they may be spreading communicable diseases, especially colds.

(10) Inspection of children by their parents each morning before they send them to school to make sure that no evidence of illness is present.

(11) Training of classroom teachers to recognize evidences of acute or chronic illnesses.[25]

b. *Isolation of Children.*—The child who is a "suspect" in regard to some communicable disease should immediately be isolated from the group. This is the rule of thumb that should be followed. Isolating a child does not constitute diagnosis. The details and procedures followed in each school regarding isolation should be in writing and clearly understood by all concerned. This is a responsibility of the school administrator. The adopted plan should have the approval of the health service staff.

The teacher should be continually on the lookout for "suspects." Some indications of communicable disease which should be recognized by the teacher are:

unusual pallor or flushed face
unusual listlessness or quietness
red, or watery eyes
eyes sensitive to light
skin rash
cough
diarrhea
nausea or vomiting
running nose, or sniffles
excessive irritability
jaundice[26]

After the teacher isolates the "suspect" from the group, the child should not be left alone. Furthermore, the nurse or school physician should be notified. In the event neither of these individuals is available, the teacher and school administrator must decide on exclusion. The best solution is to arrange for the child to return to his home where the services of a physician should be procured as soon as possible. Furthermore, the parents should report the case to the local health authorities.

c. *Readmitting Children to School.*—After having a communicable disease a child should not be readmitted to school until it is certain his return is in the best interests of the health of both the child concerned, and also the other children with whom he will come in contact. Each community should strictly conform to the law that governs communicable diseases. In addition, there should be approval for such readmission indicated in writing by a qualified physician or the local health department. In minor cases a note from the parent or the decision of the nurse or other school staff member may suffice.

d. *Immunization.*—Every child should receive immunization against preventable diseases. Most of this should be done in the preschool years when danger from such diseases is very prevalent. Every child should be immunized against

[25]*Ibid.*, p. 327.
[26]Joint Committee. *School Health Services*, p. 278.

tetanus, diphtheria, smallpox, and whooping cough.   The school can play an important part in the health education of parents to see that children are immunized against these diseases before starting school.   The children who come to school and have not received the benefit of such services need special attention.   It is a public health and medical problem and should be dealt with through members of these professions.   The school, through a strong educational program, should encourage parents to see that this essential work is done.   If the community decides

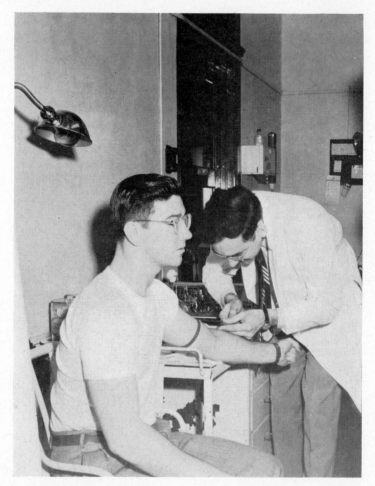

Communicable disease control.   Wisconsin State College, La Crosse, Wisconsin.

that the school is the best place for immunization, the school should cooperate fully and keep complete records on initial immunizations and booster doses.   Written permission should be secured from parents concerned.

    e. *Attendance.*—There should not be an over-emphasis on perfect attendance for school children.   This often results in children coming to school regardless of the condition of their health and the danger to others.   Furthermore, state departments of education who allocate aid to local school districts on the basis of attendance, encourage administrators, teachers, and parents to keep children in school when they should remain at home. State aid should be based on some other method which does not encourage such an unhealthful practice.

f. *Epidemics.*—The viewpoint on closing schools during epidemics has changed somewhat in recent years. Formerly it was generally believed that schools should be closed. Today, it is felt that under many circumstances they should remain open. The deciding factor is whether or not the school provides regular inspections, observations, adequate staff, and facilities to screen out those who indicate signs of having the disease. If this service can be performed and if the closing of schools will result in many contacts on playgrounds and other places where children congregate, then, according to the latest thinking, the schools should remain open. This is particularly true in urban areas. Many times in rural areas, where children will not come in contact with each other if schools are closed, it may be wise to pursue this action.

If an epidemic occurs during a vacation period, it is often wise to postpone the opening of school, since such opening might result in increased contact with the disease.

F. Emergency Care

The school is responsible for providing each child with the necessary protection and care. The school acts in *loco parentis* (in place of the parent) and it is assumed that the child will receive the same care and protection during the hours of school that he normally would receive at home. Children often become sick or injured during school hours. Therefore, the school must provide the necessary attention until this can be undertaken by the parents.

According to the Joint Committee on Health Problems the school has four responsibilities in respect to emergency care procedures. These are "(a) giving immediate care, (b) notifying parents, (c) getting the child home, and (d) guiding parents, where necessary, to sources of treatment."[27]

Some administrative guides for emergency care are as follows:

(1) Every school should have a written plan for emergency care. It should be carefully prepared by the school administration with the help of the school physician, parents, medical and dental professions, hospitals, nurse, teachers, and others interested and responsible in this area. The time to plan and decide on procedure is before an accident occurs. This should be one of the first administrative responsibilities that is accomplished.

The written plan should contain such essentials as: first-aid instructions; procedures for getting medical help, transportation, and notifying parents; staff responsibilities; supplies, equipment, and facilities available; and any other information that will help clarify exactly what is to be done in time of emergency.

The plan should be reviewed periodically and revised so that it is continually up to date. It should be posted in conspicuous places and discussed periodically with school staff and community groups, whenever necessary.

---

[27]Joint Committee. *School Health Services*, pp. 229-230.

FIRST-AID SUPPLIES AND HOW TO USE THEM[28]

SUGGESTED SUPPLIES	WHAT THEY ARE FOR
Tincture of green soap	Washing injured parts
Hospital cotton, roll	Large soft pads or dressings
Absorbent cotton, sterlized, roll, box or "picking" package	Swabs or pledgets for applying medication or wiping wounds
Dressings, large or small pads, sterilized, in individual transparent envelopes	For protecting injuries
Dressings, finger, in envelopes	For protecting very small injuries
Adhesive tape, roll, one inch	Fastening dressings, or splints
Scissors, bandage or blunt	Cutting dressings
Toothpicks	For making swabs
Alcohol 70% (water 30%) or rubbing alcohol	Disinfecting skin and minor wounds
Mercurochrome, 2% aqueous	Minor injuries especially in young children
Other disinfectant, if ordered by physician	As ordered by physician
Mineral oil, bottle, or petroleum jelly, tube or jar, white or yellow, but not medicated	For removing ointments; in eye to relieve irritation from foreign body; for burns if no other ointment is at hand
Boric acid ointment U.S.P.	For very small minor first-degree burns only
Epsom salts	In hot water, a handful to a basin, for soaking sprains, bruises, or infection when ordered by a physician
Baking soda, powder	Teaspoonful to a pint of warm water for mouthwash, or gargle if ordered
Salt, crystal or tablets	Same as baking soda, or with baking soda as directed
Hot-water bottle with cover	Local relief of pain
Ice bag	Local relief of pain
Two warm blankets	For prevention of chilling
Tourniquet (three feet of soft rubber tubing and a stick or pencil)	USE ABOVE place from where red blood spurts. Call doctor at once. Release every 15 minutes to allow circulation to reach parts, then reapply if necessary.
Eye droppers	Dropping liquid medicines. Cleanse after using and boil before using
Ear syringe, soft rubber	For ears only when ordered by physician
Graduated medicine glass*	For measuring liquid medicines

*Graduated medicine glass is most accurate and should be used whenever possible. In emergency, this table may be used:

20 drops (water solution) _____ 1 c.c. (metric)
1 teaspoon (measuring spoon, not table silver) _____ 5 c.c.
1 tablespoon (measuring spoon, not table silver) _____ 15 c.c.
1 wineglass _____ 50 c.c.
1 tumbler _____ 250 c.c.

Drugs for internal use	Only when ordered by physician and as directed by him

---

[28]American Association of School Administrators, *op. cit.*, pp. 394-395, prepared by the American Medical Association.

(2) As many staff members as possible should be trained in first-aid procedures. There is a need for special knowledge and training in respect to emergency care that might entail first aid for broken bones, use of artificial respiration, control of hemorrhage, and proper care of patients suffering from shock. The more staff members that are trained in these specific first-aid procedures, the better coverage there is for accidents which may occur at any time when school activities are in progress.

Some schools have the American Red Cross give in-service courses in first-aid procedures. Such in-service training will help to insure that the staff is competent along this line.

When a nurse is on duty it would usually be expected that her responsibility includes seeing that proper first-aid procedures are carried out.

Professional preparing institutions should give due consideration to instruction in first-aid and emergency care procedures as part of the training of all teachers and school personnel.

(3) A health room for first aid and emergency care should be available.* It should possess the necessary equipment and supplies; have good lighting; be clean, of adequate size, and always available for emergency cases.

A basic list of first-aid supplies, together with a statement as to what they are for, has been developed by the American Medical Association. See page 304.

In addition to furniture and routine equipment, the health room should also have available as a minimum the following:[29]

Stethoscope	Illuminated eye test charts
Thermometer, clinical	Tuning fork for hearing tests
Sphygmomanometer	Mouth mirror
Electric ophthalmoscope	Probes, dental
Electric otoscope	Forceps
Reflex hammer	Syringes
Tape measure	Needles
Platform scale (not a spring	Eye droppers
model)	Graduated medicine glasses

The staff responsible for the health room should be fixed and such responsibility should include training and competency in first-aid procedures.

(4) Proper emergency equipment and supplies, in addition to being located in the health room, should also be available in strategic school locations which are accident-prone because of activity courses and in places remote from the health room. Such locations might include gymnasium, laboratories, shops, school buses, annexes, and buildings housing school activities apart from the central unit.

(5) School records should contain complete information on each pupil. This would include his address; parent's name, address, and phone number; business address of parent and phone number; family physician, address and phone number; family dentist, address and phone number; parent-instructions in case of emergency; choice of hospital; and any other pertinent information.

---

*See description in chapter XII.
[29]*Ibid.*, p. 390.

(6) There should be a complete record of every accident, including first aid given and emergency care administered in the event of illness. Such information preserves for future reference the procedures followed in each case. This record is very important in the event questions arise in the future. Time results in forgetfulness, misinterpretation, misunderstanding, and inaccurate conclusions being drawn. Records can also be used to disclose hazards which should be eliminated and weak spots in procedures for emergency care which should be improved. Finally, such records aid in impressing upon pupils, staff, parents, and other individuals who are concerned* the importance of good procedures for safe and healthful living.

(7) The legal aspects of problems involved in regard to emergency care should be discussed and understood by the entire school staff. Such discussion will make for a better understanding of the laws of a particular state or locality and show the importance of avoiding negligence in duty.†

(8) Insurance plans for staff, athletes, and pupils should be made clear. They should be in writing and well publicized so that each individual will know the extent to which expenses, claims, and other items will be paid in event of accident, or the extent to which he can or should procure additional coverage.

(9) Disasters in the form of fires, floods, tornadoes, and air raids can occur at any time. In order to provide proper emergency care under such circumstances, there must be advance planning. Schools should recognize their responsibility along this line. Adequate insurance coverage should be maintained. Supplies for emergency care should be on hand. Responsibilities should be fixed in key positions. Plans should be laid for taking children to safest place possible. Drills should be conducted. Close cooperation should exist between the schools and such organizations as Civil Defense or the Red Cross.

QUESTIONS AND EXERCISES

1. What are the component parts of a school health services program? What is the importance to the child of each part?

2. What is the relationship between health services and the other phases of the school health program?

3. Prepare a speech to be given in class which could be used to point up to a parent-teacher association the importance of the development of a desirable health services program.

4. What should be the relationship between the public health department and the school health department in relation to school health services?

5. Discuss the advantages and disadvantages of the theory, "The school is a place for both education and treatment."

6. Outline what you consider to be a sound health appraisal program for an elementary school.

7. Describe the nature and scope of the school medical examination. Relate how it can be an educational experience for boys and girls.

8. Prepare a list of arguments to be presented to the board of education to justify the addition of a psychologist to the school staff.

9. What part do the teacher's observations play in a health services program? What are his or her responsibilities in this matter?

---

*See also pp. 149-152.
†See also Chapter VIII.

10. Identify: pure-tone audiometer, whisper test, Massachusetts Vision Test, caries, Snellen E Chart, follow-through, and exceptional child.

11. What are the essential health records that should be maintained to conduct a desirable health services program?

12. Prepare a mock health counseling conference with a child and his mother after a medical examination which has revealed several defects that need correction.

13. What recommendations could you make in order to insure the greatest possible correction of remediable health defects?

14. Take one type of exceptional child, do considerable research on the type of educational program that is best suited to this particular individual, and make recommendations to the class.

15. After careful study of all factors involved, outline a program for a particular community, as to how the public health department and school health education division can most effectively work together for communicable disease control.

16. Prepare a written plan for emergency care of injuries for your school, which will then be submitted to the class for approval, and then presented to the school health services division of your institution for comment.

SELECTED REFERENCES

American Association of School Administrators. *Health in Schools. Twentieth Yearbook.* Washington, D. C.: The Association, 1951.

American Dental Association, Council on Dental Health. *Dental Caries: Prevention and Control.* Chicago: the Association, 1950.

American Heart Association. *What the Classroom Teacher Should Know and Do About Children With Heart Disease.* New York: the Association, 1951.

American Medical Association. *Fourth National Conference on Physicians and Schools.* Chicago: the Association, 1953.

American Medical Association. *Physician Participation in School Health Services.* Chicago: American Medical Association, 1950.

American Medical Association. *Physicians and Schools. Conference Report.* Chicago: the Association, 1947.

American Medical Association. *Second National Conference on Physicians and Schools.* Chicago: the Association, 1949.

American Medical Association. *Third National Conference on Physicians and Schools.* Chicago: the Association, 1951.

American National Red Cross. *Red Cross First Aid Textbook. Revised Edition.* Philadelphia: Blakiston Company, 1945.

American Public Health Association. *The Control of Communicable Diseases in Man.* Seventh Edition. New York: the Association, 1950.

Crane, Marian M., et. al., "Study of Procedures Used for Screening Elementary School Children for Visual Defects," *American Journal of Public Health,* 42: 1430-39, November, 1952.

Hubbard, John P., Bain, Katherine, and Pennell, Maryland Y., "School Health Service," *American Journal of Public Health,* 39: 781-86, June, 1949.

Jacobs, Louis, "Mental Health in the School Program," *Journal of School Health,* 22: 288-95, December, 1952.

Joint Committee on Health Problems in Education of the National Education Association and the American Medical Association. *Health Appraisal of School Children.* Washington, D. C.: National Education Association, 1948.

Joint Committee on Health Problems in Education of the National Education Association and the American Medical Association. *Health Education.* Charles C. Wilson, Editor. Washington, D. C.: National Education Association, 1948.

Joint Committee on Health Problems in Education of the National Education Association and the American Medical Association. *School Health Services.* Charles C. Wilson, Editor. Washington, D. C.: National Education Association, 1953.

Kilander, H. F. *Health Services in City Schools.* Office of Education Bulletin 1952, No. 20. Washington, D. C.: U.S. Government Printing Office, 1952.

Metropolitan Life Insurance Company. *What Teachers See.* New York: the Company, 1948.

Midcentury White House Conference on Children and Youth. *Personality in the Making.* New York: Harper & Brothers, 1952, Chapter 14.

Moore, Norman S., and Summerskill, John. *Health Services in American Colleges and Universities.* Findings of the American College Health Association Survey. Ithaca, New York: Cornell University, 1953.

National Committee on School Health Policies. *Suggested School Health Policies.* New York: Health Education Council, 1946.

National Council of Chief State School Officers and the Association of State and Territorial Health Officers. *School Health Services.* Washington, D. C.: National Council Offices, 1201 Sixteenth St., NW., 1951.

National Society for the Prevention of Blindness. *An Eye Health Program for Schools.* Pamphlet No. 141. New York: the Society, 1951.

National Society for the Study of Education. *Education of Exceptional Children. Forty-Ninth Yearbook, Part II.* Chicago: University of Chicago Press, 1950.

Report of the Committee on Health Service Programs for Secondary Schools, "Suggested Standards for Health Services in Secondary Schools," *American Journal of Public Health Year Book,* 42: 139-147, May, 1952.

Schlesinger, Edward R.   *Health Services for the Child.*   New York: McGraw-Hill Book Company, 1953.

Schwebel, Milton, and Harris, Ella F.   *Health Counseling.*   New York: Chartwell House, 1951.

Shaffer, Thomas E.   "What Health Services Do School-Age Children Need? *Journal of the American Association for Health, Physical Education, and Recreation,* 23:16-18, June, 1952.

United States Office of Education, Department of Health, Education and Welfare. *Better Health for School-Age Children.* Washington, D. C.:   Children's Bureau, Office of Education and Public Health Service, 1951.

United States Office of Education, Department of Health, Education and Welfare. *Children with Impaired Hearing.* Children's Bureau Publication No. 326. Washington, D. C.:   Superintendent of Documents, Government Printing Office, 1952.

United States Office of Education, Department of Health, Education and Welfare. *Priorities in Health Services for Children of School Age.* Washington, D. C.:   Children's Bureau, Office of Education and Public Health Service, 1950.

United States Office of Education, Department of Health, Education and Welfare. *Teachers Contribute to Child Health.* Office of Education Bulletin 1951, No. 8. Washington, D. C.:   Superintendent of Documents, Government Printing Office, 1951.

Wheatley, George M., and Hallock, Grace T.   *Health Observation of School Children.*   New York: McGraw-Hill Company, 1951.

Chapter XVI

THE REQUIRED PHYSICAL EDUCATION
CLASS PROGRAM

The total school physical education program will be discussed in the next three chapters. This chapter is concerned with the required physical education class or service program. Chapter XVII deals with the intramural and extramural athletics program and chapter XVIII is concerned with the interschool athletics program.

The required physical education class program should provide students the opportunity to receive instruction, develop essential physical skills, and have enjoyable educational experiences. It is here that opinions are formed and attitudes are developed in respect to the physical education program and profession. The fact that some individuals grow into adulthood with an indifferent or unfavorable attitude toward physical education can often be traced back to the physical education they were exposed to in school. To some individuals it was something that was jammed down their throats. To others it was presented in an uninteresting manner and seemed unimportant—something to "skip" as often as possible. To still others it was experience where they were ignored because they had little skill.

Physical education should be presented in a palatable and interesting manner. Students should receive joy and satisfaction from participating in the various activities. Physical education carries its own drive and the teacher should attempt to preserve this natural drive throughout childhood years and into adulthood. It has been said that if children were exposed to good physical education programs during their formative years, there would be no necessity for required physical education programs in later school years. The individual would develop skills and attitudes toward physical education that would result in joy and satisfaction from participation. The individual on his or her own initiative would then want to continue such enjoyable experiences.

The required physical education class period cannot be conducted in a "hit-and-miss" fashion. It must be planned in accordance with the needs and interests of the individuals it serves.

Some of the initial considerations in planning and developing a physical education program are:

1. The required physical education class program, intramural, extramural, and interschool athletic programs all represent important aspects of the total physical education program. They must remain in proper balance at all school levels and be geared to the needs and interests of the student.

2. A sound philosophy is essential as a basis for the construction of any physical education program.

3. The needs of the individual and of society, as reflected in the objectives of physical education, represent a main consideration in the establishment of a program of physical education.

4. The fact that physical education contributes to the social, mental, and emotional, as well as the physical needs of the individual should be kept in mind.

5. The health and recreational aspects of the program must be emphasized. This can best be done by close coordination with the school health and school and community recreation programs.

6. Physical education should recognize the importance of coeducational activities for social growth and provide for them in the program.

A golf class in the required physical education class program for men. (Department of Physical Education and Athletics, University of Michigan.)

7. Provisions should be made so that *all* individuals may participate in and benefit from the physical education program.

8. The maxim that "physical education carries its own drive" should be preserved in every individual who comes in contact with the program. Joy and satisfaction should be outcomes from physical education that are guarded jealously.

9. Physical education should receive equal consideration with other subjects in the school offering in respect to necessary supplies, facilities, and administrative support.

10. Qualified leadership is an essential in all phases of the physical education program.

11. Physical education should be planned, organized, and conducted in a manner which will exploit the educative possibilities to the fullest.

12. The program should include a wide variety of activities which can be engaged in by all individuals, indoors and out-of-doors, and which meet safety, hygienic, and social standards.

13. Instruction in activities should be on a progressive basis and organized in a way that is systematic and most meaningful to the student.

The maxim that physical education carries its own drive should be preserved in every individual who comes in contact with the program. A basketball class in the required physical education class program for men. (Department of Physical Education and Athletics, University of Michigan.)

14. Physical education should contribute to the democratic way of life.

15. A program of measurement and evaluation should be developed so that progress toward goals may be noted and weaknesses detected.

The next step in considering the required class program is to examine some of the administrative problems surrounding its organization and administration. These include scheduling, time allotment, size of classes, teaching stations, teaching load, and grouping; administrative policies concerned with advisability of having physical education on a required or elective basis, substitutions, credit allowances, class attendance, and excuses; items of class management concerned with planning, dressing and showering, costume, roll taking, grading, and records; matters relating to activities such as criteria for their selection, classification, and coeducational aspects; and program considerations at the elementary, junior high school, senior high school and college levels; the modified program; and, finally, considerations for guarding the health of the participant.

I. SCHEDULING

The manner in which physical education classes are scheduled reflects the physical education leadership in the school and the attitude of the central administration. The physical education class will be more meaningful for students if it is scheduled in a manner which is in their interests, rather than in the interest of administrative convenience.

Scheduling should be done according to a definite plan. Physical education should not be inserted in the over-all master scheduling plan wherever there is time left over after all the other subjects have been provided for. This important responsibility cannot be handled on a "hit-and-miss" basis since that disregards the interests and needs of the students. Instead, physical education classes should be scheduled first on the master plan, along with such subjects as English and science which are required of all students most of the time they are in school. This allows for progression and for grouping according to the interests and needs of the individual participants. The three important items to take into consideration in scheduling classes are: (1) the number of teachers available, (2) the number of teaching stations available, and (3) the number of students who must be scheduled. This is a formula that should be applied to all subjects in the school offering. Physical education will be scheduled correctly as will other subjects if this formula is followed.

All students should be scheduled. There should be no exceptions. If the child can go to school, he should be enrolled in physical education. Special attention should be given, however, to the exceptional individual to insure that he is placed in a program suited to his needs. Also, special attention should be given to the so-called "dub" who needs extra help in the development of physical skills.

At the elementary and secondary levels, but especially at the elementary, scheduling should be done on a one-year basis. Special attention should be given to the needs and interests of children in respect to such items as availability of facilities, equipment, and supplies, and weather. Planned units of work will usually become increasingly longer as the child progresses in grades, because of his longer interest span, greater maturity, and the increased complexity of the activities.

Every physical educator should make a point of presenting to the central administration his or her plans for scheduling physical education classes. The need for special consideration in this area should be discussed with the principal, scheduling committee, and others who are involved. Through persistent action along this line, progress will be made. The logic and reasoning behind the formula of scheduling classes according to the number of teachers and teaching stations available and the number of students who must be scheduled cannot be denied. It must be planned in this way if there is to be progression in instruction and if a good program is to result.

Some other considerations in working out a schedule for physical education classes are time allotment, size of classes, teaching stations, teaching load, and grouping.

A. Time Allotment

Just as scheduling practices vary from school to school and state to state, so does the time allotment. In some states there are laws which are mandatory in nature and require that a certain amount of time each day or week be devoted to physical education, whereas in others permissive legislation exists. For grades one to twelve the requirement varies in different states from none or very little, to 300 minutes a week. Some require 20 minutes daily and others 30 minutes daily. Others specify the time by the week, ranging from 50 minutes to 300 minutes. The college and university level does not usually require as much physical education as grades one to twelve. The usual practice in higher education is to require physical education two times a week for two years.

The general consensus among physical education leaders is that in order for physical education to be of value it must be given with regularity. For most individuals this means daily periods. There is also agreement among experts in the field of health that exercise is essential to everyone from the cradle to the grave. Smiley and Gould[1] point out the exercise needs of individuals at various ages:

Ages 1 through 4
Free play during hours not occupied by sleeping.

Ages 5 through 8
Four hours a day of free play (running, jumping, dancing, climbing, teetering, etc.) and of loosely organized group games (tag, nine pins, hoops, beanbags, etc.).

Ages 9 through 11
At least three hours a day of outdoor active play (hiking, swimming, gymnastics, group games and relays, soccer, volleyball, broad-and-high jump, 25- and 50-yard dashes, folk dancing, etc.).

Ages 12 through 14
At least two hours a day of outdoor active play (hiking, swimming, gymnastics, group games, relays, soccer, volleyball, indoor baseball, basketball, baseball, tennis, 60-yard dash, the jumps, shot-put, low hurdles, short relays, folk and gymnastic dancing). Still no endurance contests.

Ages 15 through 17
At least one and one-half hours a day of outdoor active play (hiking, swimming, apparatus work, group games and relays, soccer, volleyball, indoor baseball, basketball, baseball, tennis, football, golf, ice hockey, 60-yard dash, the jumps, shot-put, low hurdles, short relays, folk and gymnastic dancing). Still no endurance contests.

Ages 18 through 30
At least one hour a day of active outdoor exercise (all the types listed in the preceding paragraph and, if examined and found physically fit, in addition, cross-country running, crew, wrestling, boxing, fencing, and polo).

[1]Dean F. Smiley and Adrian G. Gould. *A College Textbook of Hygiene.* New York: The Macmillan Company, 1940, pp. 346-347.

Ages 31 through 50
At least one hour a day of moderate outdoor exercise (golf, tennis, riding, swimming, handball, volleyball, etc.).

Ages 51 through 70
At least one hour a day of light outdoor exercise (golf, walking, bowling, gardening, fishing, croquet, etc.).

All individuals have exercise needs. Physical education also has mental, emotional, and social aspects and values. Therefore, there must be regular provision for this important subject.

The time-allotment recommendation usually considered adequate is a daily physical education period for each student. This should represent the minimum requirement. Some individuals feel that, especially in the elementary schools, a program cannot be adapted to a fixed time schedule. However, as a standard, there seems to be agreement that a daily experience in such a program is needed. Such a recommendation is made and should always be justified on the basis of value and contribution to the student and his needs as reflected in the objectives of education. There should be provision for regular, instructional class periods and, in addition, laboratory periods where the skills can be put to use.

On the secondary level especially, there is a feeling that a full 60-minute period is needed. Since time for dressing and showering is required, this leaves only approximately 45 minutes on the floor or playground. Some have suggested a double period every other day rather than a single period each day. This might be feasible if the daily class periods are too short. However, the importance of daily periods should be recognized and achieved wherever possible. Administrators should work toward the goal of providing adequate staff and facilities to allow for a daily period. The New York State Fitness Conference made the recommendation that "provision should be made in all schools for daily instruction in vigorous physical activities, such instruction to provide at least 150 minutes a week of physical activity at the elementary level and 225 minutes of physical activity at the secondary level."[2] Although this represents a recent recommendation, the goal of daily periods should be one toward which all physical educators work in their respective schools.

B. Size of Classes

Some school administrators feel that physical education classes can accommodate more students than the so-called academic classes, such as English or social studies. This is a misconception which has developed over the years and is in need of correction. Physical educators themselves are in many cases at fault for such a practice. Some have failed to interpret their field of endeavor adequately to the central administration. Others have followed the practice of throwing a ball to a class and utilizing free play, with little or no organization. This has led some administrators to feel that the same type of teaching job would be done with a small class, and therefore they see no reason to incur the administrative problems and extra expense of more staff and smaller classes.

The problem of size of class seems to be more pertinent at the secondary than at the elementary level. At the elementary level the classroom situation represents

[2]Report to the Commissioner of Education on the *State Fitness Conference*. Albany, New York: State Education Department, 1952, p. 10.

a unit for activity and the size of this teaching unit is usually reasonable. However, there are some schools that combine various classrooms for physical education, resulting in large classes which are not desirable.

Classes in physical education should be approximately the same size as is prevalent for the other subjects in the school offering. This is just as essential for effective teaching, individualized instruction, and progression in physical education as it is in other subjects. Physical education contributes to educational objectives on at least an equal basis with other subjects in the curriculum. Therefore, the size of the class should be comparable so that an effective teaching job can be accomplished and the objectives of education attained.

The standard established by LaPorte's committee[3] after considerable research points up the acceptable size of physical education classes. It recommends not more than 35 students as the suitable size for activity classes. Classes should never exceed 45 for one instructor. For remedial and corrective classes the suitable class size is from 20 to 25 and should never exceed 30.

The American Association for Health, Physical Education, and Recreation[4] points out that class size never should exceed 35.

C. Teaching Stations

The "teaching station" concept should be taken into consideration when scheduling physical education classes. A "teaching station" is the space or setting where one teacher or staff member can carry on physical education activities for one group of students. The number and size of teaching stations available together with the number of teachers on the staff, the size of the groups, the number of times the group meets, the number of periods in the school day, and the program of activities are important items to consider in planning.

D. Teaching Loads

The load of the physical education teacher should be of prime concern to the administrator. In order to maintain a top level of enthusiasm, strength, and other essential characteristics, it is important that the teaching load be adjusted so that the physical educator is not overworked.

The New York State Physical Fitness Conference[5] recommended that one full-time physical education teacher should be provided for every 240 elementary pupils and one for every 190 secondary pupils enrolled. If such a requirement became universal it would aid considerably in providing adequate staff members in this field and avoid an overload for so many of the teachers.

LaPorte's national study[6] made recommendations in respect to teaching load which should be considered carefully by any teacher or administrator striving for acceptable standards. It recommends that class instruction per teacher not exceed five clock hours or the equivalent in class periods per day, or 1500 minutes a week. It never should exceed six clock hours per day or 1800 minutes a week. This maximum should include after-school responsibilities. A daily load of 200 students

---

[3]William Ralph LaPorte. *The Physical Education Curriculum (A National Program)*, Fifth edition. Los Angeles: The University of Southern California Press, 1951, pp. 50-51.
[4]*Administrative Problems in Health Education, Physical Education, and Recreation*, p. 70.
[5]New York State Physical Fitness Conference, *op. cit.*, p. 7.
[6]LaPorte, *op. cit.*, p. 51.

per teacher is recommended and never more than 250.   Finally, each teacher should have at least one free period daily for consultation and conferences with students.

E. Grouping

Homogeneous grouping in physical education classes is very desirable.   To render the most valuable contribution to students, factors influencing performance must be taken into consideration in organizing groups for physical education instructional work or competition.   The lack of scientific knowledge and measuring techniques to obtain such information and the administrative problems of scheduling have handicapped the achievement of this goal in most schools.

The reasons for such grouping are sound.   Placing individuals with similar capacities and characteristics in the same class will make it possible to better meet the needs of each individual.   Grouping individuals with similar skill, ability, and other factors aids in equalizing competition.   This helps the student to realize more satisfaction and benefit from playing.   Grouping makes for more effective teaching. Instruction can be better organized and adapted to the level of the student.   Grouping facilitates progression and continuity in the program.   Furthermore, grouping makes for a better learning situation for the student.   Being in a group with persons of similar physical characteristics and skills insures some success, a chance to excel, recognition, a feeling of belonging, and security.   Consequently this helps the social and personality development of the individual.   Finally, homogeneous grouping helps protect the child.   It insures his participation with individuals who are similar in physical characteristics.   This protects the child physically and also protects him emotionally and socially.

The problem of grouping is not as pertinent in the elementary school, especially in the lower grades, as it is in the junior high school and upper levels.   At the lower levels the grade classification appears to serve the needs of children.   As children grow older, the complexity of the program increases, social growth becomes more diversified, competition becomes more intense, and consequently, there is a greater need for having similar individuals in one group.

At the present time students are homogeneously classified on such bases as grade, sex, health, physical fitness, multiples of age-height-weight, ability, physical capacity, motor ability, interests, educability, speed, skill, and previous experience. Such techniques as health examinations; tests of motor ability, physical capacity, achievement, and social efficiency; conferences with students; and determination of physiological age are utilized to obtain such information.

The Sacramento, California, public schools have outlined the various aspects of their physical education program from the elementary grades through the junior college level.   Their course of study for the senior high school girls lists the following procedure for grouping in physical education.

I. Basis of Classification

A. Physical examination

1. Personal history
2. Menstrual history
3. Posture test

4. Feet
5. Other findings
B. Medical Examination
  1. Teeth
  2. Nose, throat
  3. Heart
  4. Nutrition
  5. Blood pressure
  6. Review of findings in physical examinations
II. Classification of physical education activities based upon the above findings
  A. Active or Unrestricted Physical Education
    1. Team sports
    2. Individual sports
    3. Dancing
    4. Gymnastics and unorganized games
    5. Drill
  B. Restricted or Modified Physical Education
    1. Modified games
    2. Posture exercises
    3. Relaxation
  C. Remedial Physical Education
    1. Exercises for general muscle tone
    2. Menstrual exercises
    3. Posture exercises
    4. Feet exercises
    5. Special, individual exercises
    6. Relaxing
    7. Games
  D. Rest
    This activity includes girls who are under a physician's care and have organic or functional handicaps sufficiently serious to recommend a period of complete rest during their physical education period.

The suggestions of the American Association for Health, Physical Education and Recreation[7] are appropriate when considering recommendations for grouping.

1. The need for grouping students homogeneously for instruction and competition has long been recognized, but inability to scientifically measure such important factors as ability, maturity, interest, and capacity has served as a deterrent from accomplishing this goal.

2. The most common procedure for grouping today is by grade or class.

3. The ideal grouping organization would take into consideration all factors that affect performance—intelligence, capacity, interest, knowledge, age, height, weight, etc. To utilize all these factors, however, is not administratively feasible at the present time.

4. Some form of grouping is essential to provide the type of program that will promote educational objectives and protect the student.

5. On the secondary level, the most feasible procedure appears to be to organize sub-groups within the regular physical education class proper.

6. Classification within the physical education class should be based on such factors as age, height, and weight statistics, intelligence, and other factors such as interest and skill, which are developed as a result of observation of the activity.

---

[7]*Administrative Problems in Health Education, Physical Education, and Recreation*, pp. 71-72.

7. For those individuals who desire greater refinement in respect to grouping, utilization of motor capacity, motor ability, attitude, appreciation, and sports-skills tests may be used.

II. ADMINISTRATIVE POLICIES

The administrator of any physical education program is perennially confronted with such questions as: Should physical education be required or elective? How much credit should be given? Is it possible to substitute some other activity for physical education? What should be the policy on class attendance? How should one deal with excuses? What provision should be made for sex differences?

A. Should Physical Education Be Required Or Elective?

There is general agreement that physical education should be required at the elementary level. However, there are many advocates on both sides of the question as to whether it should be required or elective on the secondary and college levels. Both are sincere and feel their beliefs represent what is best for the student. Probably most specialists feel that the program should be required. Many school administrators feel it should be elective. Some of the arguments presented by each are as follows:

1. Required

a. Physical education represents a basic need of every child just as English, social studies, and other experiences do. It became part of the school offering as a required subject to satisfy such needs and therefore should be continued on the same basis.

b. The student is compelled to take so many required courses that the use of electives is limited, if not entirely eliminated, in some cases. Therefore, unless physical education is a required course, many students will not have the opportunity to partake of this program because of the pressures placed on them by the required courses.

c. The student looks upon those subjects that are required as being the most important and the most necessary for success. Therefore, unless physical education is on the required list, it becomes a subject of second-rate importance in the eyes of the students.

d. Various subjects in the curriculum would not be provided for unless they were required. This is probably true of physical education. Until state legislatures passed laws requiring physical education, this subject was ignored by many school administrators. If physical education were on an elective basis the course of some administrative action would be obvious. Either the subject would not be offered at all or the administrative philosophy would so dampen its values that it would have to be eliminated because of low enrollment.

e. Even under a required program, physical education is not fulfilling its potentialities for meeting the physical, social, and mental needs of students. If an elective program were instituted, deficiencies and shortages would increase, thus further handicapping the attempt to meet the welfare and needs of the student.

2. Elective

a. Physical education "carries its own drive." If a good basic program is developed in the elementary school, with students acquiring the necessary skills and attitudes, the drive for such activity will carry through in the secondary school and college. There will be no need to require such a course, because students will want to take it voluntarily.

b. Objectives of physical education are focused on developing skills and learning activities which have carry-over value, living a life which is healthful, and recognizing the importance of developing and maintaining one's body in its best possible condition. These are goals which cannot be legislated. They must become a part of each individual's attitudes and desires, if they are to be realized. A person is more or less "a master of his own fate" in regard to his body. He can do with it what he chooses. This is characteristic of life. The student should be guided in setting up his standard of values. However, he makes the final choice as to how he will achieve those values.

c. Many boys and girls do not like physical education. This is indicated in their manner, attitude, and desire to get excused from the program, and to substitute something else for the course. Under such circumstances, the values that accrue to these individuals are not great. Therefore, it would be best to place physical education on an elective basis where only those students participate who actually desire to.

The question of whether a program should be required or elective will not be decided within a few months or years. It will require considerable study. There are good points on both sides of the issue. A compromise may be possible. The present setup of our educational systems which places some subjects on a pedestal, making them required and focusing attention on them because they have been offered traditionally, may be the reason for the difficulty. Perhaps if a re-evaluation of the entire educational system were to take place with each subject evaluated on its contribution to the enriched living of the individual, its value throughout life, and the contributions it can make to an interesting, vigorous, and active life, it would be found that some of the so-called academic subjects might go the way that Latin, for example, has gone. It might be found that many of them are not practical and functional in present-day living. Sometimes the social pressures of the times and the emphasis on material values and false standards, govern individuals' choices to too great an extent. When a true set of standards can be established in the mind of every individual so that wise choices can be made in the light of what is true and good living, many subjects can be placed on an elective basis, without fear as to what choices will be made.

B. Should Substitutions Be Allowed For Physical Education?

A practice exists in some school systems which allows students to substitute some other activity for their physical education requirement. This practice should be scrutinized very carefully and resisted aggressively by every administrator.

Some of the activities that are used as substitutions for physical education are athletic participation, Reserve Officers' Training Corps, War Service, Band, and high scores on physical fitness and other tests.

There is no substitute for a good program of physical education. In addition to healthful physical activity it is concerned also with developing an individual socially, emotionally, and mentally. It develops in the individual many skills which can be utilized throughout life for worthy use of leisure time. These essentials are lost if a child is permitted to take some other activity in place of physical education. Professional persons who condone substitutions for their physical education classes are not clear as to the goals of their profession. It is important that physical educators recognize that there is no adequate substitute for a well-planned, well-organized and well-conducted physical education class.

C. Should Credit Be Given For Physical Education?

Whether or not credit should be given for physical education is another controversial problem with which the profession is continually confronted. Here again can be found advocates on both sides. There are those who feel the joy of the activity and the values derived from participation are sufficient in themselves without giving credit. On the other hand, there are those who feel that physical education is the same as any other subject in the curriculum and should also be granted credit.

The general consensus among physical education leaders is that if physical education is required for graduation and if it contributes to educational outcomes, credit should be given, just as in other subjects. The credit given should be justified by the contribution physical education makes to the achievement of outcomes toward which all of education is working.

LaPorte[8] in his national study recommends that credit be given and that physical education be a requirement for graduation.

A trend seems to be developing among colleges which allows credit to be given to physical education for college entrance. This is shown in the action of some colleges, where physical education in approved high schools is computed as part of the 15 or 16 units required for college matriculation.

D. What Policy Should Be Established On Class Attendance?

It is important for every department of physical education to have a definite policy on class attendance which covers absences and tardinesses. Many states apportion financial aid to local communities on the basis of attendance. Since it is felt that children should attend school regularly, it follows that they should also attend classes regularly, including physical education.

Regular attendance in physical education is essential in order to derive the values and outcomes that accrue from participation. Since attendance is necessary in order to achieve such outcomes, every physical education department should have a clear-cut policy on attendance regulations. These regulations should be few in number and clearly stated in writing so that they are recognized, understood, and strictly enforced by teachers and students. They should allow for a reasonable number of absences and tardinesses, which can always occur in emergency situations

---

[8]LaPorte, *op. cit.*, p. 51.

over which the student has no control. Perfect attendance should not be stressed. Many harmful results can develop if students feel obligated to attend classes when they are ill and should be home in bed. There should probably be some provision for make-up work when important experiences are missed. However, make-up work should be planned and conducted so that the student derives essential values from such participation, rather than endures it as a disciplinary measure. There should also be provision for the readmission of students who have been ill. A procedure should be established so that the program is adapted to these individuals.

A final point to remember is the importance of keeping accurate, up-to-date attendance records. Unless meaningful records are kept, administrative problems will increase.

E. What About Excuses?

The principal, nurse, or physical educator frequently receives a note from a parent or family physician asking that a student be excused from physical education. Many abuses creep in if all such requests are granted. Many times for minor reasons the student does not want to participate and obtains the parent's or family physician's support.

Some school systems have exercised control over the indiscriminate granting of such requests. Policies have been established, sometimes through conferences and rulings of the board of education, requiring that all excuses must be reviewed and approved by the school physician before they will be granted. Furthermore, family physicians have been asked to state specific reasons for requesting excuse from physical education. This procedure has worked out very satisfactorily in some communities. In other places physical educators have taken particular pains to work very closely with medical doctors. They have established a physical education program in collaboration with the school physician so that the needs of each individual are met, regardless of his or her physical condition. They have met with the local medical society in an attempt to clear up misunderstandings in regard to the purpose and conduct of the program. Family physicians have been brought into the planning. As a result of such planning, problems in regard to excuses from physical education have been considerably reduced.

There probably is a high correlation between the respect, prestige, and the degree to which physical education is understood in any community and the number of excuses that are requested. Furthermore, respect, prestige, and understanding are reflected in the type of leadership that exists. It has been found that in those communities where parents, family physicians, and the lay public in general understand physical education the number of requests for excuses is relatively small. In such communities, the values that can be derived from participation in the program are clearly recognized, and since most parents and physicians want children to have worth-while experiences, they encourage rather than attempt to limit such participation. The leadership of any program can eliminate many of the administrative problems in regard to excuses, provided physical education is properly interpreted to the public at large.

A few years ago, a conference concerned with close cooperation between physical education and medical doctors, drew up a list of statements in respect to the problem under discussion. These are as follows:

1. Orient the student, parent, and physician at an early date in regard to the objectives of the physical education program.

2. Route all requests for excuse through the school physician. In the absence of the physician the school nurse should have this responsibility. The sympathetic and informed nurse can be a real asset to the physical education program.

3. Discard permanent and blanket excuses. The school physician should share in planning certain areas of the individual physical education program. Instead of being categorically excused, boys and girls can be given an activity in keeping with their special needs.

4. Students involved in the excuse request should have a periodic re-check as to need for excuse (this tends to reduce requests up to fifty per cent).

5. Conferences between the school physicians and the head of the physical education department on the local level need to be emphasized.

6. The problem of excuse from physical education should be tied up with the total guidance program of the school. It helps also if the administrator and classroom teachers are familiar with the general physical education aims.

III. CLASS MANAGEMENT

Good class management means good planning. Forethought is needed in order to have a group of students act in an orderly manner, accomplish the tasks that have been established, and have an enjoyable, satisfying, and worth-while experience. The leader who is in charge of a class where these optimum conditions exist has spent considerable time in planning the details of the class from start to finish. Good class management does not just happen. It requires considerable thought, good judgment, and the making of many plans before the class begins.

There are many reasons for good organization. These should be recognized by every teacher and administrator. Some of these are:

1. It gives meaning and purpose to instruction and to the activities.
2. It results in efficiency, the right emphasis, and the best use of the time that is available.
3. It more fully insures that the needs and interests of the students will be satisfied.
4. It more fully insures progression and continuity in the program.
5. It provides for measurement and progress toward objectives.
6. It insures provision for child health and safety.
7. It encourages program adaptations to each individual's needs and interests.
8. It reduces errors and omissions to a minimum.
9. It helps to conserve the instructor's time and strength and aids in giving her or him a sense of accomplishment.

Some guides with which the teacher and administrator should concern themselves are as follows:

1. There should be long-term planning—for the semester and the year, as well as daily, weekly, and seasonal.

2. A definite time schedule should be planned for each period, taking into consideration time to be devoted to showering and dressing, taking roll, class activity, and other essentials.

3. The conduct of the activity should be carefully planned, so that it proceeds with precision and dispatch, with a minimum amount of standing around and a maximum amount of activity for each child.

4. The physical education class period should be regarded primarily as an instructional period. It is not one for free play. However, in order to have sustained interest and as much satisfaction and joy result from the class as possible, there should be provision for using instruction received in actual activity.

5. There should be a definite system established for such essentials as taking roll, keeping essential records, grading, adhering to policy on uniform, and dressing and showering.

6. Attention should be given to preparation of materials to be used in class. The teacher should know beforehand the materials to be used, and they should be ready when the class begins.

7. The setting for the class should be safe and healthful. The equipment should be safe, line markings, arrangements for activities, and other essential details attended to.

8. Procedure to be followed in locker room should be established to provide for traffic, valuables, clothes, and dressing and showering.

9. A procedure should be established for falling in, taking attendance, organizing for activity, and for dismissal.

10. The instructor should always use good English and explain things in a simple, clear, and informative manner. During explanations, the class should be attentive.

11. The instructor should always be prompt and punctual for class meetings.

12. The instructor should be tactful and considerate of every pupil. Pupils should not be condemned for making mistakes. It should be remembered that an educational situation is a normal and natural setting for mistakes.

13. Pupils should be encouraged and motivated to do their best.

14. All pupils should be treated in the same manner. There should be no favorites.

15. A planned program of measurement and evaluation should be provided to determine progress being made by pupils and the effectiveness of teaching.

16. The instructor and the class should dress in suitable costume.

17. There should be as few rules of behavior as possible, making sure that those which are established are adhered to. Pupils should participate in the establishment of such rules.

18. The instructor should circulate among the entire class, giving help to those who are in need of it. Individual differences should be adequately provided for.

19. The instructor should have a good command of his subject. The values of demonstrations, visual aids, and other techniques to promote learning should be recognized.

20. Desirable attitudes and understandings toward physical fitness, skill learning, good sportsmanship, and other concepts inherent in physical education should be stressed at all times.

21. Standards of achievement and specific goals which are attainable should be established. Pupils' progress should be recorded so that they know how they are advancing toward these goals.

Some of the factors concerned with class management that deserve special attention are dressing and showering, costume, taking roll, grading, and records. Each of these will be discussed in more detail.

A. Dressing and Showering

Such factors as the age of the child, time allowed, grade participating, and type of activity should be considered in a discussion of dressing and showering for physical education classes.

The problem of showering and dressing is not so pertinent at the lower elementary level where the age of the participants and type of activities as a general rule do not require special costumes and showering. Also the time allotted is too short in many cases. In the upper elementary and at the junior and senior high school and college levels, however, it is a problem.

Physical education, by its very nature, embodies activities which result in considerable running, jumping, throwing, and other vigorous movements. Participation also frequently results in perspiration. In the interests of comfort and good hygiene practices, provisions should be made for special clothing and showering. The unpleasant features of a student's returning to class after participating in physical education activity, with clothes dripping from perspiration and with the accompanying odors are not in conformance with establishing good habits of personal cleanliness and grooming. Therefore, all schools should make special provisions for places to dress in comfortable uniforms and for showering. Such places should be convenient to the physical education areas, be comfortable, and afford privacy. Although girls are increasingly becoming accustomed to using a gang shower, there are still many who prefer the private cubicles. In the interests of these individuals, such facilities should be provided. There should also be some type of towel service. In many schools there are facilities for laundering towels which have worked out very satisfactorily.

In order to insure that a maximum number of pupils take advantage of the facilities for showering and dressing it is important that proper attitudes and understandings be developed. The right attitudes toward cleanliness, personal grooming, and sanitation should be developed in each individual. If this is done, the right health practices will be followed and the question of whether or not to establish a rigid rule requiring showers will not be necessary. It should be a matter of education rather than one of coercion. In addition, there should be a reasonable time allotted for showering and dressing. This should be kept at a minimum in order to allow a maximum of time for activity, but at the same time adequate time should be allowed to dress and shower.

B. Costume

There are many reasons for the use of special costumes in physical education classes above the elementary level. Some of these are: (1) It makes for better appearance if an individual is dressed in a costume which fits the activity in which he is engaging. (2) It provides for more comfort and allows for freedom of movement. (3) It is more economical, in that it saves on street clothes. If purchased in lots by the school there can be a considerable saving to the student. Those students who cannot afford uniforms should have them provided free of charge. (4) If all have the same uniform, it aids morale and promotes equality. (5) It also is safer, without dangling sleeves or wide skirts to cause accidents.

The costumes do not have to be elaborate. For girls they can be simple, washable shorts and blouse, or one-piece suits. For boys white cotton jerseys and trunks will suffice. Of course, suitable shoes should also be worn. An important consideration is to keep the uniform clean. The instructor should establish a policy on clean uniforms and work diligently toward seeing that hygienic standards are met by all.

C. Taking Roll

There are many methods of taking roll. If a method satisfies three criteria, it is usually satisfactory. These three criteria are: (1) It is economical of time—roll taking should not consume too much time. It is essential to get into activity as soon as possible, and routine details should be kept to a minimum. (2) It should guarantee accuracy—it is important to know accurately after the class has been held who was present and who was not. This means taking into consideration those who might come to class late or leave early. (3) It should not be complicated. Any system that is used should be very simple and easy to administer.

Some of the questions that arise in respect to roll taking are: Should it be taken on the gymnasium floor, playground, in the swimming pool, shower, or locker room? Or should it be taken on the way to or from the gymnasium or place where the physical education activity is held? When should it be taken? Should it be taken at the beginning of the period; after the class has started in order to insure the inclusion of tardy students, or at the end of the period? Who should take it? Should it be taken by the instructor, an assistant instructor, the shower or locker attendant, or squad leader? These questions are pertinent and must be answered by the physical educator in each local situation and in accordance with the influences that play upon the physical education class.

Some of the methods for roll taking that may be used are as follows:

1. *Having numbers on the floor*—each member of the class is assigned a number which he must stand on at the time the signal for "fall in" is given. The person taking attendance records the numbers that are not covered.
2. *Reciting numbers orally*—each member of the class is assigned a number which he must say out loud at the time the signal for "fall in" is given. The person taking attendance then records the numbers that are not given.

3. *Tag board*—each member of the class has a number which is recorded on a cardboard, or metal tag which hangs on a peg on a board in a central place. Each member of the class who is present removes his tag from the board and places it in a box. The person taking attendance records the absentees from the board.

4. *Delaney System*—New York City has a special system developed by a man named Delaney, which involves using a folder with cards which are turned over when a person is absent. It is a cumulative system which records the attendance of pupils over a period of time. There are adaptations of this system which are used elsewhere.

5. *Squad system*—the class is divided into squads and the squad leader takes the roll for his squad and in turn reports to the instructor.

6. *Issuing Towels and Equipment*—the roll is taken when a towel is issued to each student or when it is turned in, or when a basket with uniform is issued or returned.

7. *Signing a book or register*—students are required to write their names in a book or register at the beginning of the class. Some systems require the writing of a name at the beginning of a period and crossing it out at the end of a period. The person taking attendance records the names not entered.

D. Grading

Since grading is an established custom in the educational system of this country, physical education must conform and grant grades or utilize some other method of denoting progress that has been achieved.

Grades have been issued in physical education in several ways, ranging from granting letter or numeral grades, to ranking in a class. These grades have also been based on many factors, many of which have questionable value. Present practices base grades on such factors as attendance, punctuality, effort, costume, achievement, general attitude, initiative, hygiene, skill, knowledge of rules, cooperation, posture, strength, and endurance. There seems to be no set formula or procedure. For the country as a whole it appears to be a hit-and-miss procedure, depending on what each individual instructor feels is the basis on which grades should be granted.

The following recommendations represent some of the more advanced thinking among educators in general. At the elementary level especially, the feeling is increasing that it is not wise to issue a single grade or numerical rating. It is felt that a descriptive paragraph telling in more detail what progress is being made by the pupil is much better. Discussing such items as a student's strengths and weaknesses and where he needs to improve is much more meaningful and purposeful. This type of report and talks with parents will better achieve the purpose of showing to what degree educational objectives are being attained and what needs to be accomplished in the future. This method also has implications for grading above the elementary level.

When grades are given, they should be based on the achievement of objectives —the degree to which the student has achieved the desired outcomes. These objectives should be clear in the instructor's and students' minds at the outset of the course so that the desired direction will be known. The individuals getting the best grades would be those students most nearly achieving objectives which have been listed as desirable goals for the course. In physical education the physical, motor, mental, and human relations objectives would all be kept in mind.

A further recommendation is that, as far as possible, the degree to which desired objectives are achieved should be determined objectively rather than subjectively. This means that wherever possible scientific evaluation and measurement techniques should be utilized. Since there is a dearth of such techniques, some subjective judgments will have to be made.

The State Department of Public Instruction at Bismark, North Dakota, has established some standards for grading in that state. Some excerpts[9] from their grading policy read:

The hit or miss method of purely subjective grading in physical education so widely used cannot be too strongly condemned. The grade in physical education should be an accurate reflection of how well the pupil has achieved the objectives. It is suggested that the following points be considered in grading:

(a) The system for reporting grades should conform to the system generally used by the school as a whole.

(b) Basis for the grade:

      50%, Achievement of physical skill and activity.
      30%, Specific health and social qualities.
      20%, Knowledge of rules and techniques.

An "A" student is *superior* in that he:

(a) Is keenly enthusiastic. Persists industriously at his tasks.
(b) Acts intelligently on his own initiative.
(c) Shows positive leadership.
(d) Carries out responsibilities faithfully and honestly.
(e) Displays superior general ability and form.
(f) Is well liked by most of his fellow students, tactful to those in authority and to those he leads.
(g) Is a gracious winner and a good leader and encourages the same in others.

A "B" student is *excellent* in that he:

(a) Is usually enthusiastic and generally industrious.
(b) Cooperates well with leaders.
(c) Follows directions intelligently without much help.
(d) Generally carries out his share of group activity.
(e) Has good general ability and form.
(f) Has few enemies and gets along well with others.
(g) Seldom displays poor sportsmanship.

A "C" student is *average* in that he:

(a) Is passive as a rule. Willing to do as told.
(b) Is not outstanding in understanding. A little slow at times.
(c) Usually cooperates. Never assumes leadership.
(d) Will work with assistance.
(e) Has some friends and some enemies but none outstanding.
(f) Has fair ability. Learns slowly at times.
(g) Displays poor sportsmanship occasionally.

---

[9]Department of Public Instruction. *Health Education in Secondary Schools.* Bismark, North Dakota: State Department of Public Instruction, 1950, pp. 48-49.

A "D" student is *below average* in that he:
  (a) Is disinterested and reticent. Tends to avoid work.
  (b) Does not understand directions. Makes frequent errors.
  (c) Must be led and watched.
  (d) Will avoid responsibility frequently.
  (e) Has poor ability and little form. A slow learner.
  (f) Tends to be reclusive or unsociable.
  (g) Is poor in skill. Either has no skill or won't use it.

A student will probably not be completely described by any one of the descriptive groups listed, but as a rule traits above and below the group most descriptive of the individual will level each other into the middle group.

The current thinking in regard to grading in physical education is well summarized by The American Association for Health, Physical Education and Recreation.[10]

  1. Specific goals and objectives should be established with students.
  2. Marks should relate to the attainment of these goals and objectives.
  3. Students should be informed of how marks will be determined.
  4. Marks shall be based upon several factors rather than a single item alone.
  5. Evaluation techniques should be valid, reliable, objective, and standardized whenever possible.
  6. The place of improvement shall be determined in advance.
  7. Personalities shall be removed as a factor in the final mark.
  8. The mark should not only inform but it should also suggest ways of improvement.

E. Records

Records are an essential in keeping valuable information in regard to pupils' welfare. They also are essential to efficient program planning and administration. They should, however, be kept to a minimum and should be practical and functional. They should not be maintained just as "busy" work and for the sake of filling the files. Instead they should have "use" and a place in the program.

Some of the records should be concerned directly with the welfare of the pupil and others with certain administrative factors.

Those records which concern the welfare of the student are the health record, the cumulative physical education form, anecdotal accounts, attendance reports, grades, and accident reports.

Health records are an essential. They contain information on the health examination and other appraisal techniques, health counseling, and any other data pertaining to the student's health.*

The cumulative physical education record should start when the student first attends school and contain information about activities engaged in, after-school play, tests, anecdotal accounts having a bearing on the interests, needs, and any other pertinent information that should be known in respect to the student and his participation in the physical education programs.

There should be special records for attendance and grades and any special occurrences which have a bearing on the child and are not recorded in other records.

---

*See chapter XV on "Health Services" for more complete information.
[10]*Administrative Problems in Health Education, Physical Education, and Recreation*, p. 74.

If a student is involved in an accident, a full account of the circumstances surrounding the accident should be recorded. Usually special forms are provided for such purposes.*

The records dealing with administrative factors are concerned with general administrative information and equipment records. These would include a list of the year's events: activities; records of teams; play days, sports days, intramurals; events of special interest; techniques utilized which have been helpful; budget information; and any other data which would be helpful in planning for succeeding years. The memory of the human being often fails over a period of time, with the result that many good ideas are lost and many activities and techniques of special value not utilized because they are forgotten.

There should be records in regard to equipment, facilities, and supplies. Such records should show the material needing repair, new materials needed, and also the location of various materials, so they can easily be found.

There is also a need for records in regard to such items as locker or basket assignments and any other pertinent information that is essential to the efficient running of a physical education program.

IV. PHYSICAL EDUCATION ACTIVITIES

Physical education activities represent the heart of the program. They are the means for accomplishing objectives. They represent the media which attract the attention of the student, and through participation aid him in the achievement of life's goals. Because they are so important to the physical education profession they must be selected with considerable care.

A. Criteria for Selection

1. Activities should be selected in terms of the values they have in achieving the objectives of physical education. This means they would not only possess potentialities for developing physical fitness, but also would have implications for developing the intellectual, emotional, and social make-up of the individual.

2. Activities should be interesting and challenging. They should appeal to the students and present them with situations which challenge their skill and ability. For example, golf always presents the challenge of getting a lower score.

3. They should be adaptable to the growth and developmental needs and interests of children and youth. The needs of individuals vary from age to age. Consequently, activities and the pattern of organization must also change if these needs are to be met. The activity must be suited to the child, not the child to the activity. Wherever possible, students should be allowed some choice in the activities in which they participate.

4. Activities should be modifications of racially old, fundamental movements such as running, jumping, throwing, walking, and climbing.

5. Activities, of course, must be selected in the light of the facilities, supplies, equipment, and other resources available in the school or community. One cannot plan an extensive tennis program if only one court is available.

*See pp. 149, 151.

6. Activities should be selected not only with a view to their present value while the child is in school but also with a view to post-school and adult living. Skills learned during school days have potentialities for use throughout life, thus contributing in great measure to enriched living. Patterns for many skills utilized in adult leisure hours are developed while the individual is in the formative years of childhood.

7. Activities must be selected for health and safety values. Such an activity as boxing has been questioned as to its effect on the health and safety of individuals.

8. The local education philosophy, policies, and school organization must be taken into consideration.

9. School activities should provide situations which are similar to those children experience in natural play situations outside the school environment.

10. Activities should provide the child with opportunities for creative self-expression.

11. Activities should be selected which have potentialities to elicit the correct social and moral responses through high quality leadership.

12. Activities should reflect the democratic way of life.

B. Classification

Activities that are currently used in physical education programs throughout the country may be classified in several ways. Williams and Brownell,[11] for example, utilize the following:

1. Fundamental Skills (includes running, throwing, climbing, etc.)
2. Games and Sports (includes aquatics)
3. Rhythmic Activities
4. Stunts (includes self-testing activities, gymnastics, and tumbling)
5. Corrective or Adaptive Activities
6. Recreational Activities (includes hiking, camping, trips, free play, etc.)

A survey conducted by the author[12] produced a list of physical education activities that are offered throughout the country, here classified into various categories. These do not necessarily meet criteria that have been listed. They merely indicate current offerings in physical education programs in the United States.

Team Games
baseball
basketball
code ball
field hockey (women only)
flag football (men only)
football (men only)
soccer
softball
speedball
touch football
volleyball

Rhythms and Dancing
folk dancing
gymnastic dancing
modern dancing
rhythms
square dancing
social dancing
tap dancing

Formal Activities
calisthenics
marching

[11]Jesse Feiring Williams and Clifford Lee Brownell. *The Administration of Health Education and Physical Education*. Philadelphia: W. B. Saunders Company, 1951, p. 95.

[12]Charles A. Bucher. *Foundations of Physical Education*. St. Louis: The C. V. Mosby Company, 1952, pp. 253-254.

Outdoor Winter Sports
ice hockey
roller skating
skating
skiing
snow games
snowshoeing
tobogganing

Water Activities
canoeing
diving
lifesaving
rowing
swimming
sailing
water games

Other Activities
camping and outdoor education.
combatives
correctives
fly-tying
games of low organization
relays
self-testing activities

Gymnastics
acrobatics
apparatus
obstacle course
pyramid building
rope climbing
stunts
trampoline
tumbling

Dual and Individual Sports

archery
badminton
bait and fly casting
boxing (men only)
bowling
deck tennis
checkers (women only)
darts (women only)
fencing
fishing
golf
handball

horseback riding
horseshoes
paddle tennis
rifle
rope skipping
shuffleboard
skish
table tennis
tennis
tether ball
track and field
wrestling (men only)

LaPorte[13] has compiled a list of physical education activities together with time allotments, which meet acceptable criteria.

A. Primary Level (grades 1-3)
1. Rhythmical activities _____ 25%
2. Fundamental rhythms _____ 20%
3. Hunting games _____ 20%
4. Relays _____ 15%
5. Stunts and self-testing activities _____ 10%
6. Athletic games of low organization _____ 10%
                                                          100%

B. Elementary Level (grades 4-6)
1. Athletic games of low organization _____ 25%
2. Rhythmical activities _____ 30%
3. Hunting games _____ 15%
4. Individual athletic events (self-testing) _____ 10%
5. Relays _____ 10%
6. Tumbling stunts _____ 10%
                                                          100%

C. Junior High School (grades 7-9) and Senior High School (grades 10-12)

[13]William Ralph LaPorte. *The Physical Education Curriculum (A National Program).* Fifth edition. Los Angeles: The University of Southern California Press, 1951, pp. 28-33.

| | Junior High School (Elementary) | | Senior High School (Advanced) | |
	Boys (Weeks)	Girls (Weeks)	Boys (Weeks)	Girls (Weeks)
1. *Aquatics* Swimming, Diving, Lifesaving	18	18	18	18
2. *Dancing* Folk, Square, Tap, Modern—(girls)	12	18	12	18

3. *Team Sports*
    A. Court and Diamond Games
       Volleyball, Softball, Basketball
       Nine-court Basketball—(junior high
       school girls)
	18	18	18	18

B. Field Sports
       Soccer, Speedball, Touch Football
       (boys), Field Ball (junior high
       girls), Field Hockey (senior high
       girls)
	18	12	18	12

4. *Gymnastics*
    Tumbling, Pyramids, Apparatus, Relays,
    Stunts, Body Mechanics, and Posture
    Exercises
	12	12	12	12

5. *Individual and Dual Sports*
    Tennis, Badminton, Handball, Golf, or
    Archery
	18	18	18	18

Additional sports from following: Boat-
    ing and Canoeing, Bowling, Hiking and
    Camping, Horseshoes, Fencing, Fly and
    Bait Casting, Paddle Tennis, Riding,
    Skating, Snowshoeing, Squash, Table
    Tennis, Trampoline, Wrestling
	12	12	12	12

	Total of 108 Weeks		Total of 108 Weeks	

D. College (grades 13-16) (Each activity is a one-semester course of an advanced type).

1. Apparatus	13. Social (recreational) games
2. Archery	14. Squash (or Squash Racquets)
3. Badminton	15. Swimming
4. Boxing	16. Tap and Clog Dancing
5. Diving	17. Tennis
6. Fencing	18. Tumbling
7. Folk Dancing	19. Wrestling
8. Golf	20. Team games (when needed)
9. Handball	21. Specialties (winter activities, etc., when needed)
10. Lifesaving	
11. Modern Dance (creative, interpretive)	22. Restricted and Remedial for subnor-
12. Social Dancing	mal cases

C. Coeducational Activities

The need for more coeducational activity is being recognized. Past history shows that activities for boys and girls have been combined at the lower elementary levels but at the upper elementary, secondary, and college levels they have been separated. A common sight on college campuses and even at the secondary level is separate sets of facilities for the men and women or boys and girls. In the light of education objectives, this does not seem to be in the interests of what the profession is striving to attain in the schools.

There is need for coeducational activity. Wisconsin State College, La Crosse, Wisconsin.

Men and women are continually together in work, home, social, and other situations throughout life. If they are to adjust properly in such situations, it is essential that attention be given to this matter in their childhood and youth years. Our country is faced with the problems of increased divorce rates and disintegration of family life. Individuals who have not had the opportunity to play, work, and socialize with the opposite sex in childhood and youth often find it difficult to adjust satisfactorily when they become adults. Furthermore, if family life is to be a happy experience, the various members of the families should be attuned to such items as the others' interests, temperaments, likes, dislikes, and habits. Such adjustment is obtained only through constant association in a variety of situations.

The physical education program should encourage and provide for such associations, rather than be indifferent or oppose such a natural phenomenon. The contributions this specialized field can make to such an objective are tremendous and should be utilized to the fullest.

V. PROGRAM

Many aspects of the elementary, junior high, senior high, and college physical education class programs have already been discussed. This information will not be repeated. Instead, certain administrative guides are suggested for each level to aid the administrator, teacher, or other interested person in the conduct of a physical education program.

A. Program for Kindergarten Through Sixth Grade

The various aspects of the physical education program for elementary school, including characteristics of children at various ages, opportunities they need, and activities that meet these needs and characteristics, were developed by a group of experts at the National Conference on Physical Education for Children of Elementary School Age. The following information has been taken from this report because of its value to all interested in elementary school physical education.

PROGRAM[14]

Growth is a continuous process—an emerging—an unfolding. At no time does a child abruptly complete a particular stage of development and begin the next. Neither is there a time when all children in a group are at exactly the same stage of growth.

Any classification into groups along the route of growth is artificial. The following chart is merely a device to help give a picture of activities that seem to suit the changing needs of children. The subdivisions and classifications used serve as convenient labels for periods of growth through which children gradually move, each child holding to a path that is his alone.

EARLY CHILDHOOD—5-8 YEARS OF AGE—KINDERGARTEN THROUGH THIRD GRADE

WHAT THEY ARE LIKE	WHAT THEY NEED OPPORTUNITIES	WHAT TO DO
Their large muscles (trunk, legs, and arms) are more developed than the smaller muscles (hands and feet)	To experience many kinds of vigorous activities that involve many parts of the body. To engage in many developmental activities for small muscles	Activities such as hanging, running, jumping, climbing, dodging, or throwing at an object. Bean-bag Toss, Jacks, Bouncing Balls, Hopscotch, O'Leary
They have a short attention span	To engage in many activities of short duration	Choice of activity where a child can change frequently, and activities that can be started quickly, such as Magic Carpet, Pincho, Hill Dill, and stunts

[14]Report of National Conference on Physical Education for Children of Elementary School Age. *Physical Education for Children of Elementary School Age.* Chicago: The Athletic Institute, 1951, pp. 13-20.

EARLY CHILDHOOD—5-8 YEARS OF AGE—KINDERGARTEN THROUGH THIRD GRADE—CONT'D

WHAT THEY ARE LIKE	WHAT THEY NEED OPPORTUNITIES	WHAT TO DO
They are individualistic and possessive	To play alone and with small groups To play as an individual in larger groups	Individual activities, such as throwing, catching, bouncing, kicking, climbing, stunts, running, hopping, skipping, building blocks, jumping. Dance activities which allow for expression of self, such as clowns, aviators, firemen, tops, aeroplanes. Activities which may use small numbers of children, such as Stride Ball, Cat and Rat, Hill Dill, Cowboys and Indians, Tag. Singing games such as Looby Loo, Bluebird, Sing a Song of Sixpence
They are dramatic, imaginative, and imitative	To create and explore. To identify themselves with people and things	Invent dance and game activities, such as Cowboys, Circus, Christmas Toys; work activities such as pounding, sawing, raking, and hauling. Other play activities: farmers, postmen, grocers, elevators, bicycles, leaves, scarecrows
They are active, energetic, and responsive to rhythmic sounds	To respond to rhythmic sounds such as drums, rattles, voice and nursery rhythms, songs, and music	Running, skipping, walking, jumping, galloping, dodging, swimming. Singing and folk games such as Oats, Peas, Beans, and Barley Grow; Farmer in the Dell; Dixie Polka
They are curious and want to find out things	To explore and handle materials with many types of play	Using materials such as balls, ropes, stilts, beanbags, bars, ladders, trees, blocks. Games and activities such as hiking, Run-Sheep-Run, Huckle-Buckle, Bean-Stalk.
They want chances to act on their own and are annoyed at conformity	To make choices, to help make rules, to share and evaluate group experiences	Variety of activities with minimum of rules, such as Center Base, Exchange, Midnight, and Red Light. Makeup activities, dances, and games
They are continuing to broaden social contacts or relationships	To cooperate in play and dance, to organize many of their own groups	Group games, such as simple forms of Dodge Ball, Kickball. Dance and rhythmic activities, such as Gustaf's Skoal, Dance of Greeting, Bow Belinda
They seem to be in perpetual motion	To play many types of vigorous activities	Running, jumping, skipping, galloping, rolling

MIDDLE CHILDHOOD—9-11 YEARS OF AGE—FOURTH THROUGH SIXTH GRADES

WHAT THEY ARE LIKE	WHAT THEY NEED OPPORTUNITIES	WHAT TO DO
They grow steadily in muscles, bone, heart and lungs	To engage in strenuous activity that regularly taxes these organs to the limits of healthy fatigue	Running, jumping, climbing and hard play
They enjoy rough and tumble activities	To participate in activities which use the elements of roughness	Bumping, pushing, contact activities such as King of the Ring, Poison Pen, Indian Wrestle, Hand Wrestle, Beater Goes 'Round
Sex differences begin to appear with girls taller and more mature than boys. Sex antagonisms may appear	To enjoy their roles as boys and girls, to have wholesome boy-girl relationships in activities and to participate separately for some activities	Activities such as folk dances, mixers, squares, modern, Brothers and Sisters, Last Couple Out. Group games such as Volleyball type games, Newcomb or Fist ball, Softball. Others may be enjoyed separately or together
They respond differently in varying situations	To participate in wide range of activities and organizations using many kinds of materials	Individual, dual, or small and large group activities such as swimming, tumbling, stilts, track, catch, handball, relays, Crows and Cranes, Crackers, Bombardment; folk dances, mixers, and simple square dances such as Csebogar, Captain Jinks, Life on the Ocean Wave
They have a strong sense of rivalry and crave recognition	To succeed in activities that stress cooperative play along with activities that give individual satisfaction	Self-testing activities such as track events, stunts, chinning, sit-ups, push-ups, ball-throwing, for distance and accuracy. Group and team play such as Newcomb, Kickball, Circle or Square Soccer, End Ball, Club Snatch, Progressive Dodge Ball
They may show increasing independence and desire to help	To plan, lead, and check progress	Assist with officiating, serve as squad leaders, act as scorers, help with equipment, elect captains, help with younger children and each other
They want to be liked by their own classmates, to belong. They have a strong loyalty to teams, groups, or "gangs"	To belong to groups, to be on many kinds of teams. To engage in a wide range of activities	Group games such as Bounce Volleyball, Line Soccer, Keep Away, Hit Pin Kickball, Net Ball. Partner play such as Deck Tennis (Ring Toss), Tennis, Aerial Darts, Horseshoes
They want approval, but not at the expense of their group relationships	To gain respect and approval of others	Participate in activities in which they achieve in the eyes of their group

B. Program for Grades 7 and 8

A description of children's characteristics and needs at the seventh and eighth grade levels together with physical education activities suited to these needs is taken from the report of the National Conference in Physical Education.

LATER CHILDHOOD-EARLY ADOLESCENCE—12-13 YEARS OF AGE—
SEVENTH AND EIGHTH GRADES[15]

WHAT THEY ARE LIKE	WHAT THEY NEED OPPORTUNITIES	WHAT TO DO
This is a period of rapid physical growth which is frequently uneven in various parts of the body. Awkwardness and inability to coordinate sometimes occur	To develop skill and co-ordination and to take part in activities that do not call attention to their awkwardness or put them in embarrassing situations	Skills in various activities such as batting, throwing, catching, kicking, dribbling, and serving, as used in—Softball, Soccer, Volleyball, Basketball. Skills in body controls as—how to walk, to run, to stand, to sit, to relax. Individual activities as—rope jumping, horseshoes, target throw, jumping, skating, hiking, skiiing, and swimming
Muscles, heart, lungs, and bones share liberally in the growth spurt	Vigorous activity to stimulate each of these organs to attain its fullest development	Activities conducted as vigorously as possible with respect for individual reaction
Boys and girls are showing differences in interest and in abilities. Boys tend to surpass girls in strength and speed; girls are usually more interested in dance forms than boys	To participate in some activities in separate groups and some together. For girls to have more dance in program than boys have	Activities recommended in groupings as follows:

GROUP SPORTS	BOYS ALONE	GIRLS ALONE	BOTH TOGETHER
Soccer	Yes	Yes	No
Touch football	Yes	No	No
Softball	Yes	Yes	Yes
Basketball	Yes	Yes	No
Volleyball	Yes	Yes	Yes
Individual, Dual and Group Sports			
Track	Yes	Yes	No
Badminton	Yes	Yes	Yes
Tennis	Yes	Yes	Yes
Swimming	Yes	Yes	Yes
Outing activities	Yes	Yes	Yes
Formal Dancing			
Square	Yes	Yes	Yes, preferably
Social	Yes	Yes	Yes, preferably
Creative dancing	Yes	Yes	Yes, preferably
Folk	Yes	Yes	Yes, preferably

[15]*Loc. cit.*

WHAT THEY ARE LIKE	WHAT THEY NEED OPPORTUNITIES	WHAT TO DO
Interest in members of one's own sex broadens to include an interest in members of the opposite sex	To have coeducational activities in small and large groups	Activities such as Square, Social, and Creative Dance, Tennis, Swimming, and Outing Activities, Volleyball, Table Tennis, Badminton
Great loyalty to groups as clubs, gangs, and teams, and there is a keen desire for group acceptance	To belong to various teams and to plan and develop their own groups	Many teams in all team games such as class teams, homeroom, club, counting off for teams and voting for captains who choose teams
Strong desire for individual recognition and the urge to be free of adult restrictions	To take part in activities of their own choosing, to be leaders and captains of groups, to create and modify games, and to evaluate progress	Squad-leader directed activities as: a. Testing skills—sit-up, push-up b. Officiating in games c. Assigning positions on teams
Emotions are easily aroused and swayed	To be frequently in situations requiring practice of fair play, when winning or losing	Wide variety of activities requiring individual decisions and scoring as in: a. High and broad jumps (boys only) b. Ball-throwing events. c. Running against time d. Stunts and tumbling as jump stick, Indian wrestle, pull-up, sit-up Officiating at games as umpiring in Softball, timing in races and relays
The interest span lengthens. They may want to continue in activities beyond fatigue to exhaustion	To participate in activities that are modified to overcome fatiguing factors as time, speed, distance, and pressures to win. To learn when to stop	Games that involve skills of major sports as: Line Soccer (Soccer), Keep Away (Basketball), End Ball (Basketball), Touch Football (Football), Newcomb (Volleyball), Long Base (Softball). Modifications of standard games involve changing fatiguing factors, as: a. Shortening playing periods in vigorous sports: shorter halves in soccer, shorter quarters in basketball b. Frequent time-outs c. Restricting space: Three-Court Soccer, Six-Court Basketball, One-Basket Basketball

WHAT THEY ARE LIKE	WHAT THEY NEED OPPORTUNITIES	WHAT TO DO
There is a keen interest in competitive activities	To compete in a variety of activities that involve a wide range of skills and organization	Self-testing types with competition against self as tumbling, track events. Skill tests as throwing for baskets, pitching at a target. Games not highly organized as Bombardment, End Ball, Ten Trips, Kick Over, Fist Ball
The enjoyment of organized team sports is keen	To give every boy and girl an opportunity to be a participating member on the types of teams that challenge his interest and ability	Wide variety of team sports such as Soccer, Volleyball, Softball, Basketball, Field Ball. Many teams in each sport organized on such bases as skill and ability, age-height-weight, squads

C. Program for Grades 9-12[16]

A discussion of characteristics and the physical education program for youth 14 through 17 years of age, or grades 9 through 12, is included here.

During this period students display marked characteristics in regard to physical growth and development. In respect to skeletal growth, the girls are about two years ahead of the boys. Some girls reach adult height at about 14 years, whereas others continue to grow for several years beyond this age. In the case of boys, some attain adult height at about 16 years and others continue their growth to 20 years or later. Bone growth is completed with sexual maturity.

In regards to muscular development, the "awkward age" is ending and there is a definite improvement in coordination. The muscles of boys are becoming hard and firm whereas those of girls remain softer. Posture is improving and control and grace are in evidence, especially by those who have participated in rhythmic activities such as dancing, swimming, and sports.

In respect to organic development, the heart increases in size, with a question being raised as to strenuous competitive sports, since the heart and arteries may be disproportionate in size. The puberty cycle is completed in the majority of cases. There may be a period of glandular instability with fluctuations in respect to energy level. Some characteristic ailments at this age would include headache, nosebleed, nervousness, palpitation, and acne.

The characteristics of these secondary school students are many. The boy or girl of 14 through 17 may have reached physiological adulthood but needs many new experiences for fuller development. He is emotional and is seeking a feeling of belonging in the life around him. This attempt to adjust may result in some emotional instability. The desire to conform to the standards of the "gang" or group with whom he is closely associated is often greater than the desire to conform to

[16]Much of the material in this section has been adapted from the report of the Curriculum Committee for Health, Physical Education and Safety, Elementary Schools of the Public Schools of the District of Columbia, "Child Growth and Development, Characteristics and Needs," *The Journal of the American Association for Health, Physical Education and Recreation*, April, 1949.

adult standards. However, there are cases of "hero worship," and in such cases adults have considerable influence on youth. This age group is capable of competing in more highly organized games. Groups and "cliques" evolve in accordance with interests and physical maturation. Boys as a rule like to be regarded as big, strong, and healthy, whereas girls desire to be attractive. In both sexes there is interest and an attempt to be physically attractive. As a result, good grooming increases. Appetite is good at this age. Various sexual manifestations during this age may cause undue self-consciousness. Since girls mature before boys, girls are, as a rule, more interested in boys than boys are in girls.

The needs of youth at these ages are many. There is a need for adult guidance, which should allow for considerable freedom and choice on the part of youth. Family life is important and plays a steadying influence on the child at a time when life is becoming more and more complex. There is a need for wholesome activity and experiences where excess emotions and energy can be properly channeled. Certain physical education activities require separate participation on the part of boys and girls. However, there is a need for many experiences where boys and girls play together. Coeducational activities should be adapted to both sexes so that no physiological or other harm results. Social dancing is very important at this level. Also at this age students are interested and receive much satisfaction from sports. Although individual differences determine the amount of sleep needed, most can profit from 10 hours. There is need for a planned after-school program which is adapted to the needs of youth and which includes active recreation as well as the manipulative or contemplative activities.

The types of activities that will best meet the needs of the secondary school student should be wide and varied. Team games of high organization occupy an increasingly important place at the junior high and even more at the senior high school level. The junior high and early senior high school programs should be mainly exploratory in nature, offering a wide variety of activities with the team games modified in nature and presented in the form of lead-up activities. Toward the end of the senior high school period there should be opportunity to select and specialize in certain activities which will have a carry-over value after formal education ceases. Furthermore, many of the team games and other activities are offered in a more intensive manner and in larger blocks of time as one approaches the terminal point of the secondary school. This allows for greater acquisition of skill in selected activities.

As a general rule, boys and girls at the secondary level, including both junior and senior high, can profit greatly from rhythmic activities such as clog, tap, folk, and social dancing; team sports such as soccer, field hockey, softball, baseball, touch football, volleyball, and speedball; individual activities such as track and field, tennis, paddle tennis, badminton, hiking, handball, bowling, archery and fly casting; many forms of gymnastics such as tumbling, stunts, and apparatus activities; and various forms of games and relays. These activities will comprise the major portion of the program at the secondary level. Of course the activities would be adapted to boys and to girls as they are played separately or on a coeducational basis.

D. Program for Colleges and Universities

The college and university physical education program represents the last formalized setting for physical education which many individuals will be exposed to for the rest of their lifetime. The age range of individuals in colleges and universities is very wide, incorporating those as young as 16 and some as old as 60. However, most are in their late teens or early twenties. These individuals have matured in many ways. They are entering the period of greatest physical efficiency. They have developed the various organic systems of the body. They possess a high degree of strength, stamina, and coordination. In this respect the program does not have to be restricted for the average college population. College and university students have many interests. They want to prepare themselves adequately for certain vocations. They desire to be a success in their chosen fields of work. Such an objective offers potentialities for the physical education teacher who can show how the outcomes derived from the physical education program can contribute to success in their work. College students are interested in the opposite sex and are beginning to look for a marital partner. They want to develop socially. This has implications for a broad coeducational program. They are interested in developing skills which they can use throughout life and from which they will obtain a great deal of enjoyment.

The physical education program at the college and university level should insure that these students leave school with skills in their possession for future participation in many enjoyable and worth-while sports activities. The emphasis should be on leisure-time or recreational skills. If a student possesses sufficient skill in swimming, badminton, golf, or tennis, for example, when he or she leaves school, the chances are he will engage in such activities throughout adult years. If the physical education program does not see that such skills are developed, the individual may never have another opportunity to acquire them. This responsibility rests heavily upon the physical educator's shoulders.

In formulating a program at the college and university level one needs to remember that many students enter with limited activity backgrounds. Therefore, the program should be broad and varied at the start, with opportunities to elect activities later. There should be considerable opportunity for instruction and practice in those activities in which a student desires to specialize. As much individual attention as possible should be given to insure the necessary development of skill. It has been pointed out that most colleges offer physical education twice a week for two years. There are others, however, where the requirement is for one, three, or four years' duration. It would seem that the longer the requirement the greater would be the assurance that the individual would leave school with the necessary skills. Some colleges and universities require only that the allotted time be put in, while others state that certain standards of achievement must be met. Both requirements are important if the objectives of physical education are to be realized. It would seem that sports skills are as important to the development of the "whole" individual, as being able to compute some mathematical problem, operate a typewriter, or use a slide rule.

The program of activities should be based on interests and needs of students, and facilities and staff available. There is an important place for coeducation at the college level in such activities as tennis, dancing, swimming, badminton, volleyball, and golf. Some of the experiences that might be included in the women's program are as follows: Team Activities—field hockey, soccer, speedball, basketball, softball, and fieldball; Aquatics in all forms; Dancing—folk, square, social, and modern; Individual Activities—bowling, table tennis, skating, badminton, archery, tennis, deck tennis, horseback riding, and hiking; Formal Activities—tumbling and stunts; and Camping Activities. Some of the activities that have been popular in men's programs are: Team Activities—basketball, touch football, softball, volleyball, soccer, and speedball; Aquatics in all forms; Dancing—folk, square, and social; Individual Activities—skating, fishing, squash racquets, badminton, tennis, golf, bowling, archery, hiking, horseshoes, handball, fencing, and wrestling; Formal Activities—tumbling and apparatus work; and Camping Activities.

VI. INTERRELATIONSHIPS OF ELEMENTARY, SECONDARY, AND COLLEGE AND UNIVERSITY LEVELS

Provision should be made for close interrelationships of the physical education programs at the elementary, secondary, and college levels. Continuity and progression should mark the program from the time the student enters school until he or she graduates. Over-all planning is essential to guarantee that duplication of effort, waste of time, omissions, and shortages do not occur in respect to the goal of insuring that each student become physically educated.

Continuity and progression do not exist today in many of the school systems of this country. To a great degree each institutional level is autonomous, setting up its own program irrespective of the other levels and with little regard as to what has preceded and what will follow. Many are concerned only with their own little niche and not with the over-all program. If the focus of attention is on the student—on the consumer of the product—then it would seem that program planning would provide the student with a continuous program, developed in the light of his needs and interests, from the time he starts school until the time he finishes. There should also be consideration given to adult years. Directors of physical education for the entire community should shoulder this responsibility and ensure that such a program exists. Some communities like Great Neck, Long Island, and Long Beach, California, have directors in over-all charge of the school and community physical education and recreation programs. This offers many possibilities for insuring a continuous program for community residents "from the cradle to the grave."

A system of standardized and meaningful record keeping is essential, to insure continuity and progression. Regardless of which elementary or secondary school the student attends, his records should follow him when he passes on to the next level. These records would show the activities engaged in by the student, progress made, weaknesses, measurement and evaluation results, notations on conferences and counseling, and any other pertinent information which would be helpful in planning a purposeful physical education program.

Good interrelationships among the various institutional levels is a must if physical education is to provide the best type of program possible in the light of the needs and interests of those they serve.

VII. MODIFIED PROGRAM*

The modified program refers to that particular phase of the physical education program which is concerned with students who have handicaps, either temporary or permanent in nature, and which provides activities and experiences adapted to their needs. The program is often indicated by other terms, such as adapted, corrective, prescribed, restricted, special, and individual.

The modified program helps to insure a physical education program for "all" students. Pupils should not be exempt from physical education. Programs should be provided on the basis of individual differences so that all may experience the benefits that can be derived from participation. Such a program also helps to build the morale of individuals who, as a result of a handicap, feel they are different. Being able to participate in physical education as other students do, helps to create a feeling of equality, normalcy, and adequacy, which is so important.

Whether or not special classes for the handicapped should be established will depend on many factors. Each individual case should be judged on its own merit. It should be determined whether the student will be helped more physically, emotionally, and mentally in with the regular students or in a separate section. The size of the school might have some bearing on the decision, in that the number of students needing such special attention and the facilities and staff available would have to be taken into consideration. Some physical handicaps can be aided through a modified program. Of course, any such program should be worked out closely with a qualified physician.

VIII. PROVIDING FOR THE HEALTH OF THE INDIVIDUAL

Every effort must be put forth by the physical education staff to safeguard the health of all individuals in their program. To accomplish this objective satisfactorily there must be a close working relationship with staff members in the school health program. Every child should have periodic health examinations with the results of these examinations scrutinized very carefully by the physical educator. Frequent conferences should be held with the school physician. A physical education program must be adapted to the needs and interests of each student. The physical educator must assume responsibility for health guidance and health supervision in the activities over which he is responsible. The school physician should be consulted when students return after periods of illness, when accidents occur, when students want excuses from program, and at any other time that qualified advice is needed.

Special precautions must be taken to make activity safe for the student. The desire to win in sports competition must not be used to exploit a student's health.

*See also Chapter XV on "Health Services"—"Education of the Exceptional Child."

If disagreement arises, the physician's decision should be final. These and many other phases of the physical education department's interrelationship with the school health program must be carefully attended to.

QUESTIONS AND EXERCISES

1. Write a 300-word essay on the total physical education program, bringing out the three main components and the contributions that each phase makes to the education of the individual.

2. Outline a physical education program for one of the educational levels. Show how the experiences that you include in your program contribute to the goals of physical education.

3. Select a school and evaluate its entire program in the light of the findings disclosed in this chapter.

4. What are some initial considerations that must be brought about before a program can be planned?

5. Develop a set of standards which could be used to evaluate a physical education program.

6. Develop a list of principles which would serve as guides in the scheduling of physical education activities.

7. What part does each of the following play in scheduling: (a) time allotment, (b) size of classes, (c) teaching stations, (d) teaching loads, (e) grouping, and (f) administrative philosophy?

8. Have a class discussion on each of the following:
   (a) Physical education should be elective in school.
   (b) The Reserve Officers' Training Corps is not a substitute for physical education.
   (c) Credit should be given for physical education.
   (d) Attendance should be voluntary in physical education.
   (e) All excuses should be accepted in physical education.

9. What are some essential points to keep in mind in regard to good class management?

10. Outline what you consider to be a desirable grading procedure in physical education.

11. Prepare a list of principles to guide the selection of activities in physical education.

12. What place do coeducational activities have in the physical education program? Justify your stand.

13. Develop a plan to ensure continuity in physical education from the elementary through the college level.

14. How can physical education and health education work together to help promote the health of each individual?

15. Why is a "modified" program needed in physical education?

SELECTED REFERENCES

Andrews, Gladys. *Creative Rhythmic Movement for Children.* New York: Prentice-Hall, Inc., 1954.

American Association for Health, Physical Education and Recreation. *Administrative Problems in Health Education, Physical Education and Recreation.* Washington, D. C.: the Association, 1953, Area IV.

American Association for Health, Physical Education and Recreation. *Children in Focus.* 1954 Yearbook. Washington, D. C.: the Association, 1954.

American Association for Health, Physical Education and Recreation. *Developing Democratic Human Relations Through Health Education, Physical Education and Recreation.* First Yearbook. Washington, D. C.: the Association, 1951.

American Association of School Administrators. *Health in Schools—Twentieth Yearbook.* Washington, D. C.: National Education Association, 1951, Chapter IX.

Brace, David K. *Health and Physical Education for Junior and Senior High Schools.* New York: A. S. Barnes and Company, 1948.

Bucher, Charles A. *Foundations of Physical Education.* St. Louis: The C. V. Mosby Company, 1952.

Bucher, Charles A. (Editor). *Methods and Materials in Physical Education and Recreation.* St. Louis: The C. V. Mosby Company, 1954.

Cassidy, Rosalind. *Curriculum Development in Physical Education.* New York: Harper & Brothers, 1954.

Cowell, Charles C. *Scientific Foundations of Physical Education.* New York: Harper & Brothers, 1953.

Davis, Elwood C., and Lawther, John D. *Successful Teaching in Physical Education.* New York: Prentice-Hall, Inc., 1948.

Educational Policies Commission. *Education for All American Children.* Washington, D. C.: National Education Association, 1948.

Educational Policies Commission. *School Athletics—Problems and Policies.* Washington, D. C.: National Education Association, 1954.

Irwin, Leslie W. *The Curriculum in Health and Physical Education.* St. Louis: The C. V. Mosby Company, 1951.

Knapp, Clyde, and Hagman, E. Patricia. *Teaching Methods for Physical Education.* New York: McGraw-Hill Book Company, Inc., 1953.

Kozman, Hilda Clute, Cassidy, Rosalind, and Jackson, Chester O. *Methods in Physical Education.* Philadelphia: W. B. Saunders Company, 1952.

LaPorte, William Ralph. *The Physical Education Curriculum (A National Program).* Fifth edition. Los Angeles: The University of Southern California Press, 1951.

Lee, Mabel, and Wagner, Miriam M. *Fundamentals of Body Mechanics and Conditioning.* Philadelphia: W. B. Saunders Company, 1949.

Murray, Ruth Lovell. *Dance in Elementary Education.* New York: Harper & Brothers, 1953.

Neilson, N. P., and Van Hagen, Winifred. *Physical Education for Elementary Schools.* New York: A. S. Barnes and Company, 1954.

Rathbone, Josephine L. *Corrective Physical Education.* Fifth edition. Philadelphia: W. B. Saunders Company, 1954.

Report of the National Conference on Physical Education for Children of Elementary School Age. *Physical Education for Children of Elementary School Age.* Chicago: The Athletic Institute, 1951.

Salt, E. Benton, Fox, Grace I., Douthett, Elsie M. *Teaching Physical Education in the Elementary School.* New York: A. S. Barnes and Company, 1942.

Seaton, D. C., Clayton, Irene A., Leibee, Howard C., and Messersmith, Lloyd. *Physical Education Handbook.* Second edition. New York: Prentice-Hall, Inc., 1954.

Sechon, Elizabeth L., Anderson, Marian H., Hodgins, Winifred W., and Van Fosen, Gladys R. *Physical Education Methods for Elementary Schools.* Philadelphia: W. B. Saunders Company, 1953.

Stafford, George T. *Preventive and Corrective Physical Education.* New York: A. S. Barnes and Company, 1928.

Staley, Seward C. *Physical Exercise Programs.* St. Louis: The C. V. Mosby Company, 1953.

United States Office of Education. *Physical Education in the School Child's Day.* Bulletin, 1950, No. 14. Washington, D. C.: Government Publications.

Van Hagen, Winifred, Dexter, Genevieve, and Williams, Jesse Feiring. *Physical Education in the Elementary School.* Sacramento: California State Department of Education, 1951.

Vannier, Maryhelen, and Foster, Mildred. *Physical Education for Elementary Schools.* Philadelphia: W. B. Saunders Company, 1954.

Winters, Margaret Campbell. *Protective Body Mechanics in Daily Life and In Nursing.* Philadelphia: W. B. Saunders Company, 1952.

Chapter XVII

INTRAMURAL AND EXTRAMURAL ATHLETICS

Intramurals and extramurals refer to that phase of the school physical education program which is geared to the abilities and skills of the entire student body and consists of voluntary participation in games, sports, and other activities. It offers intramural activities within a single school and such extramural activities as "play" and "sports" days which bring together participants from several schools. It is a laboratory period for sports and other activities, whose fundamentals have been taught in the physical education class program. It affords competition for all types of individuals, the strong and the weak, the skilled and the unskilled, the big and the small. It also includes both sexes, separately and in co-recreational programs. It is not characterized by the highly organized features of varsity sports, including commercialization, many spectators, considerable publicity, and stress on winning. It is a phase of the total physical education program which should receive considerable stress.

I. NATURE AND SCOPE

An intramural and extramural athletics program, although referred to by many as extracurricular, is an integral part of the total education program. Although it is usually conducted outside of regular school class hours, its educational values are great.

The following statement by James J. Reed, Director of Intramural Athletics at Princeton University, well expresses the role of the "athletics-for-all" program in the total educational offering of an institution.

> The ideal desired at Princeton is to provide a place for every boy not engaged in varsity competition to play on a team in some sport. We are as much interested in the number of men participating in the program as we are in those who win the games. To teach sportsmanship, fair play, and respect for the will of others is the goal of this department. And, since the real goal of a college education is good health, a well-rounded personality, and a well-trained mind, we attempt to realize these values in our program.
>
> Through practice, a boy develops a fondness for sports which gives him courage and self-reliance and provides him with the physical fitness so vital to carry on life's work as well as creates a sport habit which carries over and serves in later life as a wholesome recreation for his leisure time.
>
> The principles underlying the program, we think, are basically sound. They integrate intramural athletics into the fundamental outline of the college education. The program is varied and adaptable to our locality and facilities, providing activities that are at the same time economical and of a high recreational value. Con-

forming essentially to a democratic and socially-sound pattern, the intramural program has proved not only beneficial but also highly popular in the undergraduate's development, and of great interest to the student body.[1]

The activities engaged in during the intramural and extramural program are wide and varied. They cut across all seasons of the year and are played indoors as well as out-of-doors. They include individual, team, aquatic, rhythmic, and other activities. This program can be adapted to all institutional levels, from the elementary to the university. The program that is offered will vary with such local conditions as facilities, climate, personnel, and other controls that predominate and influence it.

Intramural bowling, Illinois State Normal University.

II. OBJECTIVES

The objectives of intramural and extramural athletics are compatible with the over-all objectives of physical education and also with those of education in general. The objectives as listed by one school are as follows:

The aim of the intramural department is to provide each man an opportunity to participate in his favorite type of competition and explore and enjoy others that may be new to him. This program will provide:

(1) An opportunity for better health through satisfying physical experience.

_____

[1]From the *Handbook of Intramural Sports,* Princeton University.

(2) An opportunity for each man to develop the feeling of cooperation and loyalty to a group.

(3) An opportunity to develop sportsmanship and honesty in regards to rules, officials, and opponents. The lessons learned here are important in moral education.

(4) An opportunity to enjoy hard, clean competition in favorite activities.[2]

The objectives of this program may be classified under four headings, namely, (A) Health, (B) Skill, (C) Social Development, and (D) Recreation. Each objective will be discussed briefly.

A. Health

Intramural and extramural athletics contribute to the physical, mental, social, and spiritual health of the individual. They contribute to physical health through participation in activity which affords healthful exercise. Such characteristics as strength, agility, speed, body control, and other factors that prove their worth in day-to-day living are developed. They contribute to mental health by providing opportunities for interpretive thinking, making decisions under highly charged emotional situations, and keeping one's mind occupied in worth-while pursuits. They contribute to social health through group participation and working toward the achievement of group goals. They contribute to spiritual health through practical applications of the "golden rule," fair play, sportsmanship, and high standards of conduct.

B. Skill

Intramural and extramural athletics offer the opportunity for every individual to display and develop his or her skill in various physical education activities. Through specialization and voluntary participation they offer an opportunity to excel and to experience the thrill of competition. It is generally agreed that an individual enjoys those activities in which he has developed skill. Participation in athletics offers the opportunity to develop proficiency in various activities in group situations where individuals are equated according to their skill, thus providing for equality of competition. This helps to guarantee greater success and more enjoyment of participation. In turn there will be a carry-over, into adult living, of skills which will enable many to spend leisure moments in a profitable and enjoyable manner.

C. Social Development

Opportunities for social development are numerous in intramural and extramural athletics. Through many social contacts, coeducational experiences, playing on teams, and other situations many desirable qualities are developed. Individuals learn to subordinate their desires to the will of the group, develop sportsmanship, fair play, courage, group loyalty, social poise, and other desirable traits. Voluntary participation exists in such a program and students who desire to play under its conditions will live by group codes of conduct. Such experiences offer good training for citizenship, adult living, and human relations which are so essential in present-day living.

---

[2]From the *Handbook of Intramural Athletics*. University of Rhode Island, p. 2.

D. Recreation

The intramural and extramural athletics program helps to establish a permanent interest in many sports and physical education activities. This interest and enthusiasm will carry over into adult living and provide the basis for many happy leisure hours. It also provides the basis for recreation during school days, when idle moments can have potentialities for fostering antisocial as well as constructive social behavior.

III. RELATION TO INTERSCHOOL ATHLETICS

Both intramural and extramural and interschool athletics are integral phases of the total physical education program. As has been pointed out, the total physical education program is made up of the required physical education class program, the intramural and extramural and the interschool athletics programs. Each has an important contribution to make to the achievement of physical education objectives. The important thing is to maintain a proper balance so that each phase enhances and does not restrict the other phases of the total program.

Inside the lobby of the Intramural Sports Building. (Department of Physical Education and Athletics, University of Michigan.)

Whereas intramurals and extramurals are for the entire student body, interschool athletics are for those individuals who are highly skilled in various activities. Intramurals and extramurals are conducted primarily on a school basis, while interschool athletics are conducted, as the name implies, on an interschool basis.

There is no conflict between these two phases of the program if the facilities, time, personnel, money, and other factors are apportioned according to the degree to which each phase achieves the educational outcomes desired, rather than the degree of public appeal and interest stimulated. One should not be designed as a training ground or farm system for the other. It should be possible for a student to move from one to the other, but this should be incidental in nature, rather than planned.

If conducted properly each phase of the program can contribute to the other and through an over-all, well-balanced program the entire student body will come to respect sports and the great potentials they have for improving physical, mental, social, and emotional growth. When a physical education program is initially developed, it would seem logical to first provide an intramural program for the majority of the students with the interschool athletics program coming as an outgrowth of the former. The first concern should be for the mass or majority, and the second, for the few or minority. This is characteristic of the democratic way of life. Although the intramural and extramural athletics program is designed for every student, in practice it generally attracts the poor and moderately skilled individuals. The skilled person finds his niche in the program for those of exceptional skill. This has its benefits in that it is an equalizer for competition.

IV. PLAY, SPORTS, AND INVITATION DAYS

Play, sports, and invitation days are rapidly growing in popularity and deserve a prominent place in the extramural athletics program of any school. Although they have been utilized mainly by girls' and women's physical education programs, they are equally important for boys and men at the elementary, junior high school, senior high school, and college levels. They have received the endorsement of the American Association for Health, Physical Education, and Recreation, the National Section on Girls' and Women's Athletics, and many other prominent associations concerned with physical education. They are an innovation which should receive more and more stress in those places where overemphasis on athletics, highly competitive sports for children of elementary and junior high school ages, and the desire to win at any cost are threatening the accomplishment of the goals of physical education programs.

"Sports days" refer to that phase of the program where one or several schools participate in physical education activities. Schools may enter several teams in various sports. When organized in this manner, each team is identified with the school it represents. Sports days may also be used to culminate a season of activity for participants within the same school. When several schools participate in a sports day, the number of activities may range anywhere from one to eight, although it is generally agreed that having too many activities sometimes works to a disadvantage rather than an advantage. There are no significant awards for the various events and the publicity is not of a nature that builds up the desire to win.

"Play days" usually refer to a day or part of a day which is set aside for participation in physical education activities. It may be for students from the same school, from several schools in the same community, or from many schools in various communities. In the play day each team is composed of individuals from different schools. Here the school loses its identity, whereas it was maintained in the sports day. The teams usually are labeled by distinctive, colored uniforms, arm bands, numbers, or some other device. The activities can be individual as well as team in nature, and competitive or noncompetitive. It would be noncompetitive, for example, if several students desired to engage in an activity like riding, not for the purpose of competing against one another, but simply for the sociability of the occasion.

An "invitation day" is informal in nature, as are the sports and play days. In this event two schools usually meet for competition in an activity. This practice has worked out successfully at the end of a seasonal activity, when the winning intramural team or representatives from several teams compete against a similar group from another school. The emphasis, however, is not on placing selected, highly skilled players on one team in order to enhance the chances of winning, but on the social benefits and fun that can be gained from the occasion.

The advantages of play, sports, and invitation days are very much in evidence. They offer opportunities for the entire student body to participate in wholesome competition, regardless of skill. They offer the student an opportunity to participate in many and varied activities in a spirit of friendly rivalry. They stress both social and physical values. They eliminate the pressures and undesirable practices associated with highly competitive athletics. They are available to the entire student body. They are especially adaptable for immature youngsters who should not be exposed to the practices and pressures of high-level competition. They add interest to student participation. They offer innumerable opportunities for leadership.

The general plans of organization and administration essential to the conduct of various types of play and sports days have been dealt with at length by Luther and Duff. This material is considered of such great value to those interested in organizing and administering these special events that much of the information has been reproduced here. Although it is written primarily for girls and women in physical education, the information included is equally applicable to boys and men.

PLAY DAYS AND SPORTS DAYS[3]

General Plans of Organization Common to Both Play Days and Sports Days

A successful play day or sports day requires careful planning and stimulating leadership. The activity program should be organized so that it will run off smoothly. Either day may be managed or conducted entirely by student leaders. Sponsors may help officiate or participate in the activities, however. Sponsors, too, in meeting may receive untold value from discussion of problems, methods, rule changes, and other questions pertinent to physical education programs. A play day may include any type of recreational or sport activity and usually does include a great many activities according to the equipment available in the host school and community. A play day has no "bench warmers or spectators;" therefore participation for everyone is an important item in the preliminary organization plans.

The program must be based upon a knowledge of the elements of individual differences, including age, physique, health, interests, ability, experience, and stage of physiological, emotional, and social maturity of the girls. Any limitations to the number of girls attending a play day from each school should be based upon the available space, equipment, and interest of the girls themselves.

[3]Ruth M. Luther and Charlotte Duff, "Play Days and Sports Days," *National Section on Women's Athletics, Special Events in the Physical Education Program,* Washington, D. C.: American Association for Health, Physical Education and Recreation, Revised Edition, 1951, pp. 47-54.

In every sports day be sure to check your state high school eligibility requirements for participation in such events; for example: scholarship, medical examination, permission from proper authorities to hold sports days, and parents' signatures permitting students' participation. These requirements should be listed in the invitational letter.

For the girl's protection and safety, you should have a statement from a qualified physician that she is physically fit to participate in the sports of the day.

For your own protection you should have a statement signed by the parents that they have given their permission for the student to play and make the out-of-town trip. These are common sense and safety measures.

```
┌────────────────────────────────────────────────────────────────────────┐
│                          PLAYER'S PERMIT                                 │
│                                                                          │
│ Name _____ Address _____ School _____ Date ____│
│ is physically fit and has our permission to participate in the play day to be held on │
│                                                                          │
│ _____ at _____.   │
│                                                                          │
│                          Physician _____ │
│                                                                          │
│                          Parent or Guardian _____   │
│                                                                          │
│                          High School Principal _____   │
└────────────────────────────────────────────────────────────────────────┘
```

Procedure Preliminary to the Play Day or Sports Day

1. Discussion of play days and sports days with your own girls
2. Selection of time and place and general chairman
3. Appointment of the following committees:

> Invitation
> Registration
> Programs and Awards
> Hostesses and Guides
> Food
> Entertainment
> Scheduling of Officials
> Equipment

Specific Preparations of Committees

I. Duties of Invitation Committee

A. Send out the first letter at least 6 weeks in advance.
1. State the time, place and date.
2. Indicate the type of competition (interscholastic or mixed teams).
3. List the essential regulations.
a. Registration fee (if any)
b. Representation by a woman faculty member from each school
c. The number of girls you wish each school to bring
4. Enclose a postal card for reply, stating the final date for the return of the card.

B. When replies are in, send follow-up letter.
1. Ask that permits and registration fees be sent in previous to the date of the play day or be given to person in charge at registration desk.
2. Ask each school to appoint a representative to make a short talk during the noon hour. These talks (not over three minutes each) may be about the sports in which the girls participate, the system of awards, plans for making money, types of GAA social events, etc.

3. Suggest that the stunts be demonstrations of unusual sports, tap dancing, tumbling, GAA initiation ceremonies, charades, short skits of plays, school songs, etc. State length of time each school will be allowed for its stunt.
4. Remind all entrants to bring their own gymnasium suits, shoes, sweaters or jackets, and towels.
5. Explain whether you will furnish all of the luncheon or whether you expect your guests to bring their own lunch.
6. List schools which are coming to the play day.
7. Give the exact time and place of registration. Include the telephone number of the school and of the hostess instructor.
8. Invite the visiting instructors to help officiate. State what officials will be needed and ask the visitors to indicate their choices on an enclosed card.

II. Duties of Registration Committee
   A. Registration fees
      Schools should not charge registration fees as such; however, if girls pay for lunch, use of bowling alleys, swimming pools, etc., these fees could be included and collected at this time.
   B. Register each girl as she comes in and place on a team named by a color or by a similar device.
      1. Suggestions for team divisions:
         a. Colored arm band
         b. Ribbons of different colors, such as badges
         c. Numbers may indicate squads, with girls on each squad choosing their own team name. Each girl is assigned to a specific team number as she registers.
         d. Names of conference schools, such as Big Ten, with miniature paper pennants in appropriate colors
         e. States or countries
         f. Autos: Ford, Chevy, or Packard teams
         g. Dogs: bulldogs, chows, dachshunds, etc.
      2. Give each girl a program, including general instructions, method of team rotation, schedule, etc.
      3. Give the sponsors their list of officiating duties. Example: "Miss Smith, will you please officiate at the following events?
         Referee 9:00 to 10:00 Volleyball games on Court 2.
         Sponsors' discussion 11:30 in Room 110."

III. Programs and Awards Committee
   A. Plan the program according to the number of schools accepting invitation, the type of sport event, equipment and facilities available.
   B. A mimeographed program booklet may include the program of events, songs, list of schools and sponsors, and autograph pages.
   C. Awards for winning color teams should be simple. The spirit of play day is "play for play's sake" and not for definite awards. Awards should be by-products of the event such as handmade badges or emblems.

IV. Hostesses and Guides Committee
   A. Girls from the host school should wear hostess tags. They should be prepared to give information and help at any time during the day.
   B. Begin duty by helping at registration desk.
   C. Provide checking accommodations.
   D. Show girls to dressing room.
   E. Direct teams to activities in different parts of building, or from one building to another.

V. Food Committee

  A. Luncheon

    1. Served by school cafeteria, church or Y at reasonable cost

    2. Provided and served by GAA or mothers

    3. Girls from participating schools bring own lunch and hostess school serves milk or hot drink.

  B. Light Refreshments

    Hostess school usually serves snack (milk and cookies, ice cream bars or apples) just before girls leave for home.

VI. Suggestions for the Entertainment Committee

  A. Stunts or skits

    Each school may present a stunt or a brief talk, dance, etc. Impromptu stunts may be staged by color teams. The stunts may be on a competitive basis, judged by definite points, with points being added to the team score. The stunt program helps to develop clean competition, fun, wholesome social contacts, a greater variety of activities, and to provide new ideas and material for the girls to take home.

  B. Group singing

  C. General mixers

  D. Roller skating

  E. Tour of school or campus or anything of unusual interest in host school, such as new broadcasting station

  F. Films on sport or dance technique

VII. Scheduling of Officials Committee

  A. Have qualified officials selected for each event

  B. If sponsors are officiating, have their schedules ready to hand to them when they register

  C. If your own girls are officiating, you should discuss rules and duties with them in advance

  D. Assign duties and positions and provide information regarding specific courts, team schedules, time of each event, and length of playing time

  E. Arrange signals at which all teams start and stop play

  F. Report all scores or points to head score keeper of day

Sample Play Day and Sports Day Programs

A play day program need not be a cut-and-dried affair. Catchy titles centered around a specific theme may add life and spice to the day. Originality may be used in issuing a call for "The Last Round Up" involving all the elements of a rodeo, using teams featured as the Forty-Niners, Sombrero Sisters, Dude Ranchers, Sharpshooters, and Cowboys.

Another play day theme may carry out the circus idea. Suggestions for team division might include Clowns, Aerial Artists, Lion Tamers, Bareback Riders, and Tight Rope Walkers. The possibilities for unique and clever programs are unlimited.

Example 1

ALL-CITY HIGH SCHOOL SPRING PLAY DAY

9:00-9:30 —Registration and dressing
9:30-9:50 —Welcome, general instructions, and mixers
10:00-10:50—First period

VOLLEYBALL	SOFTBALL
Red vs. Blue, Court 1	Brown vs. Pink, Diamond 1
Green vs. Yellow, Court 2	White vs. Black, Diamond 2
Winners vs. Winners, Court 1	
Losers vs. Losers, Court 2	

10:50-11:50—Second Period

VOLLEYBALL	SOFTBALL
Brown vs. White, Court 1	Red vs. Green, Diamond 1
Pink vs. Black, Court 2	Blue vs. Yellow, Diamond 2
Winners vs. Winners, Court 1	
Losers vs. Losers, Court 2	

11:50-12:10—Showers—dress, rest
12:10-12:50—Luncheon
12:50- 1:20—Talks by representatives from all schools
 1:20- 2:10—Stunts and awards in auditorium
       2:10—Farewell

Example 2

PLAY DAY BETWEEN EIGHT SCHOOLS PLUS THE HOSTESS SCHOOL FROM 1-4:30 P.M.

A. Facilities—4 tennis courts, 2 volley ball courts, 4 softball fields, archery range
B. Activities—Tennis, archery, volleyball, softball
C. Participants—10 girls (two of which specialized in tennis) from each school
D. Order of the day

Organization: A girl from each school had been placed on each of eight teams, the tennis players also being assigned to teams, while a girl from the hostess school acted as a general aide.

First activity period: Tennis players went directly to the courts for doubles games; 4 teams went to the archery range; and 4, to the volley ball courts; later those at the archery range and the volley ball courts changed places.

Break: Everyone came together to see how the teams were progressing and to learn the procedure for softball.

Second activity period: Softball games were played, the time at bat being limited to 5 minutes to make the play more interesting.

Final get-together: Songs, refreshments, and announcement of final team standings.
E. Scoring—2 for a team win, 1 for a team tie, 1 for an individual win.

Example 3

A RHYTHMIC PLAY DAY

When you think of play days, do you always think of sports and games? Are your girls interested in dancing and different types of rhythmical activities? Why not try a Rhythmic Play Day for a change? You may say, "Yes, but there are not enough schools in our locality that do very much with rhythmic activities nor enough girls who would be interested in a whole afternoon of such activity." Perhaps you would be surprised. We certainly were the first time we tried it.

Two schools, Huntington and Warren, decided to co-sponsor the play day. Invitations were sent to all fourteen of the county schools and three of the near-by state GAA groups. Each school was invited to bring 8 girls, with four dressed in slacks, four in full skirts and blouses. (This dress made it easier to direct and call.) The two hostess schools allotted themselves sixteen girls each.

Since the community gym in Huntington was more centrally located, it was decided to have the play day there with Huntington girls serving on the guide and equipment committees. Warren took over the duties allotted to the invitation and program committees. Both groups served on a joint refreshment committee, serving homemade cookies and milk at the end of the afternoon activities.

To our surprise the smaller high schools that had never come to our play days before sent in their reservations for this one. One hundred twenty-four girls representing twelve schools took part in the afternoon activities.

In the invitation we had said we would use musical mixers, singing games, and square dances. We also said that each school could lead or demonstrate a dance if they wished.

We started off the program with circle mixers which included "The Glow Worm," "The Jolly Miller," "Captain Jinks," and "Skip to My Lou." Three other schools contributed by leading "Shoo Fly," "Pop Goes the Weasel," and "Bingo."

We sat on the floor while two of the groups taught an action song, "Kookaburra," and a game, "Rhythmical Numbers."

The second part of the program was given over to square dancing, including "Hinky Dinky Parlez Vous," "Take a little Peek," "Grapevine Twist," "Split the Ring," "Elbow Swing with the Opposite Two," etc.

While the girls were enjoying their refreshments, the Warren girls did "Varsovienne" and a short modern dance demonstration.

The results of this type of play day made us realize four things:

1. As educators we have done a wonderful job in developing our play day program, but haven't we been shamefully neglectful in not utilizing rhythmical activities as a major activity once in a while, rather than centering most play days around sports?

2. We opened the gates of play day experiences to a large number of girls who had never been interested in attending a play day before.

3. The activities stimulated several of the schools to try some recreational mixers in their own school program.

4. The opportunities for developing friendly feelings and cooperation among the girls of the two schools who worked together on the project made us think we should co-sponsor more activities. Heretofore the smaller county schools had thought they could not put on a play day but this example proved that combining and sharing specific responsibilities made the burden lighter.

We are toying with the idea of asking four GAA member schools to work together on a combined type of play activity next year. We would hold it in the evening, combine sport activities with rhythmic mixers, and ask the parents of the four communities to join us. It would be a wonderful public relations project and would give the parents a real interest in the girls' physical education program.

V. ACTIVITIES

The activities that comprise the intramural and extramural athletics program represent the substance which will either attract or divert attention. Therefore, it is important that the right activities be selected. Some administrative guides that may be listed to help in the selection of these activities are as follows:

1. Activities should be selected in accordance with the season of the year and the conditions and influences that prevail locally.

2. Activities should be presented in a progressive manner from the elementary through the college level.

3. Activities should be selected in accordance with the needs and interests of the students.

4. Activities that have implications for adult living should be given a prominent place in the program.

5. Co-recreational activities should be provided.

6. The activities that are included in the physical education class program should have a bearing on the activities that are included in the intramural and extramural athletics program. The latter should act as a laboratory for the former.

7. Many desirable activities require little special equipment and do not require long periods of training in order to get the participant in physical condition.

8. Consideration should be given to such activities as field trips, story-telling, dramatics, hiking, handicraft, and others of a more recreational nature.

9. Activities in the elementary school should be selected with special attention to the ability of the child.

VI. UNITS AND TYPES OF COMPETITION FOR INTRAMURAL AND EXTRAMURAL ATHLETICS

A. Units of Competition

There are many ways of organizing competition for the intramural and extramural program. The units of competition should be such as to lend interest, create enthusiasm, and allow for identity with some group where an "esprit de corps" can be developed and add healthy and wholesome flavor to the competition.

At the elementary level, the classroom provides a basis for such activity. It may be desirable in some cases to organize on some other basis but the basic structure of the home room lends itself readily to this purpose.

At the junior and senior high school levels, several units of organization are possible. Organization may be by grades or classes, home rooms, age, height, weight, clubs, societies, residential districts, physical education classes, study groups, or the arbitrary establishment of groups by staff members. The type of unit organization will vary from school to school and community to community. The staff member in charge of the program should try to determine the method of organization best suited to the local situation.

At the college or university level there are also several possible units for organization. It can be on the basis of fraternities or sororities, classes, colleges within a university, departments, clubs, societies, physical education classes, boarding clubs, churches, residential districts, geographical units or zones of the campus, dormitories, marital status, social organizations, assignment by lot, honorary societies, or groups set up in an arbitrary manner. Again, the best type of organization will vary from situation to situation.

B. Types of Competition

There are several different ways of organizing competition. Three of the most common are on the bases of leagues, tournaments, and meets. These methods of organization take many forms, with league play popular in the major sports, elimination tournaments utilized to great extent after league play has terminated, and meets held to culminate a season or year of sports activity.

Individual and group competition may be provided. Individual competition is adaptable to such activities as tennis, wrestling, and skiing, whereas group competition is adaptable to such team activities as basketball, softball and field hockey.

Various types of tournament competition have been widely written up in books specializing in intramurals and other aspects of sports. For this reason only a brief discussion of these items will be included here.

The Round Robin tournament is probably one of the most widely used and one of the best types of competition. Each team plays every other team at least once during the tournament. It allows for maximum play. It is frequently utilized in leagues, where it works best when there are not more than eight teams.

In this type of organization, each continues to play to the completion of the tournament and the winner is the one who has the highest percentage, based on wins and losses, at the end of scheduled play.

The elimination type of tournament is economical of time but does not allow for maximum play. The winners continue to play while the losers drop out. A team or individual is automatically out when it or he loses. However, this does represent the most economical form of organization from the standpoint of time, in determining the winning player or team.

The single or straight elimination type of tournament is set up so that one defeat eliminates a player or team. Usually there is a drawing for positions and provisions for the seeding of the better players or teams on the basis of past experience. Such seeding provides for more intense competition as the tournament moves toward the finals. Under such an organization byes are awarded in the first round of play, whenever the number of entrants does not equal a multiple of two. Although such a tournament is a timesaver and is quick, it is weak in the respect that it does not adequately select the second- and third-place winners. The actual winner may achieve the championship because another player, who is better, has a bad day. Another weakness is that the majority of participants play only once or twice in the tournament.

The double elimination tournament does not have some of the weaknesses of the single elimination because it is necessary for a team or individual to have two defeats before being eliminated. This principle is also characteristic of various types of consolation elimination tournaments which permit the player or team to play more than once. In some consolation tournaments all the players who lose in the first round and those who, because they received a bye, did not lose until the second round get to play again to determine a consolation winner. In other, similar tournaments they permit any player or team who loses once, irrespective of round in which the loss occurs, to play again. There are also other tournaments such as the Bagnall-Wild Elimination Tournament which place emphasis on second and third places.

The ladder type of tournament adapts well to individual competition. Here the contestants are arranged in ladder or vertical formation with rankings established arbitrarily or on the basis of previous performance. Each contestant may challenge the one directly above or in some cases two above, and if he wins the names change places on the ladder. This is a continuous type of tournament which does not eliminate any participants. However, it is weak from the standpoint that it never ends and interest may wane.

The pyramid type of tournament is similar to the ladder variety. Here, instead of having one name on a rung or step, there are several names on the lower steps, gradually pyramiding to the top-ranking individual. A player may challenge anyone in the same horizontal row and then the winner may challenge anyone in the row above him.

The type of tournament organization adopted should be the one which is best for the group, activity, and local interests. The goal should be to have as much participation as possible for the facilities and time available. Tournaments make for more student interest and enthusiasm and are an important part of an intramural and extramural athletics program.

VII. AWARDS, POINTS, RECORDS, ELIGIBILITY

A. Awards

There are arguments pro and con in respect to awards for intramural and extramural competition. Some of the arguments for awards are that they stimulate interest, serve as an incentive for participation, and recognize achievement. Some of the arguments against awards are that they make for a more expensive program, a few individuals win most of the awards, and they are unnecessary, since individuals would participate even if no awards were given. Leaders who oppose awards also stress the ideas that there should be no expectation of awards for voluntary, leisure time participation; it is difficult to make awards on the basis of all factors that should be considered; the incentive is artificial; and the joy and satisfaction received are enough reward in themselves.

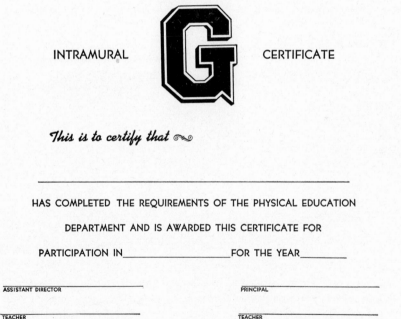

NORFOLK CITY PUBLIC SCHOOLS

INTRAMURAL CERTIFICATE

This is to certify that ◦◦◦

_____

HAS COMPLETED THE REQUIREMENTS OF THE PHYSICAL EDUCATION

DEPARTMENT AND IS AWARDED THIS CERTIFICATE FOR

PARTICIPATION IN_____FOR THE YEAR_____

ASSISTANT DIRECTOR   PRINCIPAL

TEACHER   TEACHER

Intramural certificate, Norfolk City Public Schools, Virginia.

One study indicates ". . . approximately four out of five intramural directors give awards. Letters, numerals and similar awards are used most frequently in the junior high schools. Medals and trophies are given more extensively on the junior college and college levels."[4]

When awards are given, they should be inexpensive. They can take the forms of medals, ribbons, certificates, plaques, cups, or letters.

---

[4]Deane E. Richardson. *Problems of Intramural Directors of the Southwest District*, AAHPER. A report prepared for the intramural section, men's athletics, Southwest District, American Association for Health, Physical Education and Recreation, Annual Convention, April 8-10, 1953, Logan, Utah.

Awards are symbols of achievement and should not be regarded as a prize. In Greek times the awarding of the olive wreath was the most coveted prize that could be obtained by a Greek athlete. The value of such an award was not its material value, but what it symbolized.

B. Point Systems

Most intramural programs have some type of point system which is cumulative in nature and many times figured on an all-year basis. The keeping of such points makes for continued interest and enthusiasm over the course of the school year. It also encourages greater participation.

A system of keeping points should be developed which takes into consideration those factors which stimulate wholesome competition over a period of time, maintain continued interest, and are in conformance with the objectives sought in the total program. The system should be readily understood by all and easy to administer. Under such conditions points should be awarded on the basis of such considerations as contests won, championships gained, standing in a league or order of finsh, participation, sportsmanship, and contribution to the objectives of the program.

C. Records

Efficient administration of the program will necessitate the keeping of records. These should not be extensive in nature but should contain the information that is needed to determine the worth of the program and the progress that is being made.

Such records allow for comparison with other schools of a similar nature. They show the degree to which the program is providing for the needs of the entire student body and the extent to which students are participating. They show the activities which are popular and the ones which are not as popular. They focus attention on the best units of competition, needs of the program, administrative procedures that are effective, and leadership strengths and weaknesses. Record keeping is an important phase of the program that should not be overlooked.

D. Eligibility

There is a need for a few simple eligibility rules. These should be kept to a minimum, since the intramural and extramural athletics program should render a contribution to the vast majority of the student body.

It is generally agreed that there should be no scholarship rules. There should be rules which forbid varsity players from participating in activities when they are on the varsity team or squad. Professionals should be barred from those activities in which they are professional. A student should be allowed to participate on only one team in a given activity during the season. Students, of course, should be regularly enrolled in the school and carrying what the institution rules is a normal load. Unsportsmanlike conduct should be dealt with in a manner which is in the best interests of the individual concerned, the program, and the established goals. Certain activities by their very nature should not be engaged in by individuals with certain health defects. Therefore, such individuals should be cleared by the health department of the school before participation is allowed in such activities.

The eligibility rules which were established by one school, and which have implications for high schools as well as colleges, are as follows:

1. All men students of the college in good standing shall be eligible to compete in any activity promoted by the Intramural Department, except as provided later in these articles.
2. A varsity man is one who is retained by the coach after the final cut has been made.
3. The varsity and freshman coaches are requested to pass on the list of their respective squads. Participation on these squads will automatically make a man ineligible for intramural athletics in that particular sport.
4. A man may represent but one team in a given sport in a given season.
5. A team shall forfeit any contest in which an ineligible player was used. The director shall eliminate any points made by an ineligible man in meets. These infractions of the rules must be discovered within forty-eight hours after the contest.
6. Members of the freshmen or varsity squads who become scholastically ineligible in any particular sport shall be ineligible to participate in any allied intramural activity.
7. The director may declare a man ineligible to participate in intramural athletics for unsportsmanlike conduct toward officials or opponents.
8. A man receiving a varsity award is ineligible to participate in that particular intramural sport until one complete season has passed since earning his letter.[5]

VIII. INTRAMURAL AND EXTRAMURAL ATHLETICS IN THE ELEMENTARY SCHOOL

The intramural and extramural athletics program in the elementary school should be an outgrowth of the instructional program. It should consist of a broad variety of activities including stunts, rhythmic activities, relays, and tumbling. It should be suited to the age and sex differences of the child at this level. It should be carefully supervised. The younger children in the primary grades probably will benefit most from free play. In the upper elementary grades, recess periods and after school activity can take place on both intra-grade and inter-grade bases. The program should be broad, varied, and progressive in nature, with participants similar in maturity and ability.

A committee of the American Association for Health, Physical Education and Recreation adopted the following policy statement with respect to elementary school boys and girls:

The kind of competitive sports planned for children in the elementary school must be based on what is best for the growth and development of boys and girls at this level of maturity.

In the elementary school, children grow at variable rates, and at the same chronological age there are many differences in maturity. In children who are growing rapidly growth demands much of their energy. Emotional pressures may drive the child past the stage of healthful participation. Bone ossification and development is incomplete.

In consideration of these factors, the kinds of competition indicated in the following program outline are recommended as best meeting the physical activity needs of elementary school boys and girls:

1. First, as a foundation, all children should have broad, varied, and graded physical education under competent instruction through all grades. In many of the activities in this program, the competitive element is an important factor. The element of competition provides enjoyment and, under good leadership, leads to desirable social and emotional as well as physical growth.

2. Based upon a sound, comprehensive instructional program in grades five through eight, children should have opportunity to play in supervised intramural games and contests

[5]From the *Handbook of Intramural Athletics.* Michigan State Normal College, 1953-54, pp. 9-10.

with others who are of corresponding maturity and ability within their own school. In grades below the fifth, the competitive elements found in the usual activities will satisfy the needs of children.

3. As a further opportunity to play with others, beyond the confines of their own school or neighborhood, play or sports day programs may be planned with emphasis on constructive social, emotional, and health outcomes. Teams may be formed of participants coming from more than a single school or agency, thus making playing together important.

Tackle football and boxing should not be included in the program because of common agreement among educational and medical authorities that these activities are undesirable for children of elementary school age.

Schools should plan with parents and community agencies to insure the kind of program outlined above is part of the educational experiences of every child.

It should be kept in mind that the child is important in this setting and not the teacher, parent, school, or agency.[6]

IX. INTRAMURAL AND EXTRAMURAL ATHLETICS IN THE JUNIOR HIGH SCHOOL

In the junior high school the main concentration in athletics should be on intramurals and extramurals. It is at this particular level that students are taking a special interest in sports, but at the same time their immaturity makes it unwise to allow them to engage in an interscholastic program. The program at this level should provide for both boys and girls, appeal to the entire student body, have good supervision by a trained physical education person, and be adapted to the needs and interests of the pupils.

The American Association for Health, Physical Education and Recreation, the Society of State Directors, and many other authoritative and professional groups have gone on record in favor of a broad intramural and extramural athletics program, as against an interscholastic, competitive program. They feel this is in the best interests of youth at this age level.

Watkins of Cameron Junior High School in Nashville, Tennessee, has a program which includes team and individual activities. These activities are as follows:

TEAM SPORTS[7]

Grade	Fall		Winter		Spring	
	Boys	Girls	Boys	Girls	Boys	Girls
9th	Flag Football Soccer Volleyball	Field Hockey Volleyball	Basketball	Basketball	Softball	Softball
8th	Volleyball	Volleyball	Basketball	Basketball	Softball	Softball
7th	Volleyball	Volleyball	Basketball	Basketball	Softball	Softball

INDIVIDUAL SPORTS

Grade	Fall		Winter		Spring	
	Boys	Girls	Boys	Girls	Boys	Girls
9th	Badminton	Badminton	Basketball drills	Basketball drills	Paddle Tennis	Paddle Tennis
8th	Table Tennis	Table Tennis	Basketball drills Shuffleboard	Basketball drills Shuffleboard	Horseshoes	Horseshoes

[6]National Conference on Physical Education for Children of Elementary School Age. *Physical Education for Children of Elementary School Age.* Chicago: Athletic Institute, 1951, p. 22.

[7]James H. Watkins, "Intramurals in the Junior High School," *Journal of The American Association for Health, Physical Education and Recreation,* 21: 282, May, 1950.

The junior high school provides a setting for giving students foundations and fundamental skills in many sports and activities. It is a time of limitless energy when physiological changes and rapid growth are taking place. Youth in junior high schools should have proper outlets to develop themselves in a healthful manner.

X. INTRAMURAL AND EXTRAMURAL ATHLETICS IN THE SENIOR HIGH SCHOOL, COLLEGE, AND UNIVERSITY

At both the high school and college levels the intramural and extramural athletics program should blossom forth in all its glory. At this time the interests and needs of boys and girls require such a program. These students want and need to experience the joy and satisfaction that are a part of playing on a team, excelling in an activity with one's own peers, and developing skill. Every high school, college, and university should see to it that a broad and varied program is part of the total physical education plan.

The intramural and extramural athletics program for boys and girls should receive more emphasis than it is now getting at the senior high school and college levels. It is basic to sound education. It is a setting where the skills learned and developed in the instructional program can be put to use in a practical situation, with all the fun that comes from such competition. It should form a basis for the utilization of skills which will be used during leisure time, both in the present and in the future.

There should be adequate personnel for such a program. Good leadership is needed if the program is to prosper. Each school should be concerned with developing a plan where proper supervision and leadership are available for after-school hours. Qualified officials are also a necessity in order to insure equal and good competition. Facilities, equipment, and supplies should be apportioned on an equitable basis for the entire physical education program. There should be no monopoly on the part of any group or any program.

The college and university level offers an ideal setting for play and sports days for both boys and girls.

Sports clubs should be encouraged in those activities having special appeal to groups of students. Through such clubs greater skill is developed in the activity and the social experiences are well worth while.

Co-recreational activities should play a prominent part in the program. Girls and boys need to participate more together. Many of the activities in the high school and college programs adapt themselves well to both sexes. The play and sports days that are conducted also offer a setting where both sexes can participate and enjoy worth-while competition together.

XI. INTRAMURAL AND EXTRAMURAL ATHLETICS FOR GIRLS

Most of what has been discussed thus far is applicable to girls and women as well as to boys and men. The objectives, play and sports days, activities, units of competition and programs at the various institutional levels, have been discussed with both sexes in mind. At the same time, the women have progressed so rapidly in the intramural and extramural phase of the physical education program that it seems wise to make special reference to them.

According to many leaders in the field, intramural and extramural athletics are preferred and emphasized for women as against interschool athletics. They point out that certain biological, social, and psychological characteristics of girls and women adapt better to this type of organization and program. The National Section on Girls' and Women's Athletics of the American Association for Health, Physical Education and Recreation has pointed out that sports when conducted in the right manner contribute to such desirable outcomes as fitness for living and to the development of the most desirable and attractive qualities for womanhood. These include many physical and mental as well as social qualities.

Intramural and extramural rather than interschool athletics are preferred and emphasized for women. (Department of Physical Education, University of California at Berkeley.)

The program should be composed of a wide variety of team and individual sports and other activities which may be played among the girls themselves or in mixed groups. Girls have spearheaded the drive for sports and play days and so these deserve special emphasis. There should be qualified women leaders directing all phases of the program, although men should work very closely with them and lend support and help at every opportunity. Women should officiate in their own activities. Every safeguard should be taken to protect girls from harmful practices. There should be no commercial exploitation or harmful publicity attached to the program.

XII. GENERAL ADMINISTRATIVE POLICIES FOR ORGANIZATION AND ADMINISTRATION OF INTRAMURAL AND EXTRAMURAL ATHLETICS

Some general administrative policies for the organization and administration of the intramural and extramural program are as follows:

A. General Administration

Intramural and extramural athletics should be centered in the physical education program. However, it should be a separate division of the over-all program, receiving equal consideration with the instructional and interschool athletics divisions in respect to staff, finances, facilities, equipment, supplies, and other essentials. There should be one staff member who has direct responsibility for this program. Such an individual should be one who is well trained in physical education, whose chief interest is intramural and extramural athletics and who usually is not coaching a major varsity team. This may not be possible in some smaller schools. However, it is necessary that the person in charge have adequate time and a sincere interest, to do a commendable job in this area. Along with the director there should be assistant directors, supervisors, student managers, and other staff members as needed, depending upon the size of the school. There should also be adequate provision for officials. These should be selected and trained with care because of their importance to the program. Varsity players when carefully selected make good officials. Also, varsity coaches, staff members, and student managers should be considered for this work. A list of policies governing the various features of the program should be prepared in written form and well publicized. Sometimes these are effectively publicized through a handbook.

An important feature of the over-all administration of an intramural and extramural athletics program is the establishment of a council. This usually is an elected council with representatives from the students, central administration, intramural staff, health department, and faculty. This body could be most influential in the establishment of policy and practices for a broad program of athletics for all students.

B. Health Examinations

Health examinations should be required of all participants as a safeguard to their health. Sometimes this is taken care of through the annual health examination and at other times through special examinations given before a seasonal activity starts.

C. Finances

The finances involved in an intramural and extramural athletics program are raised in various ways. Since this program has as many contributions to make to educational objectives as any other part of the educational program, or more, it should be financed out of board of education and central administration funds, just as other phases of the program are financed. It should be included in the regular physical education budget and supported through regularly budgeted school income.

There is another method of financing the program that has proved quite satisfactory in some high schools and colleges. This plan incorporates the cost of running the program in the regular activity fee which includes such student activities as dramatics, the interschool athletics program, musicals, and band concerts. This allows for stable funds that are in proportion to the student enrollment and can be anticipated in advance. Also, this method eliminates any additional charges to the student.

Other methods of financing which are utilized but which are questioned in some quarters are using money taken from athletic gate receipts, charging spectators to see the games, requiring an entry fee, and special fund-raising projects like athletic nights, carnivals, and presentation of talented athletic and other groups. Some of the arguments against such practices are that they create a wrong emphasis on gate receipts and result in many evils, that they discourage spectators from attending and students from participating, and that they require special projects to raise money—which should not be necessary for such a valuable phase of the educational program.

D. Publicity and Promotion

It is essential that the student body, faculty, and public in general understand the intramural and extramural athletics program, the individuals it serves, activities offered, and objectives it attempts to attain. Such information can be disseminated to the right individuals only through a well-planned and organized publicity and promotion program.

The newspapers should be educated and encouraged to give appropriate space to these activities. Brochures, bulletin boards, and the school newspaper can help to focus attention on the program. Notices can be prepared and sent home to parents in the elementary and secondary schools. A "Handbook" can be prepared which explains all the various aspects of the total program and given to all students and others who are interested. Record boards can be constructed and placed in conspicuous settings. Clinics can be held in the various sports. Orientation talks and discussions can be held in school assemblies and at other gatherings. Special days can be held with considerable publicity and such catch slogans as "It Pays to Play" can be adopted. Through utilizing several devices and techniques, a good job of publicity and promotion can be done, with consequent greater participation among the student body and better understanding among the public.*

E. Time

The time when intramural and extramural athletics should be held will depend upon the school level, facilities, season of year, community, and other influences.

One of the most popular and convenient times in many schools is late afternoon. This has proved best for elementary and junior and senior high schools. For some seasons of the year, namely, spring and fall, it has also been popular in college. It is a time which is economical, does not require lights, and has the out-of-doors available. It also ensures faculty supervision to a greater degree.

*See also Chapter XI on "Public Relations" for more information on publicity and promotion.

Evenings have been used quite extensively at the college level during the winter. This is not recommended at the elementary or junior and senior high school levels.

Some schools utilize hours within the school day. However, it should be remembered that the physical education class is primarily an instructional period, and to use this period for such a program does not seem to be in conformance with the standards set in the profession. However, some schools have satisfactorily utilized free, activity, and club periods for the program where facilities would allow.

Noon hour has been popular in some schools, especially at the elementary and secondary levels, and particularly in rural schools where students do not go home for lunch. Since students will be active anyway, such a period offers possibilities in selected situations, if strenuous activities are not offered.

Recess periods in the elementary school have proved to be a good time for many communities to conduct part of their intramural activity.

Saturdays have also been utilized in some situations. Although the week end has proved to be a problem in some localities because many individuals have work to do or have planned this time to be with their parents, it has worked successfully in many communities.

Before school in the morning also has proved satisfactory in a few schools. Getting up early in the morning does not seem to be a handicap to some individuals.

Special days are set aside in some schools for "field days" when classes are abandoned by administrative decree and all the students participate in a day or a half-day devoted entirely to activities that comprise the program.

QUESTIONS AND EXERCISES

1. What is the place of an intramural and extramural program in the total physical education plan of a school? How does it complement and supplement the other phases of the total program?

2. To what extent are the objectives of intramurals and extramurals compatible with those of general education? Give specific evidence to support your answer.

3. Survey at least three schools on either the high school or the college level to determine if there is proper balance between the intramural and extramural and the interschool athletics programs. Prepare a statement of findings.

4. Prepare a plan for a sports or play day that could be held in your school.

5. Why have sports, play and invitation days increased so much in popularity during the last few years?

6. Develop a set of principles which could be used as guides for the selection of activities in an intramural and extramural athletics program.

7. Draw up a seasonal list of activities that could be offered in a school of your choosing. Take into consideration facilities, climate, leadership, and other essential influences.

8. Identify the following: round robin tournament, unit of competition, straight elimination tournament, and ladder tournament.

9. Prepare a debate on the question: Should Awards Be Given In The Intramural and Extramural Athletics Program?

10. Develop what you consider to be an ideal intramural and extramural program at the elementary, junior high school, senior high school, or college level.

11. What are some important considerations in administering an athletics program for girls and women? Discuss in detail.

SELECTED REFERENCES

Ainsworth, Dorothy S., et al. *Individual Sports for Women.* Philadelphia: W. B. Saunders Company, 1949.

Bucher, Charles A., "Field Days." *The Journal of Health and Physical Education,* 19: 22, January, 1948.

Bucher, Charles A. *Foundations of Physical Education.* St. Louis: The C. V. Mosby Company, 1952.

Bucher, Charles A. (Editor). *Methods and Materials in Physical Education and Recreation.* St. Louis: The C. V. Mosby Company, 1954.

Bucher, Charles A., and Cohane, T., "Little League Baseball Can Hurt Your Boy," *LOOK,* August 11, 1953.

Cummings, Parke. *The Dictionary of Sports.* New York: A. S. Barnes & Company, 1949.

Educational Policies Commission. *School Athletics—Problems and Policies.* Washington, D. C.: National Education Association, 1954.

Forsythe, Charles E. *The Administration of High School Athletics.* New York: Prentice-Hall, Inc., 1954.

Hughes, William Leonard, and Williams, Jesse Feiring. *Sports, Their Organization and Administration.* New York: A. S. Barnes & Company, 1944.

Joint Committee (Editors). *Administrative Problems in Health Education, Physical Education and Recreation.* Washington, D. C.: American Association for Health, Physical Education and Recreation, 1953, Area V.

Leavitt, Norma M., and Price, Hartley D. *Intramural and Recreational Sports for Men and Women.* New York: A. S. Barnes & Company, 1949.

Means, Louis E. *The Organization and Administration of Intramural Sports.* St. Louis: The C. V. Mosby Company, 1952.

Meyer, Margaret H., and Schwartz, Marguerite M. *Team Sports for Women.* Philadelphia: W. B. Saunders Company, 1947.

Mitchell, Elmer D. *Intramural Sports.* New York: A. S. Barnes & Company, 1939.

Mitchell, Elmer D., et. al. *Sports for Recreation and How to Play Them.* New York: A. S. Barnes & Company, 1952.

National Section on Women's Athletics. *Special Events in the Physical Education Program.* Washington, D. C.: American Association for Health, Physical Education and Recreation, 1951.

Porter, H. V. (Editor). *All Sports Rule Book.* New York: A. S. Barnes & Company, 1952.

Report of the Joint Committee on Athletic Competition for Children of Elementary and Junior High School Age. *Desirable Athletic Competition for Children.* Washington, D. C.: American Association for Health, Physical Education and Recreation, 1952.

Rulebooks for all boys' sports are available from the National Federation of State High School Athletic Associations, 7 South Dearborn Street, Chicago 3, Illinois.

Rulebooks for all girls' sports are available from the National Section on Girls' and Women's Athletics of the American Association for Health, Physical Education and Recreation, 1201 Sixteenth Street, N.W., Washington 6, D. C.

Scheerer, William W. *High School Intramural Program.* Minneapolis: Burgess Publishing Company, 1951.

Scott, Harry A. *Competitive Sports in Schools and Colleges.* New York: Harper & Brothers, 1951.

Shaw, John H., Troester, Carl A. Jr., and Gabrielsen, Milton A. *Individual Sports for Men.* Philadelphia: W. B. Saunders Company, 1950.

Shaw, John H. (Editor), and others. *Selected Team Sports for Men.* Philadelphia: W. B. Saunders Company, 1952.

Voltmer, Carl D., and Lapp, Vernon W. *The Intramural Handbook.* St. Louis: The C. V. Mosby Company, 1949.

Watkins, James H., "Intramurals in the Junior High School," *Journal of the American Association for Health, Physical Education and Recreation,* 21: 281, May, 1950.

Yocom, Rachael D., and Hunsaker, H. B. *Individual Sports for Men and Women.* New York: A. S. Barnes & Company, 1947.

Chapter XVIII

THE INTERSCHOOL ATHLETICS PROGRAM

Each phase of the educational process must have clear-cut objectives if it is to justify its existence. This is essential in order to know where it is heading, what it is striving for, and what it hopes to accomplish. Interscholastic and intercollegiate athletics programs are no exception to this rule.

The aim of all education is the enrichment of life. This is the ultimate goal upon which attention has been focused. The objectives of athletics as part of the physical education program are more definite and specific than this aim, and through them the ultimate goal is brought nearer to realization. Therefore, it is essential that everyone associated with this work help in the achievement of these goals.

An era of great expansion in athletics started in the post-World War II period. The physical defects revealed by the draft, the value of sports in building morale, and the emphasis on physical fitness during the war and in this post-emergency period have combined to encourage athletics to a degree which has never been equalled in the history of this country. There are many fine athletics programs throughout the country.

The emphasis on athletics has been the focus of much attention and discussion and consequently various aspects of the program should be considered carefully by all interested in administration. Interschool athletics have a definite and important place in senior high school and college programs of physical education. Such competition can help players achieve a higher standard of mental, moral, social, and physical fitness, provided the over-all objectives of physical education are kept in mind.

I. RELATIONSHIP TO TOTAL PHYSICAL EDUCATION PROGRAM

Interschool athletics represent an integral part of the total physical education program. They should grow out of the intramural and extramural athletics program. It is interesting to note that at the University of Chicago athletics are organized as follows:

Intercollegiate and interscholastic athletics are administered by the staff of physical education, the same group that is responsible for the required and voluntary class programs, intramural athletics, and all forms of physical education. The Department Chairman serves as Director of Athletics.

Chicago has no athletic committee, board, or council in either advisory or controlling capacity and has had none for thirty years. The Department runs its own program, responsible only to the Dean of Students and the central administration. Because the program is conducted as an educational program for the participants, it is logical for the trained and expert staff to have full control rather than to leave important policy judgments to some committee of faculty, alumni, and students whose members are less intimately acquainted with the situation, less well qualified to make decisions, and more prone to have other interests than the welfare of students.

. . . .

All varsity squads are listed in the university time schedules as non-credit physical education classes of one-half course value. All candidates are registered for these classes. Passing grades are recorded on the record and appear on all transcripts of credits even though not credited toward degrees at this institution.[1]

Athletics, with the appeal they have to youth, should be the heart of physical education. They should be an integral part of education and aid in attaining goals which will help to enrich living for all who experience such programs.

Angell Field, Stanford University, with an intercollegiate dual meet in progress. Note the television coverage of this meet. The rim of Stanford Stadium is visible in the center background.

The challenge presented by interschool athletics is one which all physical education personnel should recognize. The challenge can be met and resolved if physical educators aggressively bring to the attention of administrators, school faculties, and the public in general the true purposes of athletics in a physical education program. It is important to stress such points as the need for having an athletics program which meets the needs of all; is organized and administered with the wel-

---

[1]T. Nelson Metcalf, "Athletics at the University of Chicago," *The North Central Association Quarterly*, XXVII: 340-345, April, 1953.

Interschool Athletics 371

fare of the individual in mind; is conducted in the light of educational objectives that are not compromised when exposed to pressures from sports writers, alumni, and townspeople; and which requires leadership trained in physical education work. The interschool athletics program can be a dynamic and worth-while experience for all youth.

Athletics, with the appeal they have for youth, should be the heart of physical education. 1950 Michigan-Michigan State Game. (Department of Physical Education and Athletics, University of Michigan.)

II. THE COACH

One of the most popular phases of physical education professional work is that of coaching. Many students who show exceptional skill in some interscholastic sport such as basketball, baseball, or football feel that they would like to become members of the profession so that they may coach. They feel that since they have proved themselves outstanding athletes in high school, they will be successful in coaching. This, however, is not necessarily true. It may seem paradoxical to the layman, but there is insufficient evidence to show that exceptional skill in any activity necessarily guarantees a good teacher of that activity. Many other factors such as personality, interest in youth, knowledge of human growth and development and the psychology of learning, intelligence, integrity, leadership, character, and a sympathetic attitude carry great weight in coaching success.

Coaching should be recognized as teaching. Because of the nature of his position, a coach may be in a more favorable position to teach concepts which make for effective daily living than any other member of a school faculty. Youth, with its inherent drive for activity and action and its quest for the excitement and competition found in sports, looks up to the coach and in many cases feels that he is the type of individual to be emulated. Therefore, the coach should recognize the influence he has over youth and see the value of such attributes as character, personality, and integrity. Although a coach must know thoroughly the game he is coaching, these other characteristics are of equal importance. The coach of an athletic team has within himself the power to build future citizens who possess traits which are desirable and acceptable to society, or citizens who have a false conception as to what is right and proper. The coach is sometimes tempted to seek outcomes not educational in nature by the insecurity of his position, the emphasis on winning teams, student and alumni pressure, the desire for lucrative gate receipts, and the publicity that goes with winning teams. Unless the coach is an individual of strong character and is willing to follow an unswerving course in the direction of what he knows to be right, many evils will enter the picture.

Coaching is characterized in some schools by insecurity of position. A great deal depends upon the school, community, and the school administration. Coaching offers an interesting and profitable career to many individuals. However, one should recognize the possibility of becoming located in a situation where the pressure to produce winning teams may be so great as to cause unhappiness, insecurity, and even the loss of a job.

It should be very clearly understood that coaching is only one phase of the physical education profession and that coaching is teaching. Because of this close relationship with physical education and the education field in general, it should be recognized that a coach should be thoroughly qualified as a physical education person. He needs a background in physical and biological science, skills, social sciences, education, and the humanities. Only in this way can he best serve youth.

The North Central Association of Colleges and Secondary Schools, an accrediting body for approximately 3,500 educational institutions covering nineteen states has the following to say about its accrediting procedure in regards to staff:

> The members of the coaching staff should be regularly constituted members of the faculty, similar in tenure and in method of appointment to other faculty members of comparable rank, with salaries comparable to the general faculty scale, and with qualifications suitable to membership on the faculty.
>
> In the accrediting procedure special attention will be given to the salaries and academic backgrounds of the athletic staff. If it appears that these persons are selected and compensated primarily on the basis of their ability to produce winning teams, rather than for their qualifications as bona fide members of a faculty with educational responsibilities, this will be regarded as a defect in faculty personnel policies and as symptomatic of undesirable athletic conditions.
>
> An institution in which the members of the athletic staff are genuine educational officers will make the same tenure provisions for these persons as for other teachers. In such an institution the record of employment of the athletic staff will reflect a policy of retaining sports instructors who exercise constructive educational influence, regardless of their success in producing winning teams. A record of a higher turnover in the athletic staff than in the faculty as a whole is evidence that the personnel policies as applied to sports instructors are not functioning properly.[2]

[2]Commission on Colleges and Universities, North Central Association of Colleges and Secondary Schools. *An Interpretation of the Revised Policy on Intercollegiate Athletics of the North Central Association.* 5835 Kimbark Avenue, Chicago 37, Illinois: the Association, 1952.

The policies that should govern such items as the appointment, tenure, promotion, and salary of the coach are clearly stated or implied in the above statements.

III. SOME ADMINISTRATIVE CONSIDERATIONS IN THE INTERSCHOOL ATHLETICS PROGRAM

There are many administrative considerations pertinent to the conduct of an interschool athletics program. Some of the more important of these are (A) Health of the Players, (B) Contracts, (C) Officials, (D) Protests and Forfeitures, (E) Game Management, (F) Schedules and Practice Periods, (G) Awards, and (H) Records. Each will be discussed in this section.

A. Health of the Players

Interschool athletics should contribute to the health of the players. Through wholesome physical activity the participant should become more physically, mentally, emotionally, and socially fit.

1. Medical Examination*

One of the first requisites for every participant in an athletics program should be a medical examination to determine physical fitness and capacity to engage in such a program. The strenuous nature of athletics and the demands placed upon the participant, make it imperative that a thorough medical examination be required. This should be a practice in all schools and for all individuals.

The medical examination may be conducted by the family or school physician. The trend appears to be to have the examination given by the family physician. However, the best method of administering the examination should be determined in the light of local conditions. The school physician should review the examination results and health histories or otherwise determine if there are any defects or other conditions which would be aggravated by participation. No student should be allowed to participate unless a physician can state that he is fit for such competition.

2. Safety

Everything possible should be done to insure that the safety of the participant is provided for. Only well-trained and qualified coaches should be permitted to be on the staff. Such a coach will always conduct his program with the health of the players in mind. He will have a knowledge of first aid. He will be continually alert to stop players from further participation if they are unduly fatigued; have received head, spine, or neck injuries; or are dazed. He will not allow a player who has been unconscious as a result of injury to resume play until a thorough check and approval have been given by a qualified physician. He will work closely with the team or school physician, trying to make every effort possible to guard the health of his players.

Proper conditioning and training should take place before any player is subjected to competition. Such conditioning and training should be progressive in nature and allow for gradual achievement of a state of acceptable physical fitness.

*See also pp. 273-279.

There should always be enough players on the squad to allow for substitutions in the event a person is not physically or otherwise fit for play.

Proper facilities and equipment should be available to guard the safety and health of the players. This means that facilities are constructed according to recommended standards in respect to size, surfacing, and various safety features. Protective equipment is provided as needed in the various sports. If desirable facilities and equipment are not available, such competition should not be provided.

Games should be scheduled which result in equal and safe competition. The desire for small schools to defeat larger schools, where the competition is not equal, often brings disastrous results to the health and welfare of the players. Under such circumstances, one often hears the remark, "They really took a physical beating." Competition should be as equitable as possible.

The strenuous nature of athletics and the demands placed upon the participant make it imperative that a thorough medical examination be required. An intercollegiate basketball game between the University of Michigan and the University of Illinois in Yost Field House. (Department of Physical Education and Athletics, University of Michigan.)

Prompt attention should be given to all injuries. Injured players should be examined by a physician and given proper treatment. There should be complete medical supervision of the entire athletics program. The trainer is not a substitute. A medical doctor should be present at all games and practices, if at all possible. The doctor should be the one to determine the extent of an injury. A player after being ill or hurt should not be allowed to participate again until the coach receives a statement from family or school physician giving such action his approval.

Proper sanitary measures should be taken. Individual towels and drinking cups should be provided. The day of the "team" towel and the "team" drinking cup has passed. Equipment and uniforms should be cleaned as often as necessary. Locker, dressing, shower, toilet, and other rooms which are used by players should be kept clean and in a sanitary condition. Playing areas should be kept clean and safe. Gymnasiums should be properly heated, and every measure taken to ensure as nearly ideal conditions as possible for students engaging in the athletics program.

3. Injuries and Insurance

Every school should have a written policy in regard to the financial and other responsibilities associated with injuries. The administrator, parents, and players should be thoroughly familiar with the responsibilities of each in regard to injuries.

Most schools do not assume responsibility for athletic injuries. Most states, however, have some form of athletic insurance. The state athletic association often sponsors such a plan. These plans pay various medical, x-ray, dental, hospitalization, and other expenses according to the terms of the plan. There are also some private insurance companies which have such plans.*

Every school should be covered by insurance. There are five types of accident insurance that can be used. "(1) commercial insurance policies written on an individual basis; (2) student medical benefit plans written on a group basis by commercial insurers; (3) state high school athletic association benefit plans; (4) medical benefit plans operated by specific city school systems; and (5) self-insurance."[3] Before adoption by any school each type of insurance should be carefully weighed so that best coverage is obtained for the type of program sponsored.

A suggested procedure to be followed as a guide for the administration of an insurance program follows: "(1) The entire school should be organized to study the insurance problems and needs, (2) a survey should be made to ascertain the need for insurance before it is purchased, (3) after the need has been established, specifications should be constructed indicating the kind and amount of insurance needed, (4) the specifications should be presented to several insurers to obtain estimates of coverage and costs, (5) the plans presented to the school by the several insurers should be studied, and the one best suited to that particular situation should be selected, (6) parents should be given full information about the insurance, (7) workable and harmonious relations should be established with the insurer selected, (8) continuous evaluation of the insurance program should be carried out, and (9) records should be carefully kept of costs, accidents, claims payments, and other pertinent data.

"School administrators should insist upon the following conditions and requirements when purchasing accident insurance: (1) the coverage should include all school activities and provide up to $500 for each injury to each pupil, (2) the medical services should include (a) cost of professional services of physician or surgeon, (b) cost of hospital care and service, (c) cost of a trained nurse, (d) cost

---

*See also pp. 152-153.

[3]Joint Committee. *Administrative Problems in Health Education, Physical Education and Recreation.* Washington, D. C.: American Association for Health, Physical Education and Recreation, 1953, p. 105.

of ambulance, surgical appliances, dressings, x-rays, etc., and (e) cost of repair and care of natural teeth, (3) the policy should be tailor-made to fit the needs of the school, (4) the coverage should be maximum for minimum cost, (5) all pupils, as well as all teachers, should be included, (6) a deductible clause should be avoided unless it reduces the premium substantially and the policy still fulfills its purpose, (7) blanket rather than schedule type coverage should be selected, and (8) claims payment must be simple, certain, and fast."[4]

B. Contracts

Written contracts are usually an essential in the administration of interschool athletics. On the college level, in particular, games are scheduled a considerable time in advance. Memories and facts tend to fade and become obscure with time. In order to avoid misunderstanding and confusion, it is best to have in writing a contract between the schools concerned. This is only good business and good administration.

Contracts should be properly executed and signed by official representatives of both schools. Many athletic associations provide specially prepared forms for use of member schools. Such forms usually contain the names of the schools, dates, and circumstances and conditions under which the contest will be held. Furthermore, they usually provide for penalties if the contract is not fulfilled by either party.

C. Officials

The officials will greatly influence the interschool athletics program and determine if it is conducted in a manner which will be of most benefit to the players and the schools concerned. Officials should be well qualified. They should know the rules and be able to interpret them accurately; recognize their responsibility to the players; be good sportsmen; and be courteous, honest, friendly, cooperative, impartial, and able to control the game at all times.

In order to insure that only good officials are utilized, machinery should be established to register and determine those who are qualified. They should be required to pass examinations on rules and to demonstrate their competency as an official. Rating scales have been developed which aid in making such estimates. Most athletic associations have some method of registering and certifying those acceptable officials whom they wish to use. The National Section on Girls' and Women's Athletics has a rating committee which certifies officials. In some states the officials who are used in turn rate the schools as to facilities, environment, and circumstances surrounding the game.

Subject to contract differences, officials usually are chosen by the home team with approval of opponents. The practice of the home team's selecting officials without any consideration of the wishes of other schools or regard for impartial officiating has resulted in relations which have not been in the best interests of players or of athletics in general. A growing practice of having the conference or association select officials to be used has many points in its favor.

[4] *Ibid.*, p. 106.

Officials should be duly notified of such details as the date and time of the contests to which they have been assigned. Officials' fees usually vary from school to school, although some associations have set up standard rates. It is usually considered best to pay a flat fee which includes salary and expenses, rather than to list both separately.

D. Protests and Forfeitures

There should be a definite procedure for handling protests and forfeitures in connection with athletic contests. There should be careful preventive action beforehand in order to avoid a situation where such protests and forfeitures will occur. Clear interpretation of the rules, good officiating, elimination of undue pressures, and proper education of schools and coaches on the objectives of interschool athletics will act as preventive measures against such action.

However, the essential procedure for filing protests and forfeitures of contests should be established. This procedure should be clearly stated in writing and contain all the details, such as person to whom the protest should be sent, time limits involved, person or group responsible for action, and any other information that is necessary. A frequent reason for protest is the utilization of ineligible players. Most associations require the forfeiture of any game in which ineligible players participate.

E. Game Management

Since there are so many details in connection with game management it is possible to include only a brief statement of the more important items. In order to have an efficiently conducted contest, it is important to have good organization. There must be someone responsible. Attention must be given to details. There must be planning. Many items must be attended to before the game, during the game, and after the game. Forsythe[5] discusses such items. The various items that he discusses are reproduced here as a check list for the administrator responsible for such management.

Before-Game Preparation (Home Contests)

a. Contracts
b. Eligibility records
c. Physical examinations
d. Parents' permission
e. Athletic officials
f. Equipment
g. Field or Court
h. Publicity
i. Courtesies to the visiting school
j. Reserve games
k. Tickets
l. Contest programs
m. Concessions
n. Ushers
o. Police protection and parking
p. Reserved areas
q. Cheer leaders
r. Score boards
s. Condition of stadium, bleachers, or gymnasium
t. Bands and half-time arrangements
u. Decorations
v. Public-address system
w. Physician at contests
x. Scorers, timers, judges

[5] Charles E. Forsythe. *The Administration of High School Athletics.* New York: Prentice-Hall, Inc., 1954, Chapter 7.

Game Responsibilities (Home Contests)

a. Supplies and equipment
b. Tickets
c. Ushers
d. Contest programs
e. Officials' quarters
f. Visiting team quarters and courtesies
g. Flag raising
h. Intermission program
i. Players' benches
j. Physician
k. Bands

l. Contracts
m. Contact guarantees and payments
n. Eligibility lists
o. Score-board arrangements
p. Guards for dressing rooms
q. Extra clothing for substitutes
r. Concessions
s. Cheer leaders
t. Police
u. Public-address system
v. Rest rooms
w. Guarding extra equipment

There are many details in connection with game management.   Michigan Stadium—Capacity 97,000. (Department of Physical Education and Athletics, University of Michigan.)

After-Game Responsibilities (Home Contests)

a. Payment of officials
b. Payment of visiting school
c. Storage of equipment
d. Contest receipts
e. General financial statement
f. Concessions report
g. Record of officials
h. Participation records
i. Filing of contest data

Preparation for Out-of-Town Games

a. Transportation
b. Parents' permits
c. Finances for trip
d. Equipment
e. Game details
f. Eligibility records
g. Game contract
h. Trip personnel
i. Participation record books

F. Schedules and Practice Periods

The trend in athletics is to limit the length of seasons for various sports. If this is not done, overemphasis often results with a particular sport monopolizing the time of students and allowing only little time for other activities. Football has often been accused of this with its fall practice before school starts, post-season games which run into the new year, spring practice, and summer work in preparation for the fall season. Such a schedule is not in the interests of the students' general welfare.

There should be defined limits in respect to the length of seasons. These should have the approval of school authorities. The length of seasons should be so arranged that they interfere as little as possible with other school work. They should provide for adequate practice before the first game so that the players are in good physical condition. There should be limits as to the total number of games, depending upon the sport, and also upon the number of games played in any one week. Post-season games are not considered advisable by many educators. Teams should be scheduled which are as nearly as possible of equal ability and equal skill.

G. Awards

The basis for awards in interschool athletics is the same as that for intramural and extramural athletics. As pointed out, there are arguments for and against giving awards. Some individuals feel that the values derived from playing a sport, joy and satisfaction, physical, social, and other values, are sufficient in themselves and no awards should be given. Others point to the fact that awards are symbolic of achievement and are traditional in our culture and should be given.

The policy that will be adopted in respect to awards should be determined locally. A definite policy should be established which cuts across all the affairs of the school. At the present time the practice of giving awards in the form of letters, insignia, or some other symbol is almost universal. It is recommended that when awards are given they should be very simple and of very little monetary value. Many state athletic associations, for example, have stated that the award should not cost more than $1.00. Furthermore, it seems wise not to distinguish between so-called major and minor sports when giving awards. They should be treated on an equal basis.

H. Records

The good administrator and coach will keep accurate records of all the details concerned with the administration of interschool athletics. There should be records of students' participation, for eligibility purposes, and to show the extent of the program; records of the conduct of various sports from year to year so that they can be compared over a period of time and also compared with other schools; statistical summaries of performance which will help the coach to determine weaknesses in game strategy or identify players' performances and other items essential to well-organized play; records of equipment and supplies; officials' records; financial records; and many other items in connection with the conduct of the total program. Good business and good administration demand good record keeping.

IV. SOME ADMINISTRATIVE PROBLEMS

There are many problems with which the administration of any interschool athletics program has to contend. Some that are particularly prominent at the present time are those concerned with (A) gate receipts, (B) tournaments and championships, (C) eligibility, (D) scholarships, (E) recruiting, (F) proselyting, and (G) scouting. Each of these will be discussed.

A. Gate Receipts

Gate receipts are the source of many evils in athletics. Too often they become the point of emphasis instead of the valuable educational outcomes that can accrue to the participant. When this occurs, athletics cannot justify their existence in the educational program. Furthermore, the emphasis on gate receipts results in a vicious cycle. The emphasis on gate receipts results in the desire for winning teams so that there will be greater financial return. This, in turn, results in greater financial outlays to secure and develop even better teams. This goes on and on with a false set of standards forming the basis for the program.

Throughout the country interschool athletics are financed through many different sources. These include gate receipts, board of education and central university funds, donations, special projects, students' fees, physical education department funds, magazine subscriptions, and concessions. In high schools a "general organization" quite frequently handles the funds for athletics. Some colleges finance part of the program through endowment funds.

It has long been argued by leaders in the physical education profession that athletics have great educational potentials. They are curricular in nature rather than extra-curricular. This means they contribute to the welfare of students just as much as any other subject in the curriculum. Upon this basis, therefore, the finances necessary to support such a program should come from board of education or central university funds. Athletics should not be self-supporting or used as a means to support part or all of the other so-called extra-curricular activities of a school. They represent an integral part of the educational program and as such deserve to be treated in the same manner as other aspects of the program. This procedure is followed in some schools with outstanding benefits to all concerned and should be an ideal toward which all should strive.

The Port Chester, New York, *Daily Item* recently ran an editorial which was entitled "Banning Greed From Gridirons—Some Schools Favor No Admission-Fee Policy." It read:

> While the coming bowl games keep alive a spark of interest in a departed football season, it may be pertinent to call attention to the sensible manner in which two Westchester (New York) municipalities conduct their high school athletic programs.
> Neither the Town of Mamaroneck nor the Village of Scarsdale charges admission to football games or other scholastic sports contests. Instead, all funds needed for support of the sports events are included in the regular school budgets. As some one has explained:
> Football, baseball and other sports are carried on just as other classes. You don't charge admission to history, English or algebra, so why charge it in football?
> There are obvious benefits in this unusual system. For one thing, a budget fixes definitely the amount which can be spent, hence income is not a variable factor. There is no

pressure upon the schoolboy participants to win in order that the next game will insure a good "take" at the gate. Nor is football made so outstanding in the program because of its revenue-producing ability to meet expenses of other less popular sports.

The Mamaroneck and Scarsdale policy might well be studied by other Westchester municipalities. For there is reason to believe that the profit-motive is a bit too strong in the gridiron policies of some of our schools.

On the college and university level the plan of free sports has won acclaim at Johns Hopkins University at Baltimore, Maryland. The *New York Times* recently carried the following story entitled, "Johns Hopkins, With Free Sports, Called 'Sanest' Athletic College—No Guarantees Given or Taken in Unique Program Which Has Been Operating With Success for 15 Years at Baltimore." The story read:

Amid all this yelling over subsidization of college athletes you wouldn't think there is in America a university where:

All home sports events are free, and

No guarantees of any sort are given or taken from opponents.

But this ideal of pure intercollegiate athletics does exist at Johns Hopkins University. It's nothing new there. It's been going on rather quietly for fifteen years.

It was started by Dr. G. Wilson Shaffer, still the athletic director, as a "sports for all and all for sports" program.

However, what made the Hopkins de-emphasize program really unique was abolishment of gate receipts, the factor that has pushed many colleges into a frenzy for a winning team.

Not only do Johns Hopkins opponents pay their way to Baltimore to play for nothing, but in return games they can keep all the gate receipts from their own crowds.

"If intercollegiate athletics have any value other than monetary," expounds Marshall S. Turner, director of physical education, "they should be financed by the university and controlled by the educational and not the monetary value.

"Our only purpose in eliminating guarantees and gate receipts is to remove any reason, or even the slightest temptation, to conduct our intercollegiate athletic program other than for educational value therein."

The "big" football colleges arguing over how much subsidization is legal didn't hear Turner at the National College Athletic Association convention in New York. His remarks were confined to a session of "minor" colleges.

Many athletic powers have excused their emphasis on winning football teams by claiming the gate receipts from filled stadiums pay for all other sports.

Well, Johns Hopkins appropriates $40,000 a year for athletics. That enables the university to field teams in thirteen intercollegiate sports—traveling expenses and all.

And out of an undergraduate student body of 1,750, between 68 and 90 per cent take part in some form of athletics depending on the season.

In a class suited to this type of program Johns Hopkins does respectably well. It's a perennial contender for the national lacrosse championship, sharing it last year with Navy. It was champion in wrestling and golf of the Mason-Dixon Conference, a loop comprising seventeen members in Maryland, Virginia and Washington, D. C.

Johns Hopkins was even invited to a football bowl—the Tangerine—in 1948 after losing only one game to Penn Military College.

It rejected the invitation.[6]

The above statements help to show how the finances of interschool athletics can be handled in a way that is sound and educational. In addition it should be pointed out that, irrespective of source, there should be a strict accounting of all funds. Accurate records should be kept so that there will never be any reflection on the school authorities who are responsible for this program.

[6]*New York Times*, January 16, 1950.

B. Tournaments and Play-offs

The question frequently arises as to whether post-season tournaments and championship play-offs should be conducted as part of an athletics program. It is generally agreed by health and physical education leaders that all the educational values that can be derived from athletics can be gained without ever playing a tournament or championship game. Furthermore, many evils enter the picture when tournaments and championships are conducted. As a result of such contests the emphasis on winning becomes more pronounced, participation often results in physical and emotional strain on players, spectator pressure increases, gambling often enters the picture, and the emphasis is on a few individuals. The main purposes of such ventures are usually to make money, to entertain the public, and to crown a winner. Such contests are frequently conducted in sports arenas and public sports palaces where evils are more prevalent.

That evils can result from emphasis on tournaments and play-offs was clearly shown not long ago when seven players of one large New York metropolitan college accepted bribes to shave points and throw games. They were the same students who played basketball brilliantly and won two national championships in one year. Some players served jail sentences. Others will never be able to live down the shame and stigma attached to their misdeeds. Their parents are still filled with remorse. The desire for a national championship, winning, and publicity led to these bribes. The first thing the New York City college did to remedy this condition was to take the games out of the Madison Square Garden and redirect the emphasis on intramurals.

The *New York Times* commented on the above incident in an editorial entitled, "The Cancer of Sports." It read:

Only last year there was a team of young athletes who achieved for their college and their classmates an almost impossible dream. They represented, in a small but significant way, something we call democracy—freedom of opportunity and choice, including the right to an education regardless of race or creed, financial or social standing. By winning, in an unprecedented feat, both the National Invitation and National Collegiate Athletic Association tournaments they brought glory to their college and their city and were a vindication of the democratic process.

Now some of these young men have, in a melancholy display of weakness, fallen from grace. According to the District Attorney, they have admitted participating in "fixing" some of the games in which they played this season. It is hard to tell on whom the heaviest blow falls—on themselves, on their families, or on their college, which having little of the advantages of other institutions pinned its faith on them through victory and defeat with eager loyalty. . . .[7]

The extent to which a state play-off can affect a high school was demonstrated in the state of Connecticut. The teaching staff gave failing grades to some star players, making them ineligible to play in the state play-offs. As a result, the student body acted in accordance with "mob" influence. As stated in an editorial in the *New Haven Register*:

The childish demonstration of poor sportsmanship staged by Hillhouse High School students last Friday over their basketball team's defeat in the current CIAC (Connecticut

---

[7]*New York Times*, Editorial, February 20, 1951.

Interscholastic Athletic Conference) tournament stems from a dangerous and unwarranted overemphasis on scholastic sports. It raises the question of whether or not the tournament should be continued.

The kids won't understand, unfortunately—their parents and education officials must— that the basic reason for organized sports in high schools is to instill good sportsmanship, fair play and tolerance in the minds of the school's students. There can be no other reason as important.

Thus, when a bunch of disgruntled students parade through the city's streets in a disorderly mob, shouting threats against members of the faculty, it becomes clear that serious and immediate consideration should be given to the cause—even if it means dropping competitive sports from the Hillhouse picture entirely.

We don't mean this step should be taken as punishment. Rather its purpose is to drop an activity that has failed to accomplish what it is supposed to do. So would any class that didn't teach students something they can use in their lives be dropped. If it doesn't do any good, there is no justification for its continuance—if it does actual harm it should be wiped off the calendar—the sooner the better. . . .

It is when the games are taken away from the high school gyms and staged in big halls seating thousands of people that "big business" enters the scene and trouble starts.

We won't go into the subject of what happens to the gate receipts. And we won't attempt here to discuss the justification of $1.50 tickets for a single high school basketball game, which, if the theory of interscholastic sports for the student's sake were carried out to the end, would be free to the students of those schools. . . .

Another school of thought, suprisingly voiced by adult fans, is that basketball is more important than studies. "They never should have flunked those guys" was one comment. "What is more important—some kid passing his Spanish grades or Hillhouse winning the tournament? You arent' going to give that kid headlines for speaking Spanish, are you?" Another reported that one of the players in question "lost" a chance for a scholarship at a leading college because he was kept on the bench.

Still another comment accused Hillhouse officials of punishing the whole school by benching the two key players. "Just because two kids didn't pass their grades is no reason to make the whole school suffer—they ought to make the kids stay after school or something— it wasn't fair to the school or the fans not to let those two guys play. Those stupid teachers forced Hillhouse right out of the state title."

If adults can't understand, who can blame the teen-age kids?

Pride in one's school is a very real and honorable feeling. Unreasoning anger at teachers who only did their duty is something else again. When that anger is allowed to grow into an undisciplined riot such as happened Thursday night and Friday then it is time to call a halt to the whole business.

One of the basic fundamentals of sport—sandlot, high school, collegiate, and professional —is to play the game according to the rules. Without that basis there would be no sport worthy of the name. The rules at Hillhouse say that if a student fails to maintain a certain average in his studies he must drop any extra-curricular activity and concentrate on his studies. It is not punishment—it is only to make sure that the student goes to school to learn—not to play.

But these wildeyed fans and these immature youngsters demand that the rules be changed. In effect they would subordinate the class room to the gym floor. They would make it more important for a boy to star in athletics than to learn to be a good citizen. They would cheapen education for the sake of victory at whatever price it takes. . . .

Until the students in the state's schools have learned beyond any possible doubt that good sportsmanship and clear thinking is a fundamental way of life, let there be no more state tournaments.[8]

It can be brought out that the tournament and state play-offs aggravated this condition, as they often do. Evils often creep in when a school and a community

---

[8]Charles W. Kellogg, *New Haven Register*, March 6, 1949, p. 2.

are attempting to win athletic laurels. Those interested in an athletics program should continually bear in mind that all its values can be derived without playing a single tournament or championship game.

C. Eligibility

Standards in regard to eligibility of contestants are essential. These should be in writing, disseminated widely, and clearly understood by all concerned. They should be established well ahead of a season's or year's play so that the student, coaches, and others will not become emotional when they suddenly realize they will lose their chance to win a championship because they cannot use a star player who is ineligible.

Standards of eligibility in interscholastic circles usually include an age limit of not more than 19 or 20 years; a requirement that an athlete be a bona fide student; rules on transfer students which frequently require their being bona fide residents in the community served by the school; satisfactory grades; a limit of three or four on number of seasons of competition allowed (playing in one game usually constitutes a season); regular attendance at school; permission to play on only one team during a season; and a requirement that participant have medical examination, amateur status, and parent's consent. These regulations vary from school to school and state to state.

On the college level eligibility rules usually revolve around the same general principles. However, there are some differences in interpretation. For example, some colleges have a freshmen rule which limits varsity competition to three years. The differences in such items as age and attendance in many cases are defined in different terms. The North Central Association makes the following statement:

> An institution should be able to show from the academic records of the students engaged in intercollegiate athletics that these students are securing a substantial and well-rounded college education, as evidenced not only by the marks received but also by the nature of the courses completed. The eligibility requirements for athletic competitors and the administration of these requirements should be such as to assure that no student whose academic standing is low is permitted to jeopardize his educational welfare by taking part in intercollegiate athletics. In this connection, the concept of normal progress toward a degree or diploma is valuable as a factor in determining eligibility.[9]

D. Scholarships

Should athletes receive scholarships or special financial assistance in schools? This subject is argued pro and con. Those in favor of scholarships and financial assistance claim that a student who excels in sports should receive aid just as much as one who excels in music or any other activity. They claim that such inducements are justified in the educational picture. Those opposed point to the fact that scholarships should be awarded on the basis of the need and general academic qualifications of a student, rather than his skill in some sport.

One solution is to have a list of criteria drawn up for the purpose of making such grants and have them handled by an all-school committee. This plan is based on the premise that scholarships and student aid should not be granted to the ath-

[9]North Central Association, *op. cit.*, p. 12.

letic or other departments. Instead, they should be handled on an all-school basis and given to students who need them most and are best qualified. In this way, those students who are in need of assistance, regardless of the area in which they specialize, will be the ones who will receive aid.

E. Recruitment

The recruitment of athletes in order to develop star and winning teams is not condoned for any educational institution. The procedure for admittance should be the same for all students, regardless of whether they are athletes, chemistry students, music students, or others. No special consideration should be shown to any particular group. The same standards, scholastic and otherwise, should prevail. In this respect the statements below apply equally well to high schools and colleges.

> The athletic teams of an institution should be composed of bona fide students who were attracted to the institution by its educational program. Special efforts to recruit students of athletic prowess for the primary purpose of developing winning athletic teams are unworthy of an institution of higher education. . . .
>
> The encouragement or condonation by an institution of outside organizations engaged in the recruitment or subsidization of athletes is symptomatic of an unwholesome athletic situation. Where such an organization exists, the institution affected by the efforts of this organization will be expected to repudiate these efforts and to take effective steps to prevent relationships between its students and the organization.[10]

F. Proselyting

"Proselyting" is a term applied to a high school or college that has so strongly overemphasized athletics that it has stooped to unethical behavior to secure outstanding talent for winning teams. High schools are not troubled with this problem as much as colleges, but in some quarters they also have difficulties along this line. There have been incidents where a father was provided employment so that he would move his family to a particular section of a city or a particular community so that his boy would be eligible to play with the local team. However, thanks to vigilant state athletic associations, such incidents have been kept to a minimum. The following represent some of the rules in force in many states to eliminate special inducements to attract athletes. These rules have been established by many state high school athletic associations.

1. A student shall not be allowed to receive for participation in athletic contests any sweater, blanket, or trophy of any sort except the unattached letter, monogram, or other insignia of the school.
2. A student shall not receive any award from an individual or an organization other than an educational institution of this Association.
3. No student shall be given any trip or excursion of any kind by any individual, group, or organization outside of this Association.
4. An Association school shall not receive any award from any individual, group, or organization outside of this Association.
5. Local individuals, local organizations, or local groups may give complimentary dinners to local athletes or members of athletic teams, provided such dinners meet with the approval of the local superintendent of schools.[11]

[10]*Ibid.*, pp. 11-12.
[11]Joint Committee, *op. cit.*, p. 126.

G. Scouting

Scouting has become an accepted practice at high school and college levels. By watching another team perform, the formations used will be known and certain weaknesses will be discovered. One coach said that his scouting consisted of watching players to determine little mannerisms they had which would give away the play that was going to be used.

Many schools are spending considerable money in this manner. However, it is being questioned in some quarters. Some schools scout a rival every game during the season. Some schools use three or four persons on the same scouting assignment. Such schools take moving pictures at length so that the opponent's play can be studied in great detail. Such money, it is felt, could be spent more wisely if used to enhance the value of the game for the participants, rather than to further any all-important effort to win.

Many unethical practices have entered into scouting. Coaches have been known to have scouts observe secret practice sessions and utilize other unethical methods. DeGroot[12] points out that the Code of Ethics of the American Football Coaches Association has the following to say on scouting, "It shall be considered unethical under any circumstances to scout any team, by any means whatsoever, except in regularly scheduled games. Any attempt to scout practice sessions shall be considered strictly unethical. The head football coach of each institution shall be held responsible for all scouting. This shall include the use of moving pictures."

Many coaches feel that the only reason they want to scout, is that they themselves are being scouted. Therefore, it will work to their disadvantage unless they follow the same procedure. If something could be done to eliminate or restrict scouting, considerable time and money could be put to much more advantageous use.

V. ATHLETIC ASSOCIATIONS

An individual school, by itself, finds it difficult to develop standards and control athletics in a sound educational manner. However, by uniting with other schools such a project is possible. This has been done on local, state and national levels in the interests of better athletics for high schools and colleges. By establishing rules and procedures well in advance of playing seasons, the necessary control for conducting a sound athletics program is provided educators, coaches, and others. It aids them in resisting pressures of alumni, students, spectators, townspeople, and others who do not always have the best interests of the program in mind.

There are various types of athletic associations. The ones that are most prevalent in high schools and colleges are student athletic associations, local conferences or leagues, state high school athletic associations, National Federation of State High School Athletic Associations, National Collegiate Athletic Association and various college conferences.

The student athletic association is an organization within a school which is designed to promote and participate in the conduct of the athletics program of that school. It is usually open to all students in attendance. Through the payment of

[12]Dudley S. DeGroot, "Code of Ethics of the American Football Coaches Association," *The Journal of the American Association for Health, Physical Education and Recreation*, 24: 51, February, 1953.

fees it often helps to support the athletics program. Such associations are found in many of the high schools throughout the country. They can be very helpful in the development of a sound athletics program.

There are various associations, conferences, or leagues that bind together athletically several high schools within a particular geographic area. These are designed in the main to regulate and promote wholesome competition among the member schools. They usually draw up schedules, approve officials, handle disputes, and have general supervision over the athletics program of the member schools.

The state high school athletic association which now exists in almost every state is a major influence in high school athletics. It is open to all professionally accredited high schools within the state. It has a constitution, administrative officers to conduct the business, and a board of control. The number of members on the board of control varies usually from six to nine. Fees are usually paid to the association on a flat basis or according to the size of the school. In some states there are no fees, since the necessary revenue is derived from the gate receipts of tournament competition. State associations are interested in a sound program of athletic competition within the confines of the state. They concern themselves with the usual problems that have to do with athletics, such as rules of eligibility, officials, disputes, and similar items. They are interested in promoting good high school athletics, equalizing athletic competition, protecting participants, and guarding the health of players. They are an influence for good and have won the respect of educators in the various states.

The National Federation of State High School Athletic Associations was established in 1920 with five states participating originally. At the present time nearly all the states are members. The National Federation is particularly concerned with the control of interstate athletics. Its constitution states this purpose:

> The object of this Federation shall be to protect and supervise the interstate athletic interests of the high schools belonging to the state associations, to assist in those activities of the state associations which can best be operated on a nationwide scale, to sponsor meetings, publications and activities which will permit each state association to profit by the experience of all other member associations, and to coordinate the work so that waste effort and unnecessary duplication will be avoided.

The National Federation has been responsible for many improvements in athletics on a national basis, such as doing away with national tournaments and working toward a uniformity of standards.

The National Collegiate Athletic Association began in the early 1900's. The alarming number of football injuries and the fact that there was no national control of the game of football led to a conference of representatives of universities and colleges, primarily from the eastern section of the United States, on December 12, 1905. Preliminary plans were made for a national body to assist in the formulation of sound requirements for intercollegiate athletics, particularly football, and the name of "Intercollegiate Athletic Association" was suggested. At a meeting March 31, 1906, a constitution and by-laws were adopted and issued. On December 29, 1910, the name of the association was changed to "National Collegiate Athletic Association." The purposes of the NCAA are designed to uphold the principle of institutional control of all collegiate sports; maintain a uniform code of amateurism in conjunction with sound eligibility rules, scholarship requirements, and good sportsmanship; promote and assist in the expansion of intercollegiate and intramural sports; formulate, copyright, and publish the official rules of play (in eleven sports); sponsor and supervise regional and national meets and tournaments for member institutions; preserve athletic records; and serve as headquarters for collegiate athletic matters of national import. The Association is composed of approximately 450 members at the present time.

Also on the college and university levels is the National Association of Intercollegiate Athletics which has a large membership, especially among the smaller schools. This organization has recently become affiliated with the American Association for Health, Physical Education and Recreation.

In higher education, there are in addition many leagues, conferences, and associations formed by a limited number of schools for athletic competition. Examples are the "Ivy League" and the "Big Ten Conference." These associations regulate athletic competition among their members and settle problems which may arise in connection with such competition.

VI. GIRLS' INTERSCHOOL ATHLETICS*

Procedures and practices in respect to interschool athletic competition for girls vary from state to state. Some states have broad programs of interschool athletics, others do not have any, and some have modified programs. In those having modified programs, play days, sports days, invitation games, and telegraphic meets are increasingly playing a more prominent part. Most states do not set up specific requirements for girls' athletics but feel that their established regulations apply to both girls and boys. A few states have athletic associations for girls which are similar to those for boys.

The question of athletics for girls is a highly controversial matter. The questions of how much, how little, and what is a happy medium are frequently raised with enthusiastic supporters on all sides of the issue. There seems to be a general consensus of opinion that athletics can render a valuable service to girls. The question arises as to what type of program can best render this service. Girls can develop a better state of total fitness, skills for worthy use of leisure time, and other desirable qualities and attributes just as boys and men can. However, it must be recognized that girls and women are not boys and men. There are many biological, social, and other differences which must be taken into consideration. It is impossible to take the boys' program and duplicate it for the girls without any changes.

The girls' program should be concerned especially with the individual sports and activities, as well as the team games. The women in charge and those doing the officiating should be qualified. Official girls' rules should be followed. The girls' games should be separated from the boys', except in coeducational activity, which should occupy a prominent place in the program. The social aspects should be stressed, jumping and body contact should be limited or eliminated altogether. Health safeguards should be observed, limited seasons and restrictions on the

---

*See also Chapter XVII.

amount of competition of any one girl should be enforced. Publicity and commercial aspects should be controlled so that the girls are not exploited.

If athletics for girls are conducted in a sound manner, many benefits can accrue. Some of these benefits have been brought out by the American Association for Health, Physical Education and Recreation.

> The values or purposes may be summarized thus: to satisfy the human desire of belonging to a group which represents the school; to stimulate greater interest in the physical education class program, and wider participation in the intramural program; to develop and maintain physical fitness among players; to provide opportunities for girls to become participants as well as spectators; to strengthen individual qualities, such as initiative, resourcefulness, loyalty, cooperation, and other similar qualities, through game experiences of great importance to the individual; to encourage girls to become skilled in activities as a personal and social asset; to offer challenging competition to the accelerated or gifted student in physical education; to offer opportunities for participation in activities that may be continued throughout life.[13]

VII. INTERSCHOOL ATHLETICS AT THE ELEMENTARY AND JUNIOR HIGH SCHOOL LEVELS

There has been considerable discussion in recent years on the advisability of athletic competition for children of elementary and junior high school age. The resolutions passed by professional organizations and stands taken by leaders in the field point to the fact that highly organized interschool athletics programs should not be a part of elementary and junior high school programs. The needs and interests of children should be the major factor in determining the type of program These needs and interests are not furthered through such a practice.

The author, writing in *Look* magazine, pointed out: "The drive to win is traditional in America and must be preserved. But a boy will absorb that lesson soon enough in high school. In his grammar school years, it is more important that his recreation be guided toward other objectives: the fun of playing rather than the winning; the child rather than the game; the many rather than the few; informal activity rather than formal; the development of skills in many activities rather than specialization. . . .[14]

The feeling expressed by the profession is incorporated in the publication, *Desirable Athletic Competition For Children* which is the report of the Joint Committee on Athletic Competition for Children of Elementary and Junior High School Age. This Joint Committee was composed of representatives from the American Association for Health, Physical Education and Recreation, the Department of Elementary School Principals of the National Education Association, and the National Council of State Consultants in Elementary Education. This committee's report[15] recommended:

> *Instruction in Physical Education for All:* The best interests of all children are served when school and community give priority—in the professional personnel, space and facilities,

[13]Joint Committee, *op. cit.*, p. 117.

[14]Charles A. Bucher and T. Cohane. "Little League Baseball Can Hurt Your Boy," *Look,* August 11, 1953, p. 74.

[15]Report of the Joint Committee on Athletic Competition for Children of Elementary and Junior High School Age. *Desirable Athletic Competition for Children.* Washington, D. C.: American Association for Health, Physical Education and Recreation, 1952.

equipment and supplies, time and money—to a broad program of *instruction* in physical education, based upon individual and group needs, for all boys and girls.

Voluntary Informal Recreation and Intramurals: Next in importance is a broad and varied program of voluntary informal recreation for children of all ages, and an interesting extensive program of intramural activities for boys and girls in upper elementary grades and above. "Intramural activities" means individual, dual, and team sports with competition limited to contests between teams within the individual school (or neighborhood recreation center).

Play Days, Sports Days, Informal Games: Activities such as play days, sports days, and occasional invitational games which involve children of two or more schools, and which have high social values are to be encouraged. The emphasis should be upon social participation with the competitive aspect subordinated. Play days involve teams or groups made up of children from several schools all intermixed. Sports days include activities in which the playing units are composed of members of the same school. A few *invitational* contests in certain sports between schools (or natural neighborhood groups) on an *informal* basis might be carried on—but only as a supplement to good instruction in physical education, recreational opportunities for all children within the school, and additional informal recreational opportunities during out-of-school hours.

Activities should be appropriate to the level of maturity, skills, and interests of the participants. Tackle football for children below the ninth-grade age and boxing for children and youth of all ages are definitely disapproved.

No Interschool Competition of a Varsity Pattern: Interschool competition of a varsity pattern and similarly organized competition under auspices of other community agencies are *definitely disapproved* for children below the ninth grade.

Participation in any program involving high pressure elements of the kind mentioned below would be considered a violation of this principle. Boxing (all levels) and tackle football (below the ninth grade) are considered undesirable under any conditions.

High Pressure Practices To Be Avoided: The terms "invitational" and "informal" are to be taken literally. This *means avoidance of such high pressure elements of an interscholastic pattern as:*

Highly organized competition in the form of leagues or championships

Overemphasis by means of newspapers, radio, television, or similar media

Stress on individuals rather than teams, such as selection of "all star" teams

Tournaments, frequent contests, long seasons, "little" bowl games, or other procedures that cause pressures or that may make undue physical demands on young boys or girls.

Games or contests played at night or at other times outside usual school or recreational hours

Travel beyond the immediate neighborhood (or in the case of small rural schools, a nearby community)

Encouragement of partisan spectators and supporters—any pressures that come from social situations that place undue value on an informal game

"Grooming" of players for a high school or college team, proselyting, or inducements of any kind to cause a good player to leave his normal group and play with another team

Commercial promotions which, under various guises, seek to exploit youth for selfish purposes

Competitions in which a selected few players are given a large and disproportionate share of facilities and of the time and attention of staff members, with the resultant neglect of a large number of children. . . .

VIII. INTERSCHOOL ATHLETICS AT THE HIGH SCHOOL LEVEL

The responsibility of the school for the interschool athletics program is one that cannot be avoided. Therefore, it is essential that all administrators be aware of the best practices that are recommended for the various phases of the total program.

The Joint Committee on Standards for Interscholastic Athletics of the National Association of Secondary School Principals, the National Federation of State High School Associations, and the American Association for Health, Physical Education and Recreation has established standards.[16] These make it possible for every school to examine its athletics program in a critical manner and see how well it meets recommended practices. They are as follows:

Basic to any consideration of acceptable standards in interscholastic athletics for secondary schools is this statement of the GUIDING POLICIES for the organization, administration, and development of a program of athletics for the youth of our schools:

1. Athletics are to be an integral part of the secondary school program and should receive financial support from tax funds on the same basis as other recognized parts of the total educational program. As a part of the curriculum, high school sports are to be conducted by secondary school authorities and all instruction provided by competent, qualified, and accredited teachers so that desirable, definite educational aims may be achieved.

2. Athletics are for the benefit of all youth. The aim is maximum participation, a sport for every boy and every boy in a sport, in a well-balanced intramural interscholastic program with emphasis on safe and healthful standards of competition.

3. Athletics are to be conducted under rules which provide for equitable competition, sportsmanship, fair play, health, and safety. High school sports are for amateurs who are bona fide undergraduate high school students. These youths must be protected from exploitation and the dangers of professionalism. Pre-season, post-schedule, post-season, all star-games, or similar types of promotions are not consistent with this principle. It is necessary to develop a full understanding of the need for observance of local, league, sectional, state, and national standards in athletics.

Recommendations: For the purpose of promoting and stimulating safe and healthful participation among a high percentage of secondary school boys in a wide variety of wholesome athletic activities and after careful study of the problems which have been created by certain types of interscholastic contests (including meets, tournaments, national championships, contests which require distant travel, contests which are sponsored by individuals or organizations other than a high school or group of high schools, and contests between teams of high school all-stars), the Joint Committee makes the following recommendations. The Joint Committee urges that all of the organizations represented adopt these MAJOR INTERPRETATIONS and place them in the form of policies, standards, or regulations in accordance with the established practice of each organization:

Standards:

1. The program of athletics should be developed with due regard for the following standards of health and safety.

   a. A health examination should be required previous to participation, preferably on a seasonal basis with annual examination a minimum.

   b. A physician should be present at all contests involving activities where the injury hazard is pronounced.

   c. A contestant who has been ill or injured should be readmitted to participation only on the written recommendation of a physician.

   d. A contestant upon returning to participation after illness or injury should be carefully observed, and if there is any doubt as to his condition he should immediately be referred to a physician.

   e. The coach (faculty member in charge) should be competent in first aid and thoroughly versed in sports conditioning and training. It is also strongly recommended that all players be given basic instruction in first aid.

---

[16]Joint Committee Report. "Standards in Athletics for Boys in Secondary Schools," *The Journal of the American Association for Health, Physical Education and Recreation*, 22: 16, September, 1951.

f. In case of head, neck, or spine injury or suspicion thereof, the player should be removed from play, placed at rest, and be given the immediate attention of a physician.

g. Every school should have a written policy regarding the responsibility for injury incurred in athletics, and this policy should be known to all participants, their parents, and other responsible adults. Arrangements should be made for obtaining and paying for medical and hospital care of injured participants, in accord with local policy.

h. The best obtainable protective equipment should be provided for all participants, and special attention should be given to proper fitting of such equipment.

i. Competition should take place only between teams of comparable ability, and playing seasons should be limited to reasonable duration.

j. No preseason games should be played until players are well drilled in fundamentals and have had a minimum of two weeks of physical conditioning.

k. Playfields should meet standard requirements for size of area, playing surfaces, and facilities for safety, and all reasonable precautions should be taken to prevent accidents.

l. Contests should be selected, and rules and lengths of playing periods should be such that they will not overtax the physical abilities of high school students.

2. Good citizenship must result from all coaching and from interschool competition. The education of the youth of the nation fails unless it creates the proper ideals and attitudes, both in the game and off the field.

a. The contribution of athletics to citizenship, indeed, to life itself, will be judged according to the contribution they make to fine living.

b. Athletics should contribute a feeling, on the part of the athlete, of personal worth, excellence in performance, self-respect, and desirable personal and social growth and development.

c. Educationally, winning is not the only important item. While the will to win within the rules of good sportsmanship is an important attribute to good citizenship, there is always a tendency to overdo the importance of winning in athletics. Other important contributions are those desirable changes made in skills, habits, and attitudes of the participants.

d. Athletics are responsible jointly with education for establishing among boys and girls those standards of behavior that represent the best in good citizenship. Athletics must contribute to those virtues which are socially sound for a democracy, such as truthfulness, fair play, honesty, modesty, give-and-take, courtesy, self-discipline, courage, generosity, self-restraint, and loyalty to team, state, and nation.

3. The ten "Cardinal Athletic Principles" are accepted as expressing the policies of our organizations, and it is urged that these be displayed in the literature of our organizations. To be of maximum effectiveness, the athletics program will:

a. Be closely co-ordinated with the general instructional program and properly articulated with the other departments of the school.

b. Be such that the number of students accommodated and the educational aims achieved justify the use of tax funds for its support and also warrant the use of other sources of income.

c. Justify the time and attention which is given to the collection of "other sources of income" which will not interfere with the efficiency of the athletics program or of any other departments of the school.

d. Confine the school athletic activity to events which are sponsored and supervised by the proper school authorities so that any exploitation or improper use of prestige built up by school teams or members of such teams may be avoided.

e. Be planned in such a way as to result in opportunity for many individuals to explore a wide variety of sports and to set reasonable season limits for each listed sport.

f. Be controlled in such a way as to avoid the elements of professionalism and commercialism which tend to grow up in connection with widely publicized "bowl" contests, barnstorming trips, and interstate or intersectional contests which require excessive travel expense or loss of school time or which are claimed to be justified by educational travel values.

g. Be kept free from the type of contest which involves a gathering of so-called "all-stars" from different schools to participate in contests which may be used as a gathering place for representatives of certain colleges or professional organizations which are interested in soliciting athletic talent for their teams.

h. Include educative exercises to reach all nonparticipating students and community followers of the school teams in order to insure a proper understanding and appreciation of the sports skills and of the need for adherence to principles of game ethics.

i. Encourage a balanced program of intramural activity in grades below the ninth to make it unnecessary to sponsor contests of a championship nature in these grades.

j. Engender respect for the rules and policies under which the school conducts its program.

4. All schools should use reasonable care in avoiding any participation in a contact sport between participants of normal high school age and participants who are appreciably above or below normal high school age.

Senior high school competition should be limited to participation in games, meets, and tournaments between participants enrolled in grades 9 through 12. Junior high school competition should be limited to participation in games, meets, and tournaments between participants enrolled in grades 7 through 9. These games, meets, and tournaments should be approved and conducted by appropriate secondary school authorities.

a. All school personnel should utilize *every precaution* and *procedure* to assure competition in secondary school athletics on the basis of comparable parity.

b. A significant phase in the growth of a living organism is maturity. Wide differences in maturity place in jeopardy the well-being of athletic competitors. School personnel should permit competition between teams composed of comparable maturity.

c. Certain stages of maturity can be distinguished and should be utilized as one of the bases for determining parity in athletic competition.

d. Outstanding features of adolescence are insecurity, awkwardness, and excessive competitiveness. One can adjust himself to these factors only by becoming more mature, wiser, and more self-reliant. These are additional evidences that parents and school personnel should use protective procedures in setting up competition between individuals and groups of pre-adolescent and adolescent ages.

e. A high school pupil or team should not compete with members of a college or university, a preparatory school, other schools which include post-graduates on their teams, or against any independent team sponsored by an "outside" organization.

f. A junior high school pupil or team should not compete with members of a team representing a senior high school, elementary school, or an outside organization. This would not, however, exclude the participation of ninth-grade pupils as members of a senior high school team if the ninth grade was under the administrative direction of the high school principal and if the other conditions stated above are met.

g. Appropriate secondary school authorities consist of all legally certified teaching, supervisory, and administrative personnel directly under the superintendent of schools. These personnel should see that the items noted above are observed.

5. All schools shall fully observe and abide by the spirit and letter of established eligibility requirements which have been democratically developed by each of the state athletic associations.

6. Each state athletic association should attempt to secure the co-operation which would provide a plan of continuous eligibility from high school to college.

7. For competition in which only one state is involved, no school shall participate in a meet or tournament involving more than two schools unless such contest has been approved by its state high school association or its delegated constituent or allied divisions.

8. The use of school facilities or members of the school staff shall not be permitted in connection with any post-season or all-star contest unless such contest has been sanctioned by the state athletic association.

9. A school shall not permit any employee or official to encourage or collaborate in any negotiations which may lead a high school athlete to lose his eligibility through the signing of a professional contract.

10. The solicitation of athletes through tryouts and competitive bidding by colleges and universities is unethical, unprofessional, and psychologically harmful. It destroys the amateur nature of athletics, tends to commercialize the individual and the program, promotes the use of athletic skill for gain, and takes an unfair and unjust advantage of competitors.

11. In all interstate athletic contests, each athlete shall compete under eligibility rules which are at least as restrictive as those adopted by the state high school athletic association of his state, except in the case of nonmember schools which are not eligible for membership in their state associations.

12. No school shall compete in any of the following contests unless such contest has been sanctioned by each of the interested state high school athletic associations through the National Federation: (a) any interstate tournament or meet in which three or more schools participate; (b) any interstate two-school contest which involves a round trip exceeding 600 miles; (c) any interstate two-school contest (regardless of the distance to be travelled) which is sponsored by an individual or an organization other than a member high school.

13. No basketball tournament which is purported to be for interstate high school championship shall be sanctioned, and no basketball tournament involving schools of more than one state shall be sanctioned unless the tournament is purely community in character.

14. No contest which is purported to be for a national high school championship in any sport shall be sanctioned.

IX. INTERSCHOOL ATHLETICS AT THE COLLEGE AND UNIVERSITY LEVEL

It is at the college and university level that overemphasis has taken place to the largest extent in the field of interschool athletics. Commercialization flourishes when 60,000 people gather for a sports spectacle, the cost of tickets range from $2.00 to $6.00, and large stadia, long trips, and many scholarships predominate. A few schools have established "easy courses" in the curriculum so that athletes will not have to meet the usual academic standards. Records have been falsified to enable some to meet entrance requirements. Others have been given tuition, board, spending money, and sometimes even a car to attract them. Players have been recruited from various sections of the country through unethical means. Alumni pressure for winning teams, the firing of coaches, and other undesirable practices have been in evidence in some quarters.

The College of William and Mary is one of the schools where athletic abuses crept into athletics recently. The faculty of this school issued a statement which was commented on editorially in the *New York Times*.

The faculty of the College of William and Mary has said some things about overemphasis of intercollegiate athletics that the student body, administration and particularly the alumni of most other American colleges would do well to ponder. The statement was occasioned by an athletic scandal that broke out at William and Mary hard on the heels of the one at West Point. Illicit activity at the two institutions took different forms, but in both cases the fundamental cause was the same: an unreasonable stress on the necessity of producing winning teams in intercollegiate competition. This the William and Mary faculty has recognized; and we regret that in their analysis of the situation at West Point the military authorities did not see fit to make a similar admission. Many institutions of higher education in America are to a greater or less degree guilty of this tendency, which if not checked will destroy amateur athletics as well as the character of athletes and the integrity of the institutions themselves.

The "increasingly ambitious intercollegiate athletic program" at William and Mary, said the faculty, had "sapped the academic standards" of the college, "become a commercial enterprise demanding winning teams at any cost," "vitiated the most elementary standards of honesty and right conduct" and "weakened the moral fiber of the college and its students and alumni." It takes courage for the faculty (including the new president) of a college that has had a succession of winning football teams to say this, and to add: "Big-time athletics is an expensive undertaking . . . [for which] the necessary money is usually forthcoming. But . . . it seems that the college is incapable of financing essential improvements which . . . would be considerably more beneficial to the whole student body. The result is a distortion of values. . . ."

Interschool athletics at the college level. Varsity basketball, Illinois State Normal University.

Athletics are an important part of the college curricula. But in our view winning teams are not; and the whole meaning of amateur sport is inverted by the unbearable pressures now so often exercised to produce victory on the athletic field. If intercollegiate athletics is to regain an honorable reputation in this country, college administrations, alumni, faculty and students must cooperate to reduce it to its proper proportions. The first business of colleges still is education.[17]

---

[17]Editorial, *New York Times*, September 21, 1951.

Much of the responsibility for eliminating the abuses from college athletic circles has been placed upon the shoulders of the various regional accrediting agencies. One of the largest of these has the following to say in regard to policy:

1. Some of the most serious abuses of athletics really arise from the abuses of instruction. It is not good university and college practice to permit soft spots in the curriculum. Students call these "snap" courses. They are too easy or too frivolous to occupy the time of university or college students. Their presence aids and abets corruption of athletics. The same applies to low standards of entrance and performance in any of the colleges or courses of the university. Sub-college standards of academic work anywhere in the institution afford a hiding place for youths who lack the ability to be university students or young men whose athletic duties prove too exacting to permit them to pass courses of truly university grade.

2. The notion that institutions of higher education have a responsibility for providing public entertainment in the form of athletic spectacles is alien to the true functions of such institutions.

3. The manner in which an institution spends its funds is the best possible evidence of the values it fosters. A college or university will give financial support to programs and activities in proportion to the importance it attaches to them. A first-rate educational institution will in the very nature of things devote as much of its income as possible to functions that bring a high educational return. This applies to all phases of operation, not alone to athletics.

4. The chief administrative officer of a college or university is ultimately responsible for the wholesome conduct of intercollegiate athletics in his institution, and this ultimate responsibility he cannot properly delegate to subordinate officers. It is his duty to be well informed about the athletic policies and practices of his institution and to take the necessary steps to assure that the athletic program is making its full contribution to the attainment of educational objectives.

5. A high quality institution does not resort to athletic renown as a means of securing public support. Rather, it makes its appeal on the basis of its educational merit. If athletic prominence is an indispensable element in the public relations of a college or university, that fact is of itself a reflection on the academic worth of the institution.

6. When the winning of contests per se becomes the major emphasis of an athletic program, this results almost inevitably in practices that are detrimental to the moral tone and educational seriousness of purpose of the institution. This emphasis can have such far-reaching consequences, sometimes penetrating to the very core of institutional integrity, that the existence of an unsatisfactory athletic situation in an institution will be regarded as a serious enough weakness to justify the denial of accreditation.[18]

Although the University of Chicago is not being held up as a model, it has incorporated many features in its athletic program which are worthy of mention. Metcalf[19] points up some of these features:

The University of Chicago takes pride in the fact that it conducts its athletic program for sport, recreation, and its educational values rather than for business, public entertainment, prestige, publicity, or financial return.

There is a common misconception that Chicago has withdrawn from the intercollegiate athletic field and engages in only intramural sports. This misunderstanding is probably due to the fact that Chicago is rarely mentioned in the headlines of the sports pages since it dropped varsity football in 1939 and resigned from the Western Conference in 1946. The fact of the matter is that Chicago's extramural sports program was never more extensive than it is today. The following table shows the extent of the varsity sports program in 1951-52.

[18]North Central Association, *op. cit.*
[19]Metcalf, *op. cit.*, p. 340.

Varsity Teams	*Junior Varsity Teams*	*Informal Varsity and Club Teams*
Baseball	Baseball	Badminton Club
Basketball (+B Team)	Basketball	Baseball (Summer)
Cross Country	Fencing	Basketball (Professional Schools)
Fencing	Golf	Fencing Club
Golf	Gymnastics	Gymnastics Club
Gymnastics	Soccer	Ice Hockey Club
Soccer	Swimming	Rifle Club (two teams)
Swimming	Tennis	Sailing Club
Tennis	Indoor Track	Squash Club (three teams)
Indoor Track (+B Team)	Outdoor Track	Tennis (Summer)
Outdoor Track (+B Team)	Wrestling	Track Club
Wrestling		Weight Lifting Club

The *Varsity Teams* play without any conference affiliation. Since Chicago withdrew from the Western Conference each team has endeavored to find its proper level of competition. In the arrangement of schedules an effort is made to secure opponents of approximately equal strength. In fencing and gymnastics the competition is at the "Big Ten" level. In the other ten varsity sports we play primarily at the college rather than the university level.

The *Junior Varsity Teams* are restricted to students in the first two years of the College of the University of Chicago. Since the College admits students who have completed the Sophomore year of high school, these boys in the first two years are 11th and 12th grade students. Theirs is high school level competition against public and parochial city and suburban high schools and in the Private School League of Greater Chicago. For these teams, membership in the Illinois High School Association is maintained.

The *Club Teams* are open to faculty, employees, and in some instances to alumni as well as to students. Only eight of the fifteen club teams receive regular coaching. The schedules of the club teams include athletic clubs, YMCA's, colleges, industrial teams, and A.A.U. championship meets.

Many of the practices and policies of Chicago's athletic program are unique, at least among large universities. Some of the more unusual features which will be explained in the following paragraphs are:

1. The predominant emphasis that is placed on the educational values of athletic participation.

2. The autonomy of the athletic staff in the conduct of the program.

3. The complete integration of varsity sports, administratively and financially, in the general physical education program.

4. The complete absence of athletic recruiting.

5. The absence of detailed rules of eligibility.

6. The freedom from the abuses and pressures so commonly associated with varsity athletics, especially at the university level. . . .

. . . These paragraphs express the basic athletic philosophy under which the program is conducted.

Intercollegiate athletics are conducted primarily for the benefit of the participants. In the coaching and training of teams and in the conduct of contests, the welfare of the athletes must outweigh all other considerations.

The opportunity to participate in intercollegiate athletics is considered not so much a service which the athlete renders to the university as a privilege which the university permits the athlete to enjoy.

The athletics program is so conducted as to assure, in so far as possible, that students will devote only as much time and effort to athletics as is beneficial to their general welfare.

X. SUMMARY

The standards for athletics at every school level have been clearly stated. There should be no doubt in any individual's mind as to the types of interschool programs that are sound educationally and in the best interests of the boys and girls who will participate in them. It is the responsibility of administrators and others concerned with such programs to implement the various standards that have been established. If they are truly interested in a sound athletics program they will see that this is done. *In every case, it is not a question of de-emphasis, but a question of re-emphasis along educational lines. Good leadership will make the interschool program a force for good in education which has no equal.*

Athletics are a part of the total physical education program. The objectives that have been stated earlier in this book for physical education also apply to interschool athletics. The administrator can evaluate his or her program in terms of the extent to which the listed objectives are being achieved. There should be no question as to where a school stands.

The Educational Policies Commission Report on School Athletics[20] should be read by every physical educator, every coach, every administrator, and other individuals interested in a sound school athletics program. This report contains 100 questions which can be used to evaluate any school athletics program. *The information in this report represents the ideals toward which all educators should be striving.* It will take some time to achieve such goals but all should make sure they are proceeding in the right direction.

QUESTIONS AND EXERCISES

1. Develop a set of standards which could be used to appraise an interschool athletics program at the high school or college level.

2. Describe the main features of the interschool athletics program at the University of Chicago.

3. Have a debate on the question, Resolved: That all gate receipts for interscholastic athletic contests should be abolished.

4. Write a profile of what you consider to be the ideal coach.

5. As a Director of Athletics what plans would you have to make for a season of play in basketball? Outline in detail.

6. What are some essential points to keep in mind in respect to each of the following: (a) contracts, (b) officials, (c) protests and forfeitures, (d) game management, (e) schedules, (f) awards, (g) records, and (h) medical examinations?

7. Describe in detail how athletic insurance works.

8. As a Director of Athletics, what administrative policy would you recommend in respect to each of the following: (a) gate receipts, (b) tournaments and championships, (c) eligibility, (d) scholarships, (e) recruiting, (f) proselyting, and (g) scouting?

9. What is the role of the Athletic Association in the conduct of athletics?

10. Develop a set of guiding administrative principles for girls' athletics.

11. Write an essay of 500 words on the topic: "Desirable Sports Competition for Children."

12. Debate the following question: "Do National Play-offs in Sports Constitute a Desirable Activity for Children Under Twelve Years of Age?"

---

[20]Educational Policies Commission. *School Athletics—Problems and Policies.* Washington, D. C.: National Association, 1954.

13. What practical suggestions can you make for eliminating the "big business" aspects of intercollegiate athletics?

14. Read the Educational Policies Commission report on "School Athletics" and give a report to the class.

SELECTED REFERENCES

American Association for Health, Physical Education and Recreation. *Administrative Problems in Health Education, Physical Education and Recreation.* Washington, D. C.: the Association, 1953, Area V.

American Association of School Administrators. *Health in Schools. Twentieth Yearbook.* Washington, D. C.: National Education Association, Chapter IX.

Bucher, Charles A., (Editor). *Methods and Materials in Physical Education and Recreation.* St. Louis: The C. V. Mosby Company, 1954.

Bucher, Charles A. *Foundations of Physical Education.* St. Louis: The C. V. Mosby Company, 1952.

Bucher, Charles A., and Cohane, Tim. "Little League Baseball CAN Hurt Your Boy," *LOOK,* Aug. 11, 1953, p. 74.

Educational Policies Commission. *School Athletics—Problems and Policies.* Washington, D. C.: National Education Association, 1954.

Forsythe, Charles E. *The Administration of High School Athletics.* New York: Prentice-Hall Inc., 1954.

Hughes, William Leonard, and Williams, Jesse Feiring. *Sports, Their Organization and Administration.* New York: A. S. Barnes & Company, 1944.

Joint Committee on Athletic Competition for Children of Elementary and Junior High School Age. *Desirable Athletic Competition for Children.* Washington, D. C.: American Association for Health, Physical Education and Recreation, 1952.

Katchmer, George A. *Finance Your Athletic Program.* Minneapolis: Burgess Publishing Company, 1953.

Leavitt, Norma M., and Price, Hartley D. *Intramural and Recreational Sports for Men and Women.* New York: A. S. Barnes & Company, 1949.

Meyer, Margaret H., and Schwartz, Marguerite M. *Team Sports for Women.* Philadelphia: W. B. Saunders Company, 1947.

Mitchell, E. D. *Sports for Recreation and How to Play Them.* New York: A. S. Barnes & Company, 1952.

National Section on Women's Athletics. *Standards in Athletics for Girls and Women.* Washington, D. C.: American Association for Health, Physical Education and Recreation, 1953.

Porter, H. V., (Editor). *All Sports Rule Book.* New York: A. S. Barnes & Company, 1952.

Rogers, Frederick Rand. *The Future of Interscholastic Athletics.* New York: Bureau of Publications, Teachers College, Columbia University, 1929.

Rugen, Mabel E. (Editor). *The Physical Educator Asks About Health.* Washington, D. C.: American Association for Health, Physical Education and Recreation, 1951.

Rule Books for all boys' sports. Available from the National Federation of State High School Athletic Associations, 7 South Dearborn Street, Chicago 3, Illinois.

Rule Books for all girls' sports. Available from the National Section on Girls' and Women's Athletics of the American Association for Health, Physical Education and Recreation, 1201 Sixteenth Street, N.W., Washington, D. C.

Scott, Harry A. *Competitive Sports in Schools and Colleges.* New York: Harper and Brothers, 1951.

Shaw, John H., (Editor). *Selected Team Sports for Men.* Philadelphia: W. B. Saunders Company, 1952.

Shaw, John H., Troester, Carl A., Jr., and Gabrielsen, Milton A. *Individual Sports for Men.* Philadelphia: W. B. Saunders Company, 1950.

Shepard, George E., and Jamerson, Richard E. *Interscholastic Athletics.* New York: McGraw-Hill Book Company, Inc., 1953.

Yocom, Richard D., and Hunsaker, H. B. *Individual Sports for Men and Women.* New York: A. S. Barnes & Co., 1947.

Chapter XIX

COMMUNITY RECREATION

Recreation may be defined as that field of endeavor concerned with those socially acceptable and worth-while activities in which a person voluntarily participates during leisure hours and through which he may better develop physically, mentally, emotionally, and socially.

I. OBJECTIVES OF RECREATION[1]

Community recreation is a field of endeavor which deserves increasing recognition for the work that it is doing in enriching individual lives. The objectives reflect this contribution. These objectives are the (A) Health Development Objective, (B) Human Relations Objective, (C) Civic Development Objective, and (D) Self-Development Objective.

A. The Health Development Objective

The health development objective is important in the field of recreation. Health to a great degree is related to activity during leisure hours as well as during hours of work. The manner in which a person spends his free time determines in great measure whether his physical, mental, emotional, and spiritual health is of high quality. Through recreation, adaptive physical activity is available which is conducive to organic, mental, emotional, and spiritual health. A range of activities exists which offers opportunities for every individual to promote his organic health. Activities are available in which the individual may relax, escape from the tensions of work, forget about problems, and thereby improve mental health. Activities are planned and conducted which provide the individual enjoyment and pleasure and in this way contribute to emotional health. Activities are included which require the participation of many individuals and are conducive to better social relations and higher standards of moral and spiritual values, thus promoting spiritual health. Public recreation programs are designed to provide activities which counteract the deteriorating effects of strenuous or routine work or study and thus complement the over-all routine that an individual follows. They overcome many of the shortages that exist when the man leaves the office, the child leaves school, or the housewife completes her work. In this way they contribute to the integration and development of the whole individual.

B. The Human Relations Objective

The human relations objective represents a major contribution of recreation to enriched living. Recreational programs develop many individual qualities which

[1]Charles A. Bucher (Editor). *Methods and Materials in Physical Education and Recreation.* St. Louis: The C. V. Mosby Company, 1954, pp. 25-27.

make for better adjustment. Such attributes as courage, justice, patience, tolerance, fairness, and honesty are only a few that are possible of development while individuals are playing and recreating together in the many activities that comprise the total recreation program. Attitudes which promote good human relations are also developed. Wholesome attitudes of social cooperation, loyalty to the group, recognition of the rights of others, and the idea that one receives from a group in direct proportion to what one gives it are a few that make for better relations and enable worthy goals and projects to be accomplished. The growth of family recreation is a trend which also helps to make for a more unified home life. This is very

The human relations objective represents a major contribution of recreation to enriched living. "Canoemanship"—one of the activities of recreation course, University of Connecticut.

important, since the family group represents the foundation on which good human relations are built. Furthermore, to develop good social traits it is necessary to bring people together in a situation where there is a feeling of belonging and where each individual is recognized. There are innumerable opportunities for such interaction in the many recreational programs that exist throughout the country.

C. The Civic Development Objective

The civic development objective is a noteworthy goal for recreation. Recreation contributes in many ways to the development of any community. It contributes to community solidarity by uniting people in common projects regardless of race, creed, economic status, or other discriminatory factors. It helps to build the morale of the members of the community. It is a contributing factor in alleviating crime in that it provides settings and activities in which youth and other individuals may engage in constructive, worth-while activities, rather than in destructive, antisocial activities. It helps make the community a safer place in which to live through providing adequate playgrounds and other recreational centers, which keep children and youth off the streets. It helps make the community more prosperous by contributing to the health of the individual, by cutting down on the dollar appropriation for crime, and by increasing the total work output of an individual. It helps the growth and development of the individual so that he becomes a more valuable citizen in the community and has more to contribute in its behalf.

D. The Self-Development Objective

The self-development objective refers to the potentialities which participation in a program of recreational activities has for developing the individual to his fullest capacity. Recreation does this through a variety of means. It contributes to the balanced growth of an individual. It allows for growth in ways other than in mere production of material things for utilitarian purposes. In other words, it satisfies the human desire for such things as creative music, art, literature, and drama. It allows an individual to create things not for their material value but for the joy, satisfaction, and happiness that go with creating something through one's own efforts. It allows for the development of skills and abilities which are latent and dormant in the individual until they are aroused by leisure hours with proper settings and leadership. These skills help to make a better integrated individual. Recreation provides an avenue for the individual to experience joy and happiness through some activity in which he has the desire to engage. In this chaotic world where there are so many sorrows, heartbreaks, and frowns, it is essential for people to revitalize themselves through the medium of activities. They provide smiles and hearty laughs and release from the tension associated with day-to-day routine. They afford a place for many individuals to excel. Such an urge is many times not satisfied in one's regular job or profession. An opportunity is provided in recreation to satisfy this desire. It offers an educational experience. The participant learns new skills, new knowledges, new techniques, and develops new abilities. He is filing away new and different experiences which will be helpful in facing the situations he will encounter from day to day.

II. RECREATION IN RETROSPECT

In looking back over the last half century of recreation a few shortcomings and many accomplishments can be noted. The accomplishments stand out in one's mind in historical review, but at the same time it is necessary to examine the shortcomings, if progress is to be made in the years ahead. This is an important field of work and only as weaknesses are overcome and eliminated will the profession achieve its many potentialities. These shortcomings are not listed as criticism, but as suggestions for helping recreation to achieve a greater role in society, which it justly deserves.

A. Shortcomings

One of the shortcomings that seems to stand out is the weakness of not recruiting the highest and best qualified type of leadership for this field of work and also the failure of professional preparing institutions to provide the highest quality of preparation to those who are recruited.

Another weakness appears to be the lack of co-ordination of all agencies at the community level engaged in recreation work. Many communities have several organizations, all of which are trying to induce the individual to participate in their respective programs, with consequent duplication of such items as services, efforts, and financial outlay. Co-ordination would prevent much of the waste and inefficiency that exist. Furthermore, it would result in better service to the public.

A third weakness is that recreation could serve the older population to a greater degree than it is at the present time. It is estimated that there are 10,000,-000 individuals over 65 years of age today and that by 1975 there will be 20,000,000. By 1975 it is estimated that the average length of life will be 74 years and thereafter will continue until it reaches 100 years. There must be greater provision for the older population. With many of these individuals being forced to retire and finding many idle moments on their hands, it is essential that they have the benefits of a broad and varied recreation program. This will provide them with constructive leisure time activities, challenges to make life interesting and satisfying, and will help to maintain their health. Recreation can offer this age group more than they are finding at the present time.

There could be a stronger professional organization of the workers in the recreation profession. Individuals in this field of endeavor should be closely united, working together to set higher standards, attempting to eliminate weaknesses, exchanging ideas, and promoting their profession.

There is an overemphasis on so-called physical education activities in many recreation programs. Many educators still confuse recreation with physical education and feel they are offering a good recreation program through physical education activities. This, of course, is erroneous, in that recreation has different goals and a much broader range of activities.

There is insufficient stress on family recreation today. With some experts contending that the family and home are disintegrating, there is greater need for activities and programs in which the entire home and family can engage. The facts that there have been 200,000 to 600,000 divorces annually in the last decade and an approximately 50 per cent increase in the number of infants born outside of marriage in the last ten years, and that nearly one quarter of all married women who live with husbands work offer some evidence of the need for bringing the family together in forms of wholesome and enjoyable recreation activity.

These are some of the weaknesses of recreation today. There are three others which deserve a more detailed consideration: (1) failure to interpret recreation sufficiently to a great bulk of the American people, (2) failure of the schools to develop resources for leisure, and (3) lack of adequate stress on moral and spiritual values.

Recreation is not interpreting its program sufficiently to a great bulk of the American people. A great majority of people still pursue forms of recreation that are unwholesome, unhealthy and noneducational. This is evidenced by the billions of dollars spent on certain forms of recreation—10 billions spent on liquor annually, television sets approaching the 50,000,000 mark and still rising, the tremendous number of individuals continually in attendance at race tracks, and the numbers who flock to see poor movies and purchase low-grade literature. America is largely a nation of spectators. Television appears to be one of the most serious fads or abuses of leisure time at the present. There are many good television programs on the networks and if this medium is used with discretion it has many advantages.

There is insufficient stress on family recreation today.

However, many are using it four, six, eight or more hours daily, viewing robberies, assaults, unrealistic dramas and programs of little value. Even among children, surveys have shown that a great amount of time is spent in this manner. Without a doubt, some of this is good. However, when it interferes with a child's obtaining skills that will be essential to his present and future happiness, it becomes harmful. It should not replace or be a substitute for experiences which develop useful skills. Children should have skill in many activities. They should be able to play many games and have many hobbies in which they are active doers, rather than merely spectators.

Recreation must be made more appealing. Television should be used to stimulate people to action. Incentives should be provided to develop hobbies around the house and other leisure time activities. People should be helped to do better those things they are going to do anyhow. There are over 2000 television channels and over 200 have been allotted to education. Recreation could play a prominent part in education through television.

Schools do not gear their programs to the mass of the American people. Formal education is too compartmentalized. It is still catering too much to the persons going to college and into certain professions. It should be recognized that the majority do not go on to college and into the professions. Subject-matter areas are too fixed. They should be flexible and taught so that their recreational implications are emphasized. Dr. Paul Douglass, a former president of American University conducted a survey among women graduates. He discovered that of 30,-000 women graduates only three per cent thought that their education had been valuable for the development of resources for leisure time pursuits. This is an indictment of American education. If it is going to be practical and functional, then surely it should develop skills and other resources for leisure time activities, especially in this age when leisure time is continually increasing. The science subjects should emphasize to a greater degree than they are at present a study of birds, trees, rocks, and flowers as an incentive to forming hobbies. The art department should be concerned with making jewelry and artificial flowers, decorating furniture, painting designs on materials, and painting as a hobby, instead of with turning out the work of masters. English could do a greater job with informal dramatics, story-telling, and creative writing. The social sciences could create a greater desire to participate in community activity and to develop a better environment in which to live. They could also use the study of furniture of various periods in history as an incentive to antique collecting. Why not include more costume designing in home economics and stimulate to a greater degree the creative joy of cooking? Geography classes while studying the various countries of the world could obtain stamps from each as an incentive to stamp collecting. Physical education could emphasize to a greater degree the individual activities such as fishing, golf, tennis, and tying trout flies. When it is realized that only about one out of every 1000 individuals ever plays football after leaving school, it can be seen there should be at least equal stress on such activities as swimming and golf. Educators must be brought to realize that recreation is not related only with physical education, but with all areas. One survey of 1000 adults found that only 2 per cent utilized sports and games for their leisure time activities. As one grows older there is a tendency to do other things.

The last shortcoming in recreation to be discussed is that it is not stressing moral and spiritual values sufficiently. There is ample evidence of the low morality of the times. The extent of gambling, misuse of public office, exploitation of the masses, family disintegration, and other facts show this to be true. Recreation is in position to help combat this low morality. Moral and spiritual values can be developed and instilled at times when recreational activities are in progress. As one person has said, "they are developed in the 'teachable moments' of human association and informal activity. Some of these teachable moments occur: when a person craves activity, seeks a thrill, wins or loses, is lonely and seeks companionship, wants approval, emulates a hero, or wants the satisfaction of creative response." Moral and spiritual values must permeate the entire recreation program. Recreation leaders must teach by example as well as precept. They must be careful not to exploit youth or to do anything that would tend to develop values not in accordance with what is known to be the best way of life.

These are some of the shortcomings of the profession which must be eliminated if recreation is to become great as a field of endeavor.

B. Accomplishments

The accomplishments of the recreation profession stand out as one looks back over the years in perspective. The field is attaining professional status; increasingly being recognized as requiring trained workers with special training to do the work; has its own professional preparing curricula; and has its own professional organizations and journals. It has grown in prestige in the eyes of the public.

The recreation profession has accomplished much in industry. It has increased production, decreased absenteeism, and made for a much happier and more contented working population.

Recreation has resulted in benefits to churches. Youth attendance has increased 10 per cent over the last decade. This increase is partially due to a spiritual revival among the young, but the development of recreation programs in churches as means of attracting youth to its doors cannot be overlooked.

Recreation has resulted in benefits to hospitals and penal institutions. It is increasingly being used as a means of therapy for rehabilitating the ill and the anti-social.

There are many other accomplishments of the field of recreation. Limited space prevents a discussion of all. A fuller discussion, however, will be devoted to three accomplishments which seem to stand out over the last fifty years.

Recreation can look with pride to the great growth of the camping movement. Camps are being sponsored by government agencies, municipalities, churches, youth serving agencies, and especially the schools. Many school systems now utilize camping as part of their regular education program. John W. Studebaker, former United States Commissioner of Education, stated that by 1960 camping would be one of the most important phases of the educational program. The state of Michigan is only one example. It has access to 45,000 acres of forest as a result of a cooperative agreement worked out with the State Conservation Department. Other states are acquiring land and developing camps. Camping is proving its value in the development of the child mentally, socially, and emotionally.*

Another accomplishment of recreation is that as a result of their programs school buildings are being opened all year round, and at night as well as in the day time. Gymnasiums, classrooms, shops, home economics rooms, and other parts of the school plant are being opened to the community. A great variety of courses and activities are being offered, ranging everywhere from how to play canasta to classes for expectant fathers. Staffs are being provided on a year-round basis. The school is becoming a community center, a place for coming together and having fun, obtaining education, and participating in many enjoyable activities. Education

*See also Chapter XX.

is on its way to a twelve-month year which will make more and more room for recreational activities.

Buildings are being constructed with community recreation programs in mind. Sections of school buildings are being separated for community and recreation use. Facilities are being arranged so that convenience and efficiency are insured for the adult population that wishes to take advantage of such offerings. Storage space for recreational equipment and supplies is being taken into consideration. In many buildings small activity rooms are being installed for many features of the program.

A third accomplishment of recreation is that it is helping to build a brighter future for many individuals. In these chaotic times there is a great need for programs of activities where individuals can lose themselves in constructive activity. Recreation has resulted in increased joy of living for many persons. Many individuals now can go home after long hours of work with something to look forward to, a recreational activity which will give them a great deal of satisfaction and enjoyment. Furthermore, the development of many recreation skills enables them to look forward to retirement with confidence because they know they will be able to spend their increased leisure in a profitable manner. Recreation is combating divorce and is making families happier. Certainly a man who has a hobby around the house is more likely to be a better husband and father than one who spends his time in a bar or corner saloon. Recreation is helping to combat the tensions associated with modern-day living. In this day of hot wars, cold wars, atom and hydrogen bombs, many individuals find it hard to adjust to the fast pace of living. The bright lights, noises, crowds, and rushing madness associated with city living continually keep them in emotional and physical turmoil. Man finds it is difficult not to stress material values and not to compete with his neighbors for higher salaries and better jobs. He finds it difficult to relax and enjoy living. The incidence of heart disease, the facts that one-half of all hospital beds are occupied with individuals suffering from mental disorders and that 50 per cent of all patients who consult doctors are mentally ill, are evidence of this statement. However, recreation is helping to combat these maladies. According to Dr. Menninger, recreation activities afford an outlet for aggressive drives, encourage relaxation, and are of great psychological value in affording the opportunity to create. He also points out that the aim of psychiatric prescription is to take troublesome feelings and direct them into socially approved outlets.

These are only a few of the accomplishments of recreation. There are many more. They will continue as the years go by. Recreation has a bright future. Weaknesses should be turned into strengths. Recreation leaders should redouble their efforts. The years ahead are bright if aims are set high and the profession keeps on the right course. As one poet has said:

> The winds blow east
> The winds blow west
> The self same breezes blow
> 'Tis not the gale
> But the set of the sail
> That determines where we'll go.

III. THE RECREATION LEADER

The recreation leader should have most of the qualifications of the health education and physical education specialists and in addition some which are pertinent especially to his field of work.

Various personal attributes are important for the recreation leader who is working with people so much of the time. These include such characteristics as integrity, friendly personality, enthusiasm, initiative, organizing ability, and others which will aid in the achievement of recreation objectives.

Recreaton leaders should possess a broad cultural background, with an understanding of the needs and problems facing society. This implies a fundamental knowledge of history, sociology, and anthropology. In addition, they should have the skills and competencies necessary for coping with such needs and problems. This would include the communicative arts, knowledge of psychology, and other allied areas.

It is especially important that the recreation leader have a broad understanding and appreciation of human beings. He or she must have respect for the human personality; a broad social viewpoint; the desire to inculcate a high standard of moral and spiritual values; a recognition of the needs, interests, and desires of individuals; an appreciation of the part that recreation can play in meeting these needs and interests; and a desire to serve humanity.

There is special need for an understanding and appreciation of community structure and the place of recreation at the "grass roots" level of this structure. The ability to utilize scientific survey techniques and other methods of social research is also an essential qualification.

There should be ability in the performance of skills in many of the areas with which recreation is concerned. These skills should not be limited to games and sports but in addition should branch out into such areas as arts and crafts, dramatics, camping and outdoor education, music, social recreation, and other important aspects of the total offering.

The philosophy of recreation, with the importance of constructive leisure time activities to human beings, should be understood. In addition, there is the necessity for the special knowledge, attitudes, and skills concerned with such things as methods and materials, safety, first aid, principles of group work, health, juvenile delinquency, and crime prevention.

QUESTIONS AND EXERCISES

1. Survey a community recreation program. In the light of this survey list the contributions the program makes to the community, its organization aspects, relation to schools, activities included in its program, and degree to which it is achieving professional objectives.

2. What are the objectives of recreation? Develop a group of guiding principles for the achievement of each of these objectives.

3. To what degree is recreation understood by the American public in general?

4. Discuss what you consider to be the outstanding accomplishments of the recreation profession during the last fifty years.

5. How can the recreation profession turn its shortcomings into accomplishments during the next fifty years?

6. Develop a plan whereby physical education, health education, and recreation can work together most productively in the community.

7. To what extent is your school achieving recreational objectives through its educational offering?

8. Read and critically review one article in *Recreation* magazine.

9. How can television be utilized most advantageously by the recreation profession?

10. Describe what you consider will be a community recreation program in the year 2000.

SELECTED REFERENCES

American Association for Health, Physical Education and Recreation. *Administrative Problems in Health Education, Physical Education and Recreation.* Washington, D. C.: the Association, 1953.

Brightbill, Charles K., and Meyer, Harold D. *Recreation.* New York: Prentice-Hall, Inc., 1953.

Bucher, Charles A. (Editor). *Methods and Materials in Physical Education and Recreation.* St. Louis: The C. V. Mosby Company, 1954.

Butler, George D. *Introduction to Community Recreation.* New York: McGraw-Hill Book Company, Inc., 1949.

Butler, George D. *Playgrounds—Their Administration and Operation.* New York: A. S. Barnes & Company, 1950.

Corbin, H. Dan. *Recreation Leadership.* New York: Prentice-Hall, Inc., 1953.

Danford, Howard G. *Recreation in the American Community.* New York: Harper & Brothers, 1953.

Fitzgerald, Gerald B. *Community Organization for Recreation.* New York: A. S. Barnes & Company, 1948.

Fitzgerald, Gerald B. *Leadership in Recreation.* New York: A. S. Barnes & Company, 1951.

Hjelte, George. *The Administration of Public Recreation.* New York: The Macmillan Company, 1948.

Hutchinson, John L. *Principles of Recreation.* New York: A. S. Barnes & Company, 1949.

Jacks, L. P. *Education Through Recreation.* New York: Harper & Brothers, 1932.

Larson, Leonard A., Fields, Morey R., and Gabrielsen, Milton A. *Problems in Health, Physical and Recreation Education.* New York: Prentice-Hall, Inc., 1953.

Lipovetz, Ferd J. *Recreation.* Minneapolis: Burgess Publishing Company, 1950.

Meyer, Harold D., and Brightbill, Charles K. *Community Recreation.* Boston: D. C. Heath & Company, 1948.

Meyer, Harold D., and Brightbill, Charles K. *State Recreation.* New York: A. S. Barnes & Company, 1950.

Nash, Jay B. *Philosophy of Recreation and Leisure.* St. Louis: The C. V. Mosby Company, 1953.

National Recreation Workshop. *Recreation for Community Living.* Chicago, Illinois: The Athletic Institute, 1952.

Neumeyer, M. H., and Neumeyer, E. S. *Leisure and Recreation.* New York: A. S. Barnes & Company, 1949.

Olsen, Edward G. *School and Community.* New York: Prentice-Hall, Inc., 1945.

Rohrbough, Lynn. *Handy I and II.* Delaware, Ohio: Co-operative Recreation Service, 1949.

Slavson, S. R. *Recreation and the Total Personality.* New York: Association Press, 1948.

Chapter XX

CAMPING AND OUTDOOR EDUCATION

In May, 1948, representatives of such well-known organizations and agencies as the American Association for Health, Physical Education, and Recreation; United States Office of Education; National Secondary School Principals Association; American Association of School Administrators; and the American Council on Education made recommendations that camping should be a part of every child's educational experience, that cooperative arrangements should be worked out with conservation departments and other agencies directly related to natural resources, and that experimental camping programs, as a phase of the educational program, should be established in Michigan and any other states that were interested in trying out this educational trend. Since 1948, camping and outdoor education have grown tremendously in this country.

Camping and outdoor education are rapidly being recognized as having an educational value that should be experienced by every boy and girl. Although there are comparatively few camps throughout the United States that are associated with school systems, the trend is more and more in the direction of required camping and outdoor education as part of the educational offering.

Many teacher education institutions preparing teachers of science, elementary education, health education, recreation, and physical education recognize the value of camping and its importance in education. Prospective teachers in some training programs are required to spend one or more sessions at a camp. The experience orients the student in camp living and in the organization and administration of a camp and emphasizes the value of outdoor education. It is also felt by some professional preparing institutions that the student should have a broad understanding of camping in education. This should include such things as a study of the role of camping and outdoor education in the total educational process, the aims and objectives of camping and outdoor education, procedures essential in the conduct of a camp, qualifications and duties of the camp counselor in his relation to the director and to the campers, safety precautions and procedures, the program of activities for all types of weather conditions, and facilities.

The values of school camping and outdoor education are very much in evidence as a result of the many experiments that have been conducted throughout the United States. For purposes of discussion, it might be said that the values of such experiences are threefold: (1) they meet the social needs of the child, (2) they meet the intellectual needs of the child, and (3) they meet the health needs of the child.

A camping experience is an essential part of every child's school experience because it helps to develop the child socially. In a camp setting children learn to live democratically. They mix with children of various creeds, national origin, color, economic status, and ability. They aid in planning the program that will be

Camping and outdoor education are rapidly being recognized as having an educational value that should be experienced by every boy and girl.

followed during their camp stay; they assume part of the responsibility for the up-keep of the camp, such as making their own beds, helping in the kitchen, sweeping their cabins, and fixing the tennis courts; and they experience cooperative living. The children get away from home and from their parents. They lose their feeling of dependency upon others and learn to do things for themselves. The child learns to rely on his own resources. The camp also provides an enjoyable experience for the child. A child is naturally active and seeks adventure. This experience provides the opportunity to release some of this spirit of adventure and satisfy the "wanderlust" urge.

A camping experience is an essential part of every child's school experience because it helps to develop the child intellectually. While living in a camp, the child learns about such things as soil, forests, water, and animal and bird life. He learns about the value of the nation's natural resources and how they should be conserved. He learns by doing rather than through the medium of textbooks. Instead of looking at the picture of a bird in a book, he actually sees the bird chirping on the branch of a tree. Instead of reading about soil erosion in a textbook, he sees how it actually occurs. Instead of being told about the seven basic groups of food, he has the opportunity to live on a diet that meets the right standards. Instead of reading about the values of democratic living, he actually experiences it. The child experiences many new things which he cannot possibly do at home or within the four walls of a school building. Camping is also of especial value to children who do not learn easily from books. In many cases the knowledge accumulated through actual experience is much more enlightening and beneficial.

Camping is an essential part of every child's school experience because it helps to meet the health needs of the child. Camps are located away from the turmoil, confusion, noise, and rush of urban life. Children experience having their meals at a regular time, obtaining sufficient sleep, and participating in wholesome activity in the out-of-doors. They wear clothing that does not restrict movement, that shields from the sun, and which they are not afraid to get dirty. The food is good. They are doing things that are natural for them to do. It is an outlet for their dynamic personalities. It is much more healthful, both physically and mentally than living in a "push button" existence with its lack of recreation, relaxation, and opportunity for enjoyable experiences. It is like living in another world, and children come away refreshed from such an experience.

The program in most camps consists of such sports activities as swimming, boating, fishing, horseback riding, tennis, badminton, hiking, horseshoes, basketball, and softball; such social activities as campfires, frankfurter and marshmallow roasts, dancing mixers, and cookouts; and opportunities to develop skills and an appreciation in arts and crafts, photography, Indian lore, drama, music, and nature study.

The educational aspects can include a variety of experiences. Some of these are campfires, outdoor cooking, woodcraft, camp sites, canoeing, conservation, astronomy, birds, animals, indoor and outdoor gardening, fishing, hiking, hunting and orienteering.

A publication of the American Association for Health, Physical Education and Recreation points out some experiences that might take place and yield educational results:

"While the camp program is well integrated with the aims and purposes of general education, there are many implications for essential learnings usually associated with health, physical education and recreation. A student at a school camp, as a member of a program group made up of boys and girls, might have some of the following experiences: (a) a trip over the area with a cookout; (b) a work project such as planting trees, building shelter for game, repairing boats and others; (c) responsibility for the common living activities for the day, such as preparation of food, cleaning of the camp, cutting wood for the fire, and the like; (d) participation in activities of interest, such as crafts, dramatics, and music; (e) helping to plan the evening activities for the camp; (f) helping evaluate the day's program; (g) meeting with the camp council; (h) participating in a special camp-fire program; and (i) countless other kinds of experiences appropriate to the age of the group and the location of the camp."[1]

These are some outstanding examples of school systems that are using camping as an effective and worth-while educational experience.

The sixth grade children in the city of San Diego and San Diego County, California, have the opportunity to experience one week of camp life at Camp Cuyamaca. This is a former Civilian Conservation Corps Camp and is located in the nearby mountains. Year-round camping is included as part of the education of the boys and girls going to these schools. The staff is made up largely of school personnel, and the financial outlay is assured by the city council and county board of supervisors. From sixty to seventy children at a time experience all sorts of camp activities including arts and crafts, nature study, hikes, and how to take care of living quarters. Teachers accompany the children on camping trips. One main emphasis in the camp is to have children experience living together with other children in a democratic, healthful, and stimulating environment.

Another notable school camping experience takes place in the public school system of Battle Creek, Michigan, at Saint Mary's Lake Camp. As provided in the arrangements established in this educational setup, children have the opportunity of two weeks' camping experience, which may occur at any time during the year. The camp staff is made up of faculty members of the Battle Creek schools. A novel feature of this camp is the banking experience that each child has. All boys and girls deposit their money in the camp bank, and a banking system is established analogous to that used by commercial banks. The campers also run their own post office. The only cost to each child for this valuable experience is the price of the food.

Long Beach, California, also offers a valuable camping experience to the children and faculties of its schools. Their camp, Camp Hi-Hill, is located about fifty miles from Long Beach in the San Gabriel Mountains. This camp is primarily for sixth graders and faculty members, and the emphasis is on giving these children an opportunity to cope with various problems that arise when a group of individuals start living together in a democratic manner. This camp is also conducted on a year-round basis with winter activities playing just as important a role as summer activities.

Some states have passed legislation making tax money available to the schools for the support of camping provided for the public school children. This trend in state level provision for camping in the public schools means that more and more

[1]Joint Committee (Editors). *Administrative Problems in Health Education, Physical Education and Recreation.* Washington, D. C.: American Association for Health, Physical Education and Recreation, 1953, p. 47.

SCHOOL CAMPING IS AN EXTENSION OF THE CLASSROOM[2]

BASIC SCIENTIFIC UNDERSTANDINGS AND
  APPRECIATIONS

How soil is formed
How plants grow
The rain-water cycle
How forest animals live
Dependence of man upon plants and animals
Causes of soil erosion and prevention
Operation of a weather station
Use of map and compass
Significance of fire damage
Study of stars
Meaning of contour, grade, and slope

STUDY OF SEASONAL CHANGES

Bird, animal, and insect life
Uses of flood control dams
How snow is used for protection and water
  supply for vegetation
Migration, fire hazards
Barometric pressure
Weather observations
How animals use the food they have stored
Watersheds

WORTHY SKILLS IN RECREATION

Hiking to discover, study, explore, and collect
  native craft materials
Outdoor cooking techniques
Outdoor survival skills
Outdoor sports such as: skiing, boating,
  canoeing, fly-casting, bait-casting, swim-
  ming, skating, and mountain climbing
Crafts
Nature workshop
Square dancing
Building outdoor shelters
Appreciating wholesome outdoor recreation

SPIRITUAL VALUES

Experiencing the beauty of nature
Appreciation of living things developed from
  personal contact
Better appreciation of the personal worth of
  others, from living together
Development of finer group unity
Appreciation of the beauty and worth of the
  out of doors

WHOLESOME WORK EXPERIENCES

Conservation projects
Planting and terracing to arrest erosion
Repairing trails
Building small check dams
Planting and maintaining a forest nursery
Setting tables
Washing dishes
Cleaning cabins
Caring for animals and pets
Learning safe use and care of simple hand
  tools

DEMOCRATIC SOCIAL LIVING

Cooperative planning by groups
Evaluation by students
Discussing camp safety standards
Living in cabin groups
Participating in campfire activities
Solving problems arising from living together
Understanding duties of the forest ranger
Acting as host, hostess, and hopper at dining
  table
Improving relationships of pupils and teacher
Enriching and fostering democratic living

HEALTHFUL LIVING

Maintaining personal health, cleanliness
Maintaining regular hours of sleeping
Keeping cabin neat and clean
Participating in wholesome exercise
Developing better table manners and eating
  habits
Planning menus
Practicing first aid

opportunities are going to be made available for children to have this worth-while experience. For example, in the state of Michigan a bill was passed providing that boards of education, with the exception of those in primary school districts,

[2]Adapted from State Board of Education, Concord, New Hampshire. *School Camping and Outdoor Education,* and from Division of Instruction, Long Beach, California, Public Schools. *Guide for The Camp Hi-Hill Program.* Long Beach: June, 1952.

could operate camps independently or jointly with other boards of education or governing bodies for purposes of recreation and instruction. Provision was made for the charging of fees, if necessary, to cover expenses incurred in maintaining the camp. However, these camps are to be run on a nonprofit basis. Provisions were also made for boards of education to employ personnel to operate these camps, to maintain essential facilities, and to locate camps on property other than that owned by the board of education, provided that the consent of the owner of said property had been secured. Finally, a provision was made stipulating that the cost of operating a school camp should not be included in the determination of per capita costs of the regular school program.

In the state of New York legislation has provided that boards of education may operate camps on land secured by the school district for camp purposes. The legislature of the state of New York passed the Desmond School Camp Bill, which made it possible for school districts to appropriate funds for instructional programs deemed advisable for school children. Camping is one experience which is being recognized more and more as being an essential for all children of school age.

When historians look back at the twentieth century there is a good possibility they will credit the school camping movement as the greatest educational innovation of the era and acclaim Michigan as one of the pioneer states in proving that nature's classroom helps to prepare the child much more effectively for living in today's world. The state of Michigan deserves special credit for its part in the school camping movement. The history of school camping in this state goes back some twenty-five years. In the early 1930's, Tappan Junior High School in Ann Arbor utilized a camp setting for its junior high school students, and the Cadillac board of education developed a summer camp for its elementary school children. A little later, schools in Battle Creek, Decatur, and Otsego utilized camps in their educational programs. In 1945 the state government passed legislation making it possible for school districts to acquire and operate camps as part of their educational program. In 1946 their Departments of Public Instruction and Conservation, together with the W. K. Kellogg Foundation, joined forces to develop the program further. The late Lee M. Thurston, State Superintendent of Public Instruction, and P. J. Hoffmaster, State Director of Conservation, set as the goal for the state of Michigan, "A week of school camping for every boy and girl in the state in 1960."

The rapid development of camping in Michigan has resulted to a great degree because of the educationally significant way in which the program is operated. The groups going to camp usually include fifth or sixth graders on the elementary level, or home rooms and special subject-matter areas on the secondary level. The camps are run by the teachers and students. Pre-planning takes place in the classroom where such essentials as clothing that is needed, projects that are to be developed, and job assignments are arranged. The usual procedure is to have two teachers for the average classroom-size group, plus extra help for food preparation and camp maintenance. The parents assume the cost of food, with special provisions being made for those children whose families are unable to pay the expenses. Any child who wants to go to camp is given the opportunity. Schools assume the instructional cost. The school district or government agency bears the cost of the camp and its facilities. In Dearborn, Ann Arbor, and Highland Park, for example, special budgetary provisions are made to pay for camp costs.[3]

Over 100 educational systems include camping in their school programs at the present time in the state of Michigan. This state is pioneering in an educational movement which has many potentialities for furthering the social, mental, physical and emotional growth of children. The fact that fewer than 10 per cent of the children of camp age in America ever get any type of camp experience presents a challenge for other states to follow Michigan's lead.

The years ahead will undoubtedly find camping becoming more and more a part of the school program. Administrators, teachers, and educators in general should examine the potentialities that camping and outdoor education have for their own school systems.

QUESTIONS AND EXERCISES

1. Prepare a speech to be given to a parent-teachers association on the importance of camping in education. Point up the values of camping to the children in the community.

2. What is the responsibility of professional preparing institutions in the field of camping and outdoor education?

3. Make a study of the program of camping and outdoor education in the state of Michigan and give a report to the class.

4. Cite specific examples to show how camping and outdoor education can develop a child socially and intellectually.

5. Prepare a report for a board of education to justify taking all the sixth grade children of a school to camp on school time.

6. What should constitute some of the experiences provided in a camp setting?

7. Make a study of school camping in the forty-eight states and report to class on the progress that has been made during the last five years.

8. How can school camping contribute to the wise use of natural resources?

9. What is meant by enabling legislation? What type of enabling legislation is needed in your state to promote school camping? List a series of logical steps that should be followed to achieve such legislation.

10. Write an essay of 250 words on the subject: "School Camping Is an Extension of the Classroom."

SELECTED REFERENCES

Burns, Gerald P. *Program of the Modern Camp.* New York: Prentice-Hall, Inc., 1954.

Burns, Gerald P. "The Role of Sports and Games in Organized Camping," *The Journal of the American Association for Health, Physical Education and Recreation,* 20: 314, May, 1949.

"Camping and Outdoor Education," *The Journal of Educational Sociology* 23: (Entire Issue), May, 1950.

Carlson, Reynold E. "The Place of Organized Camping in State Parks," *Recreation* XLVI: 452, January, 1953.

Clark, Leslie. "The School Camp in Winter," *Journal of the American Association for Health, Physical Education and Recreation* 23: 10, January, 1952.

Clarke, James M. *Public School Camping.* Stanford, California: Stanford University Press, 1951.

Cumbee, Frances. "Basic Campcraft Skills," *Journal of the American Association for Health, Physical Education and Recreation* 22: 7, June, 1951.

Joy, Barbara Ellen. "Getting More Real Camping Into Camps," *Journal of Health and Physical Education* 19: 18, January, 1948.

---

[3]Julian W. Smith, "The Michigan Story of Camping and Outdoor Education," *The Journal of Educational Sociology* 23: 508, May, 1950.

Makechnie, George K. "Camping Round the Calendar," *Hygeia* 27: 838, December, 1949.

Manley, Helen, and Drury, M. F. *Education Through School Camping.* St. Louis: The C. V. Mosby Company, 1952.

Masters, Hugh B. "Values of School Camping," *Journal of the American Association for Health, Physical Education and Recreation* 22: 14, January, 1951.

McQuarrie, Agnes M. "A Camp of 'Firsts'," *The Journal of the American Association for Health, Physical Education and Recreation* 24: 16, May, 1953.

Mortensen, Martin. "Training Leaders in Camping and Outdoor Education," *Journal of the American Association for Health, Physical Education and Recreation* 23: 14, June, 1952.

Pike, Kenneth V. "School Camping Has Come to Stay," *Journal of the American Association for Health, Physical Education and Recreation* 22: 23, June, 1951.

Report of the Committee on Camping in Education. "The Place of Camping in Education," *Journal of the American Association for Health, Physical Education and Recreation* 21: 15, January, 1950.

Roth, Charles B. *The Sportsman's Outdoor Guide.* New York: Prentice-Hall, Inc., 1953.

Smith, Julian W. "Community School Camping," *Journal of the American Association for Health, Physical Education and Recreation* 22: 4, June, 1951.

Smith, Leon H. "Family Camping—20-Year Success Story," *Camping,* March, 1952, p. 21.

Tour, Cy La. "Summer Camp—Paradise for Boys," *Today's Health* 31: 32, June, 1953.

Vinal, William G. *The Outdoor Schoolroom for Outdoor Living.* Cohassett, Massachusetts: Vinehall, R.F.D., 1952.

Weakley, Jim, and Bleier, T. J. "Summer-School Camping at a Blimp Base," *National Education Association Journal* 39: 368, May, 1950.

Weil, Truda T. "The School Camp—Our Outdoor Classroom," *Journal of the American Association for Health, Physical Education and Recreation* 21: 284, May, 1950.

Willard, Lotene. "Year-Round Public-School Camping," *National Education Association Journal* 38: 576, November, 1949.

INDEX

A

Accident reports, 148-152
Accident-prone settings in physical education, 144-146
Administration:
  camping and outdoor education and, 410-417
  definition of, 17-18
  democracy in, 62-72
  facilities and, 204-231
  governmental aspects in, 73-94
  health education and, 101-102, 245-267
  health services and, 102, 221-222, 268-308
  history of, 18-20
  importance of, 20-22
  interschool athletics and, 369-399
  intramurals and extramurals and, 346-368
  legal liability and, 133-154
  management in, 47-61
  meaning of, 17-31
  measurement and evaluation and, 171-185
  personnel policies in, 32-46
  physical education class and, 309-345
  practices for healthful environment and, 232-244
  professional preparation and, 155-170
  public relations and, 59-60, 186-203
  relationships of health and physical education and, 119-132
  school and community organization in, 95-118
Administrative policies in physical education class program, 318-322
Administrative practices and health, 232-244:
  attendance and, 235-236
  discipline and, 236-237
  homework and, 235
  human relations and, 240-241
  organization of school day and, 233
  personnel policies and, 236
  physical environment and, 239-240
  play and recreation and, 235
  professional services and, 242-243
  school-community relationships and, 241-242
  student achievement and, 233
  teacher and, 238-239
Administrative relationships of health and physical education, 119-132
Administrator:
  administrative practices and, 232-244
  code for, 30
  development and selection of, 25-26
  duties of, 26-30
  legal liability and, 133-154

Administrator—Cont'd
  objectives of health and physical education and, 130-131
  public relations and, 188-189
  pupil and teacher health and, 232-244
  qualifications of, 22-25
Adult health education, 259
Alabama College, 224, 241
Alcohol and tobacco education, 253-254
American Football Coaches Association, 386
Athletic administrative problems, 380-386:
  eligibility, 384
  gate receipts, 380-381
  proselyting, 385
  recruitment, 385
  scholarships, 384-385
  scouting, 386
  tournaments and play-offs, 382-384
Athletic associations, 386-388
Athletic contracts, 376
Athletic eligibility, 384
Athletic game management, 377-380
Athletic injuries, 375-376
Athletic medical examinations, 279
Athletic protection funds, 152-153, 375-376
Athletic records, 379
Athletic schedules and practices, 379
Athletic scholarships, 384-385
Athletics (*see* Interschool athletics; Intramurals and extramurals)
Attendance in physical education, 320
Authority:
  fallacy of, 33-35
  problem of, 67
Auxiliary rooms, 225
Awards, 359-360, 379

B

Board of education, 95-97
Budgeting, 29, 56-57, 365-366

C

Cafeteria, 223
Cameron Junior High School, Tennessee, 362
Camp Hi-Hill, 413, 414
Camping, 410-417
  examples of school, 413-414
  facilities for, 230
  history of school, 410
  program in school, 412-413
  recreation and, 406
  values of school, 410-412
Camping and recreation, 406, 410-417
Chandler Junior High School, Worcester, 99, 101, 103

City-manager government, 114
Clark Street School, Worcester, 124
Classification of physical education activities, 330-333
Class management in physical education, 322-329
Classrooms, 221-223
Coach, 371-373
Coeducational activities, 333-334
College health education, 257-259
College intramurals and extramurals, 363
College of William and Mary, 394-395
College physical education class program, 341-342
Commercial organizations and health, 265-266
Commission form of city government, 112-113
Communicable disease control, 298-303:
  attendance and, 302-303
  epidemics and, 303
  healthful environment and, 300-301
  immunization and, 301-302
  isolation and, 301
  measures for, 300-303
  responsibility for, 299-300
Communication, personnel relations and, 43-45
Community recreation, 400-409:
  accomplishments, 406-407
  camping and, 406, 410-417
  civic development and, 401-402
  defined, 400
  health and, 400
  human relations and, 400-401
  interpretation of, 404-405
  moral and spiritual values and, 404-406
  objectives of, 400-402
  recreation leader and, 408
  schools and, 404-405, 407
  self-development and, 402, 407
  shortcomings, 403-406
Community structure, 109-118:
  municipal government in, 110-115
  public health organization in, 115-117
  village government in, 109-110
Competition, 357-358
Concentrated health education, 259-260
Content areas of health education, 254-258
Controversial health education areas, 253-254
Coordination, 28-29, 53-54
Correction of remediable defects, 290-292
Correlated health education, 260-261
Costume in physical education, 325
Council-manager government, 110-112
Credit for physical education, 320
Criteria for good health teaching, 256
Criteria for test construction and selection, 179-180

D

Decision making, 35-36
Democratic administration, 62-72:
  elements of, 67-70
  group process in, 62-73
  problems in, 64-67
Dental certificate, 281
Dental examinations, 279-281
Directing and administration, 27-28

Discipline and health, 236-237
Dressing and showering, 324
Duties of administrator, 26-30

E

Education:
  camping and, 410-417
  facilities and, 204-231
  government and, 73-94
  group process in, 62-63
  public relations and, 196-198
  purpose of, 73-74
  recreation and, 404-405, 407
Education and group process, 62-63
Educational Policies Commission, 398
Elective physical education, 319
Elementary school health education, 254-256
Elementary school intramurals and extramurals, 361-362
Elementary school physical education class program, 334-337
Emergency care, 303-306
Examination of athletes, 279
Exceptional child, care and education of, 292-298:
  educational program and, 294-298
  identifying, 293-294
  nature of, 293
  personnel for, 298
Excuses in physical education, 321-322
Extramurals (*see* Intramurals and extramurals)

F

Facilities, 204-231
  furniture, 215
  health features of, 211-216
  heating and ventilation of, 214-215
  indoor, 216-225
    administrative and staff offices, 216, 218
    auxiliary rooms, 225
    cafeteria, 223
    classrooms, 221-223
    gymnasiums, 219-220
    health services suite, 221, 222
    locker, shower, and drying rooms, 218
    special activity areas, 220-221
    swimming pool, 223-225
  lighting of, 213-214
  outdoor:
    camps, 230
    school play areas, 225-229
    swimming pools, 229-230
  planning, 204-210
  sanitation and, 215
  school building, 212-213
  school site, 211-212
  trends in, 210-211
Fallacy of final authority, 33-35
Family physician's report, 276
Family recreation, 403
Fayol's administrative duties, 29-30
Finance (*see* Budgeting)
First-aid supplies, 304
Four-cycle plan of health instruction, 250
Framework for measurement and evaluation, 172-178
Furniture, 215

G

Gate receipts, 380-381
Girls' interschool athletics, 388-389
Girls' intramurals and extramurals, 363-364
Governmental and proprietary functions, 141
Governmental aspects of educational adminis-
    tration, 73-94:
  federal government, 78-81, 87-89, 91
  government and health, 87-91
  governmental relationships, 86-87
  growth of education in relation to govern-
    ment, 74-78
  local government, 85-86, 90-91, 93
  state government, 81-85, 89-93
Grading, 326-328
Grouping for physical education classes, 316-
    318
Gymnasiums, 219-220

H

Health (*see also* School health program):
  administrative practices and, 232-244
  camping and, 410-412
  community recreation and, 400
  facilities and, 204-231
  government and, 87-91
  health education for, 101-102, 245-267
  health services for, 102, 221-222, 268-308
  interscholastic athletics and, 373-376
  intramurals and extramurals and, 365
  physical education class and, 343-344
  public, 115-117
  relationship to physical education, 119-132
Health and physical education class, 343-344
Health appraisal, 273-288:
  athletic examinations, 279, 373
  dental examinations, 279-281
  health records in, 287-288
  medical examinations, 273-279
  psychological examinations, 279
  screening for vision and hearing defects,
    282-285
  teachers' observations, 285-287
Health attitudes, 123
Health council, 103-104, 248
Health counseling, 288-290:
  conference method in, 290
  counselor in, 289-290
  purposes of, 288-289
Health education, 101-102, 245-267:
  adult, 259
  college and university, 257-259
  concentrated, 259-260
  content areas of, 248-254
  controversial content areas, 253-254
  correlated, 260-261
  defined, 100-102
  elementary level, 254-256
  health needs for, 249-253
  incidental, 261
  organization of classes in, 261-263
  relation to school health programs, 245-267
  resources for, 263-267
  secondary level, 256-257
Health educator, 160-161, 248
Health knowledge, 122-123, 245-267

Health of teacher, 238-239
Health practices, 123-124
Health records, 278, 287-288
Health service suite, 221, 222
Health services:
  care and education of exceptional children
    in, 292-298
  communicable disease control in, 298-303
  correction of remediable defects in, 290-
    292
  defined, 102
  emergency care in, 303-306
  health appraisal in, 273-288
  health counseling in, 288-290
  place in schools of, 269-271
  program of, 268-308
  responsibility for, 271
  suite for, 221, 222
Healthful school living:
  administrative practices for, 232-244
  defined, 102-103
  facilities and, 204-231
Heathcote School, Scarsdale, 209, 212
Heating and ventilation, 214-215
Height-weight records, 287
Highland Park, Illinois, High School, 278
Housing (*see* Facilities)
Human relations, 240-241, 400-401

I

Illinois State Normal University, 156, 166,
    167, 169, 193, 199, 347, 395
Incentives, 41-43
Incidental health education, 261
Indiana State Department of Health, 246,
    272, 274, 280, 284
Insurance, 152-153, 375-376
Interschool athletics, 369-399:
  administrative considerations in, 373-379
  administrative problems in, 380-386
  associations for, 386-388
  coach and, 371-373
  college and university, 394-397
  defined, 108-109
  elementary and junior high school, 389-390
  facilities for, 204-231
  girls', 388-389
  high school, 390-394
  insurance for, 152-153, 375-376
  medical examinations for, 279
  relation to physical education, 369-371
Intramurals and extramurals, 346-368:
  activities in, 356-357
  administrative policies for, 365-367
  awards, points, records, eligibility for, 359-
    361
  college, 363
  defined, 107-108
  elementary school, 361-362
  finances for, 365-366
  girls', 363-364
  health examinations for, 365
  junior high school, 362-363
  nature and scope of, 346-347
  objectives of, 347-349
  play, sports, and invitation days, 350-356
  publicity and promotion for, 366

Intramurals and extramurals:—Cont'd
  relation to interschool athletics, 349-350
  senior high school, 363
  time for, 366-367
  units and types of competition, 357-359
Invitation days, 350-356

J

Johns Hopkins University, 381
Joint Committee on Athletic Competition, 389-390
Junior high school intramurals and extramurals, 362-363
Junior high school physical education class program, 337-339

K

Kent State University, 258
Kester Avenue School, Los Angeles, 210, 214

L

Leadership, 36-37
Legal liability, 133-154:
  accident-prone settings and, 144-146
  athletic protection funds and, 152-153
  board members and, 142-143
  fees in, 141
  governmental versus proprietary functions in, 141
  municipality and, 142
  negligence, 136-139
  nuisance, action in, 139-140
  safety and, 146-152
  school district and, 142
  supervision and, 152
  teachers and leaders and, 143-144
  tort, 135-136
  waivers and consent slips and, 152
Liability (*see* Legal liability)
Lighting, 213-214
Line and staff, 51-53
Locker, shower, and drying rooms, 218
Los Angeles City School District, 96

M

Management, 47-61
  budgeting and financial control in, 56-57
  coordination in, 53-54
  line and staff in, 51-53
  office management in, 60-61
  organizational patterns in, 48-51
  planning in, 57-59
  public relations in, 59-60
  purpose of organization in, 47-48
  reorganization in, 54-56
  research in, 59
Massachusetts Department of Public Health, 276
Measurement and evaluation, 171-185:
  administrative guides in, 178-179
  criteria for test construction and selection, 179-180
  framework for, 172-178
  materials available in, 181-183

Measurement and evaluation:—Cont'd
  minimum and desirable standards in, 183-184
  purposes of, 171-172
  standardization of, 181
Medical examinations, 273-279, 365
Michigan camping, 410, 414-416
Municipal government, 110-115:
  charter in, 115
  city-manager government in, 114
  commission government in, 112-113
  council-mayor government in, 110-112
  health department in, 115-117
  home rule in, 115

N

National Association of Intercollegiate Athletics, 388
National Collegiate Athletic Association, 387, 388
National Conference on Elementary School Physical Education, 334-339
National Council, Y.M.C.A., 21, 411
National Federation of State High School Athletic Associations, 387
National Section on Girls' and Women's Athletics, 364, 389
Negligence, 136-139
New Trier Township, Illinois, High School, 281
New York State Fitness Conference, 314, 315
Norfolk, Virginia, Public Schools, 255, 359
North Central Association, 372, 384, 385, 396
North Dakota State Department of Public Instruction, 327

O

Objectives of physical education, 124-130
Objectives of recreation, 400-402
Objectives of school health, 120-124
Office management, 60-61
Offices, 216, 218
Official health agencies, 264-265
Officials, 376-377
Organization of health education classes, 261-263
Organization of school day, 233
Organizational patterns, 48-51:
  according to associated materials or persons, 49, 51
  according to process, 49-50
  according to purpose, 48-49, 50
  according to setting, 51
Organizing, 26-27
Outdoor education, 410-417

P

Personnel management, 38-41
Personnel policies, 32-46:
  communication, 43-45
  decisions, 35-36
  fallacy of final authority, 33-35
  health and, 236

Personnel policies:—Cont'd
  incentives, 41-43
  personnel management, 38-41
  persuasion, 43
  principles of cooperation, 32
  staff morale, 36-38
Personnel policies and health, 236
Persuasion and administration, 43
Physical education:
  defined, 104
  facilities for, 204-231
  government and, 91-93
  interschool athletics, 369-399
  intramurals and extramurals, 346-368
  legal liability in, 133-154
  measurement and evaluation in, 171-185
  professional preparation for, 155-170
  public relations and, 186-203
  required class program, 309-345
  terminology in, 105-106
  within school structure, 104-109
Physical education school relationships, 342-343
Physical educator, qualifications, 161-163
Planning and administration, 26, 57-59
Planning physical education classes, 309-312
Play and recreation and health, 235
Play days, 350-356
Principal, 97-98
Principles of cooperation, 32
Problems in democratic administration, 64-67
Professional health agencies and associations, 263-264
Professional preparation, 155-170:
  accrediting colleges engaging in, 168-170
  competencies developed by, 165-168
  cultural background in, 164-165
  directions of, 155-160
  qualifications of health educators, 160-161
  qualifications of physical educators, 161-163
Proselyting, 385
Protests and forfeitures, 327
Psychological examinations, 279
Public relations, 59-60, 186-203:
  administration and, 188-189
  definition, 186-188
  education and, 196-198
  health and physical education and, 198-202
  media of, 189-193
  principles of, 195-196
  qualifications for, 194-195
Public relations media, 189-193
Pupils' medical report, 277
Purpose of education, 73-74

Q

Qualifications of administrator, 22-25

R

Records, 278, 287-288, 328-329, 379
Recreation (*see* Community recreation)
Recreation, accomplishments, 406-407
Recreation, interpretation, 404-405
Recreation leader, 408
Recruitment of athletes, 385

Reorganization and administration, 54-56
Reporting and administration, 29
Required physical education class program, 309-345:
  activities in, 329-334
  administrative policies for, 318-322
  college and university, 341-342
  defined, 106-107
  elementary, 334-337
  facilities for, 204-231
  grouping in, 316-318
  junior high, 337-339
  management of, 322-329
  planning for, 309-312
  senior high, 339-340
  teaching loads in, 315-316
  teaching stations in, 315
  time allotment for, 313-314
Research, 59
Resources for health education, 263-267
Rhythmic play day, 355-356
Roll taking, 325-326

S

Sacramento, California, School District, 28, 316-317
Safety, 146-152, 373-376
Saint Mary's Lake Camp, 413
Sanitation, 215
Scheduling physical education classes, 312-318
School committee (*see* Board of education)
School construction, 204-231 (*see also* Facilities)
School Facilities Survey, 205, 206, 207, 208
School health program:
  administrative practices and, 232-244
  aspects of, 100-104
  facilities in, 204-231
  health education in, 101-102, 245-267
  health services in, 102, 221-222, 268-308
  measurement and evaluation in, 171-185
  professional preparation for, 155-170
  public relations and, 186-203
  qualifications for health educators in, 160-161
  relationship to physical education, 119-132
  terminology in, 99-100
  within school structure, 98-104
School plant sanitation, 215
School play areas (outdoor), 225-229
School site, 211-212
School structure, 95-109:
  board of education in, 95-97
  health within, 98-104
  lay groups in, 98
  physical education within, 104-109
  principal in, 97-98
  superintendent of schools in, 97
Schools and recreation, 404-405, 407
Scouting in athletics, 386
Screening for vision and hearing defects, 282-285
Secondary school level health education, 256-257
Selection of physical education activities, 329-330

Senior high school intramurals and extramurals, 363
Senior high school physical education class program, 339-340
Sex education, 253-254
Size of physical education classes, 314-315
Southeast Missouri State College, 217
Special activity areas, 220-221
Sports days, 350-356
Spring play day, 354-355
Staff morale, 36-38
Staffing, 27
Standards:
    administrative practices, 232-244
    camping and outdoor education, 410-417
    facilities, 204-231
    health education, 245-267
    healthful environment, 204-244
    health services, 268-308
    interschool athletics, 369-399
    intramurals and extramurals, 346-368
    measurement and evaluation, 183-184
    physical education class, 309-345
    public relations, 195-196
    recreation, 400-409
Stanford University, 134, 370
State of Nebraska, 253
Student achievement and health, 233
Substitutions for physical education, 319-320
Superintendent of schools, 97
Supervision, 152
Swimming pools, 223-225, 229-230

T

Teachers' observations, 285-287
Teaching loads, 315-316

Teaching stations, 315
Third national conference on health in colleges, 258
Time allotment for physical education, 313-314
Tort, 135-136
Tournaments and play-offs, 382-384
Types of competition, 357-358

U

United States Department of Health, Education, and Welfare, 76
United States Office of Education, 76, 295, 296
Units of competition, 357
University of California, 105, 125, 127, 364
University of Chicago, 369-370, 396-397
University of Connecticut, 224, 401
University of Florida, 147
University of Michigan, 217, 310, 311, 349, 371, 374, 378
University of Tampa, 226

V

Value of camping, 410-412
Village government, 109-110

W

Waivers and consent slips, 152
Washington Irving Elementary School, Iowa, 121, 213, 219, 237
Wisconsin State College, LaCrosse, 188, 302, 333